Enhancing Motivation for Change in Substance Abuse Treatment

Treatment Improvement Protocol (TIP) Series

35

William R. Miller, Ph.D.

Consensus Panel Chair

U.S. DEPARTMENT OF HEALTH AND HUMAN SERVICES
Public Health Service
Substance Abuse and Mental Health Services Administration
Center for Substance Abuse Treatment

Rockwall II, 5600 Fishers Lane
Rockville, MD 20857

Acknowledgments

This publication was written under contract number 270-95-0013 with The CDM Group, Inc. (CDM). Sandra Clunies, M.S., I.C.A.D.C., served as the CSAT government project officer. Rose M. Urban, M.S.W., J.D., LCSW, CCAC, CSAC served as the CDM TIPs project director. Other CDM TIPs personnel included Raquel Witkin, M.S., project manager; Jonathan Max Gilbert, M.A., managing editor; Y-Lang Nguyen, production editor; Janet G. Humphrey, M.A., editor/writer; Paddy Cook, freelance writer; Joanna Taylor, editor; Cara Smith, editorial assistant; Paul Seaman, editorial assistant; and Kurt Olsson, editor/writer.

Disclaimer

The opinions expressed herein are the views of the Consensus Panel members and do not necessarily reflect the official position of CSAT, SAMHSA, or DHHS. No official support of or endorsement by CSAT, SAMHSA, or DHHS for these opinions or for particular instruments, software, or resources described in this document are intended or should be inferred. The guidelines in this document should not be considered substitutes for individualized client care and treatment decisions.

Electronic Access and Copies of Publication

Copies may be obtained free of charge from SAMHSA's National Clearinghouse for Alcohol and Drug Information (NCADI), (800) 729-6686 or (301) 468-2600; TDD (for hearing impaired), (800) 487-4889, or electronically through the following Internet World Wide Web site: www.ncadi.samhsa.gov.

Recommended Citation

Center for Substance Abuse Treatment. *Enhancing Motivation for Change in Substance Abuse Treatment*. Treatment Improvement Protocol (TIP) Series, Number 35. DHHS Pub. No. (SMA) 05-4081. Rockville, MD: Substance Abuse and Mental Health Services Administration, 1999.

Originating Office

Practice Improvement Branch, Division of Services Improvement, Center for Substance Abuse Treatment, Substance Abuse and Mental Health Services Administration, 1 Choke Cherry Road, Rockville, MD 20857.

DHHS Publication No. (SMA) 05-4081
Printed 1999
Reprinted 2000, 2001, 2002, 2003, 2004, and 2005

Contents

Figures

What Is a TIP?

Treatment Improvement Protocols (TIPs) are best practice guidelines for the treatment of substance abuse, provided as a service of the Substance Abuse and Mental Health Services Administration's Center for Substance Abuse Treatment (CSAT). CSAT's Office of Evaluation, Scientific Analysis and Synthesis draws on the experience and knowledge of clinical, research, and administrative experts to produce the TIPs, which are distributed to a growing number of facilities and individuals across the country. The audience for the TIPs is expanding beyond public and private substance abuse treatment facilities as alcoholism and other substance abuse disorders are increasingly recognized as major problems.

The TIPs Editorial Advisory Board, a distinguished group of substance use experts and professionals in such related fields as primary care, mental health, and social services, works with the State Alcohol and Other Drug Abuse Directors to generate topics for the TIPs based on the field's current needs for information and guidance.

After selecting a topic, CSAT invites staff from pertinent Federal agencies and national organizations to a Resource Panel that recommends specific areas of focus as well as resources that should be considered in developing the content of the TIP. Then recommendations are communicated to a Consensus Panel composed of non-Federal experts on the topic who have been nominated by their peers. This Panel participates in a series of discussions; the information and recommendations on which it reaches consensus form the foundation of the TIP. The members of each Consensus Panel represent substance abuse treatment programs, hospitals, community health centers, counseling programs, criminal justice and child welfare agencies, and private practitioners. A Panel Chair (or Co-Chairs) ensures that the guidelines mirror the results of the group's collaboration.

A large and diverse group of experts closely reviews the draft document. Once the changes recommended by these field reviewers have been incorporated, the TIP is prepared for publication, in print and online. The TIPs can be accessed via the Internet on the National Library of Medicine's home page at the URL: http://text.nlm.nih.gov. The move to electronic media also means that the TIPs can be updated more easily so they continue to provide the field with state-of-the-art information.

Although each TIP strives to include an evidence base for the practices it recommends, CSAT recognizes that the field of substance abuse treatment is evolving and that research frequently lags behind the innovations pioneered in the field. A major goal of each TIP is to convey "front line" information quickly but responsibly. For this reason, recommendations proffered in the TIP are attributed to either Panelists' clinical experience or the literature. If there is research to support a particular approach, citations are provided.

This TIP, *Enhancing Motivation for Change in Substance Abuse Treatment*, embraces a fundamentally different way to conceptualize motivation. In this approach, motivation is viewed as a dynamic and changeable state rather than a static trait. This TIP shows how clinicians can influence this change process by developing a therapeutic relationship, one that respects and builds on the client's autonomy and, at the same time, makes the treatment counselor a participant in the change process. The TIP also describes different motivational interventions that can be used at all stages of change, from precontemplation and preparation to action and maintenance. The goal of this TIP is to make readers aware of the research, results, and promise of motivational interventions in the hope that they will be used more widely in clinical practice and treatment programs across the United States.

Other TIPs may be ordered by contacting SAMHSA's National Clearinghouse for Alcohol and Drug Information (NCADI), (800) 729-6686 or (301) 468-2600; TDD (for hearing impaired), (800) 487-4889.

Editorial Advisory Board

Consensus Panel

Chair

William R. Miller, Ph.D.
Regents Professor of Psychology and
Psychiatry
Director of Research
Center on Alcoholism, Substance Abuse, and
Addictions
Department of Psychology
University of New Mexico
Albuquerque, New Mexico

Workgroup Leaders

Edward Bernstein, M.D., F.A.C.E.P.
Associate Professor and Academic Affairs
Vice Chairman
Boston University School of Medicine
Boston, Massachusetts

Suzanne M. Colby, Ph.D.
Assistant Professor of Psychiatry and
Human Behavior
Center for Alcohol and Addiction Studies
Brown University
Providence, Rhode Island

Carlo C. DiClemente, Ph.D.
Department of Psychology
University of Maryland, Baltimore County
Baltimore, Maryland

Robert J. Meyers, M.A.
Center on Alcoholism, Substance Abuse, and
Addictions
University of New Mexico
Albuquerque, New Mexico

Maxine L. Stitzer, Ph.D.
Professor of Psychiatry and Behavioral
Biology
Johns Hopkins University School of
Medicine
Baltimore, Maryland

Allen Zweben, D.S.W.
Director and Associate Professor of Social
Work
Center for Addiction and Behavioral Health
Research
University of Wisconsin at Milwaukee
Milwaukee, Wisconsin

Panelists

Ray Daw
Executive Director
Northwest New Mexico Fighting Back, Inc.
Gallup, New Mexico

Jeffrey M. Georgi, M.Div., C.S.A.C., C.G.P.
Program Coordinator
Duke Alcoholism & Addictions Program
Clinical Associate
Department of Psychiatry and Behavioral
Science
Duke University Medical Center
Durham, North Carolina

Cheryl Grills, Ph.D.
Department of Psychology
Loyola Marymount University
Los Angeles, California

Rosalyn Harris-Offutt, B.S., C.R.N.A., L.P.C., A.D.S.
UNA Psychological Associates
Greensboro, North Carolina

Don M. Hashimoto, Psy.D.
Clinical Director
Ohana Counseling Services, Inc.
Hilo, Hawaii

Dwight McCall, Ph.D.
Evaluation Manager
Substance Abuse Services
Virginia Department of Mental Health,
   Mental Retardation and Substance Abuse
   Services
Richmond, Virginia

Jeanne Obert, M.F.C.C., M.S.M.
Director of Clinical Services
Matrix Center
Los Angeles, California

Carole Janis Otero, M.A., L.P.C.C.
Director
Albuquerque Metropolitan Central Intake
Albuquerque, New Mexico

Roger A. Roffman, D.S.W.
Innovative Programs Research Group
School of Social Work
Seattle, Washington

Linda C. Sobell, Ph.D.
Professor
NOVA Southeastern University
Fort Lauderdale, Florida

Foreword

The Treatment Improvement Protocol (TIP) series fulfills SAMHSA's mission of building resilience and facilitating recovery for people with or at risk for mental or substance use disorders by providing best-practices guidance to clinicians, program administrators, and payors to improve the quality and effectiveness of service delivery, and, thereby promote recovery. TIPs are the result of careful consideration of all relevant clinical and health services research findings, demonstration experience, and implementation requirements. A panel of non-Federal clinical researchers, clinicians, program administrators, and client advocates debates and discusses its particular areas of expertise until it reaches a consensus on best practices. This panel's work is then reviewed and critiqued by field reviewers.

The talent, dedication, and hard work that TIPs panelists and reviewers bring to this highly participatory process have helped to bridge the gap between the promise of research and the needs of practicing clinicians and administrators to serve, in the most scientifically sound and effective ways, people who abuse substances. We are grateful to all who have joined with us to contribute to advances in the substance abuse treatment field.

Charles G. Curie, M.A., A.C.S.W.
Administrator
Substance Abuse and Mental Health
    Services Administration

H. Westley Clark, M.D., J.D., M.P.H.,
    CAS, FASAM
Director
Center for Substance Abuse Treatment
Substance Abuse and Mental Health
    Services Administration

Executive Summary and Recommendations

This TIP is based on a fundamental rethinking of the concept of motivation. Motivation is not seen as static but as dynamic. It is redefined here as purposeful, intentional, and positive—directed toward the best interests of the self. Specifically, motivation is considered to be related to the probability that a person will enter into, continue, and adhere to a specific change strategy. This TIP shows how substance abuse treatment staff can influence change by developing a therapeutic relationship that respects and builds on the client's autonomy and, at the same time, makes the treatment clinician a partner in the change process. The TIP also describes different motivational interventions that can be used at all stages of the change process, from precontemplation and preparation to action and maintenance, and informs readers of the research, results, tools, and assessment instruments related to enhancing motivation.

The primary purpose of this TIP is to link research to practice by providing clear applications of motivational approaches in clinical practice and treatment programs. This TIP also seeks to shift the conception of client motivation for change toward a view that empowers the treatment provider to elicit motivation. These approaches may be especially beneficial to particular populations (e.g., court-mandated offenders) with a low motivation for change.

Despite the preponderance of evidence supporting the efficacy of motivation-focused interventions, their use in the United States has occurred primarily in research settings. One obstacle to their implementation may be ideological: low motivation, denial, and resistance are often considered characteristic attributes of those diagnosed with substance abuse disorders. The cognitive–behavioral emphasis of motivational approaches, however, requires a different perspective on the nature of the problem and the prerequisites for change. This approach places greater responsibility on the clinician, whose job is now expanded to include engendering motivation. Rather than dismissing the more challenging clients as unmotivated, clinicians are equipped with skills to enhance motivation and to establish partnerships with their clients.

The Consensus Panel recommends that substance abuse treatment staff view motivation in this new light. Motivation for change is a key component in addressing substance abuse. The results of longitudinal research suggest that an individual's level of motivation is a very strong predictor of whether the individual's substance use will change or remain the same. Motivation-enhancing techniques are associated with increased participation in treatment and such positive treatment outcomes as reductions in consumption, higher abstinence rates, better social adjustment, and successful referrals to treatment. In addition, having a positive attitude toward change and being committed to change are associated with positive treatment outcomes. This is not a new insight. However, until relatively recently motivation was more commonly viewed as a static trait that the client either did or did not have. According to this view, the clinician has little chance of influencing a client's motivation. If the client is not motivated to change, it is the client's—not the clinician's—problem.

Recent models of change, however, recognize that change itself is influenced by biological, psychological, sociological, and spiritual variables. The capacity that each individual brings to the change process is affected by these variables. At the same time, these models recognize that although the client is ultimately responsible for change, this responsibility is shared with the clinician through the development of a "therapeutic partnership."

Chapter 1 of this TIP presents an overview of how the concepts of motivation and change have evolved in recent years and describes the "stages-of-change" model, developed by Prochaska and DiClemente and upon which this TIP is based. Chapter 2 presents interventions that can enhance clients' motivation, highlights their effective elements, and links them to the stages-of-change model. Developed by Miller and Rollnick, motivational interviewing is a therapeutic style used to interact with substance-using clients that can help them resolve issues related to their ambivalence; this is discussed in Chapter 3.

Chapters 4 through 7 address the five stages of change and provide guidelines for clinicians to tailor their treatment to clients' stages of readiness for change. Various tools and instruments used to measure components of change are summarized in Chapter 8. Chapter 9 provides examples of integrating motivational approaches into existing treatment programs. As motivational interventions are still a

relatively new field, there are many unanswered questions; Chapter 10 offers directions for future research.

In order to avoid awkward construction and sexism, this TIP alternates between "he" and "she" for generic examples.

Throughout this TIP, the term "substance abuse" has been used in a general sense to cover both substance abuse disorders and substance dependence disorders (as defined by the *Diagnostic and Statistical Manual of Mental Disorders*, 4th Edition [DSM-IV] [American Psychiatric Association, 1994]). Because the term "substance abuse" is commonly used by substance abuse treatment professionals to describe any excessive use of addictive substances, commencing with this TIP, it will be used to denote both substance dependence and substance abuse disorders. The term does relate to the use of alcohol as well as other substances of abuse. Readers should attend to the context in which the term occurs in order to determine what possible range of meanings it covers; in most cases, however, the term will refer to all varieties of substance use disorders as described by the DSM-IV.

Summary of Recommendations

The Consensus Panel's recommendations, summarized below, are based on both research and clinical experience. Those supported by scientific evidence are followed by (1); clinically based recommendations are marked (2). References for the former are cited in the body of this document, where the guidelines are presented in detail.

Conceptualizing Motivation

In the past 15 years, considerable research has focused on ways to better motivate substance-using clients to initiate and continue substance abuse treatment. A series of motivational approaches has been developed to elicit and enhance a substance-using client's motivation to change. These approaches are based on the following assumptions about the nature of motivation:

- Motivation is a key to change. (2)
- Motivation is multidimensional. (2)
- Motivation is a dynamic and fluctuating state. (2)
- Motivation is interactive. (2)
- Motivation can be modified. (2)
- The clinician's style influences client motivation. (2)

To incorporate these assumptions about motivation while encouraging a client to change substance-using behavior, the clinician can use the following strategies:

- Focus on the client's strengths rather than his weaknesses. (2)
- Respect the client's autonomy and decisions. (2)
- Make treatment individualized and client centered. (1)
- Do not depersonalize the client by using labels like "addict" or "alcoholic." (2)
- Develop a therapeutic partnership. (2)
- Use empathy, not authority or power. (1)
- Focus on early interventions. Extend motivational approaches into nontraditional settings. (2)
- Focus on less intensive treatments. (1)
- Recognize that substance abuse disorders exist along a continuum. (2)
- Recognize that many clients have more than one substance use disorder. (1)
- Recognize that some clients may have other coexisting disorders that affect all stages of the change process. (1)
- Accept new treatment goals, which involve interim, incremental, and even temporary steps toward ultimate goals. (2)
- Integrate substance abuse treatment with other disciplines. (2)

Motivational approaches build on these ideas. They seek to shift control away from the clinician and back to the client. They emphasize treating the client as an individual. They also recognize that treating substance abuse is a cyclical rather than a linear process and that recurrence of use does not necessarily signal failure.

Transtheoretical Model of Change

Substantial research has focused on the determinants and mechanisms of personal change. Theorists have developed various models for how behavior change happens. One perspective sees external consequences as being largely responsible for influencing individuals to change. Another model views intrinsic motivations as causing substance abuse disorders. Others believe that motivation is better described as a continuum of readiness than as one consisting of separate stages of change.

The transtheoretical stages-of-change model, described in Chapter 1, emerged from an examination of 18 psychological and behavioral theories about how change occurs, including components that make up the biopsychosocial framework for understanding addiction. This model of change provides the foundation for this TIP. The five stages of change are precontemplation, contemplation, preparation, action, and maintenance. These stages can be conceptualized as a cycle through which clients move back and forth. The stages are not viewed as linear, such that clients enter into one stage and then directly progress to the next. Framing clients' treatment within the stages of change can help the clinician better understand clients' treatment progress.

This model also takes into account that for most people with substance abuse problems, recurrence of substance use is the rule, not the exception. After a return to substance use, clients usually revert to an earlier change stage—not always to maintenance or action, but many times to some level of contemplation. In this model, recurrence is not equivalent to failure and does not mean that a client has abandoned a commitment to change. Thus, recurrence is not considered a stage but an event that can occur at any point along the cycle of recovery. Based on research and clinical experience, the Consensus Panel endorses the transtheoretical model as a useful model of change (1, 2); however, it is important to note that the model's use has been primarily conceptual and that no current technology is available to definitively determine an individual's stage of readiness for change.

Motivational Interventions

A motivational intervention is any clinical strategy designed to enhance client motivation for change. It can include counseling, client assessment, multiple sessions, or a 30-minute brief intervention. To understand what prompts a person to reduce or eliminate substance use, investigators have searched for the critical components—the most important and common elements that inspire positive change—of effective interventions. The Consensus Panel considers the following elements of current motivational approaches to be important:

- The FRAMES approach (1)
- Decisional balance exercises (1)
- Developing discrepancy (1)
- Flexible pacing (2)
- Personal contact with clients who are not actively in treatment (1)

The FRAMES approach consists of the following components:

- *Feedback* regarding personal risk or impairment is given to the individual following an assessment of substance use patterns and associated problems. This feedback usually compares the client's scores or ratings on standard tests with normative data from the general population or specified treatment groups.
- *Responsibility* for change is placed squarely and explicitly with the individual. Clients have the choice to either continue their substance use behavior or change it.
- *Advice* about changing—reducing or stopping—substance use is clearly given to the individual by the clinician in a nonjudgmental manner. It is better to *suggest* than to *tell*. Asking clients' permission to offer advice can make clients more receptive to that advice.
- *Menu* of self-directed change options and treatment alternatives is offered to the client.
- *Empathic* counseling, showing warmth, respect, and understanding, is emphasized. Empathy entails reflective listening.
- *Self-efficacy* or optimistic empowerment is engendered in the person to encourage change.

Research has shown that simple motivation-enhancing interventions are effective for encouraging clients to return for another clinical consultation, return to treatment following a missed appointment, stay involved in treatment, and be more compliant.

The simplicity and universality of the concepts underlying motivational interventions permit broad-scale application in many different settings and offer great potential to reach individuals with many types of problems and in many different cultures. This is important because treatment professionals work with a wide range of clients who differ with regard to ethnic and racial background, socioeconomic status, education level, gender, age, sexual orientation, type and severity of substance abuse problems, physical health, and psychological health. Although the principles and mechanisms of enhancing motivation to change seem to be broadly applicable, there may be important differences among populations and cultural contexts regarding the expression of motivation for change and the importance of critical life events. Therefore, clinicians should be thoroughly familiar with the populations with whom they expect to establish therapeutic relationships. (2)

Because motivational strategies emphasize clients' responsibilities to voice personal goals and values as well as to make choices among options for change, clinicians should understand and respond in a nonjudgmental way to expressions of cultural differences. They should identify elements in a population's values that present potential barriers to change. Clinicians should learn what personal and material resources are available to clients and be sensitive to issues of poverty, social isolation, or recent losses in offering options for change or probing personal values. In particular, it should be recognized that access to financial and social resources is an important part of the motivation for and process of change. (2)

Motivational Interviewing

Motivational interviewing is a therapeutic style intended to help clinicians work with clients to address their ambivalence. While conducting a motivational interview, the clinician is directive yet client centered, with a clear goal of eliciting self-motivational statements and behavioral change from the client, and seeking to create client discrepancy to enhance motivation for positive change. The Consensus Panel recommends that motivational interviewing be seen not as a set of techniques or tools, but rather as a way of interacting with clients. (2) The Panel believes that motivational interviewing is supported by the following principles:

- Ambivalence about substance use and change is normal and constitutes an important motivational obstacle in recovery. (2)

- Ambivalence can be resolved by working with the client's intrinsic motivations and values. (2)
- The alliance between client and clinician is a collaborative partnership to which each brings important expertise. (2)
- An empathic, supportive, yet directive counseling style provides conditions within which change can occur. (Direct argument and aggressive confrontation tend to increase client defensiveness, reducing the likelihood of change.) (2)

The motivational interviewing style facilitates an exploration of stage-specific motivational conflicts that can potentially hinder further progress. (1) However, each dilemma also offers an opportunity to use the motivational style as a way of helping clients explore and resolve opposing attitudes.

The Consensus Panel recognizes that successful motivational interviewing will entail being able to

- Express empathy through reflective listening. (1)
- Communicate respect for and acceptance of clients and their feelings. (2)
- Establish a nonjudgmental, collaborative relationship. (2)
- Be a supportive and knowledgeable consultant. (2)
- Compliment rather than denigrate. (2)
- Listen rather than tell. (2)
- Gently persuade, with the understanding that change is up to the client. (2)
- Provide support throughout the process of recovery. (2)
- Develop discrepancy between clients' goals or values and current behavior, helping clients recognize the discrepancies between where they are and where they hope to be. (2)

- Avoid argument and direct confrontation, which can degenerate into a power struggle. (2)
- Adjust to, rather than oppose, client resistance. (2)
- Support self-efficacy and optimism: that is, focus on clients' strengths to support the hope and optimism needed to make change. (2)

Clinicians who adopt motivational interviewing as a preferred style have found that the following five strategies are particularly useful in the early stages of treatment:

1. *Ask open-ended questions.* Open-ended questions cannot be answered with a single word or phrase. For example, rather than asking, "Do you like to drink?" ask, "What are some of the things that you like about drinking?" (2)
2. *Listen reflectively.* Demonstrate that you have heard and understood the client by reflecting what the client said. (2)
3. *Summarize.* It is useful to summarize periodically what has transpired up to that point in a counseling session. (2)
4. *Affirm.* Support and comment on the client's strengths, motivation, intentions, and progress. (2)
5. *Elicit self-motivational statements.* Have the client voice personal concerns and intentions, rather than try to persuade the client that change is necessary. (2)

Tailoring Motivational Interventions to the Stages of Change

Individuals appear to need and use different kinds of help, depending on which stage of readiness for change they are currently in and to which stage they are moving. (2) Clients who are in the early stages of readiness need and use different kinds of motivational support than do clients at later stages of the change cycle.

To encourage change, individuals in the precontemplation stage must increase their awareness. (2) To resolve their ambivalence, clients in the contemplation stage should choose positive change over the status quo. (2) Clients in the preparation stage must identify potential change strategies and choose the most appropriate one for their circumstances. Clients in the action stage must carry out change strategies. This is the stage toward which most formal substance abuse treatment is directed. During the maintenance stage, clients may have to develop new skills that help maintain recovery and a healthy lifestyle. Moreover, if clients resume their problem substance use, they need help to recover as quickly as possible and reenter the change process.

From precontemplation to contemplation

According to the stages-of-change model, individuals in the precontemplation stage are not concerned about their substance use or are not considering changing their behavior. These substance users may remain in precontemplation or early contemplation for years, rarely or never thinking about change. Often, a significant other finds the substance user's behavior problematic. Chapter 4 discusses a variety of proven techniques and gentle tactics that clinicians can use to address the topic of substance abuse with people who are not thinking of change. Use of these techniques will serve to (1) create client doubt about the commonly held belief that substance abuse is "harmless" and (2) lead to client conviction that substance abuse is having, or will in the future have, significant negative results. The chapter suggests that clinicians practice the following:

- Commend the client for coming to substance abuse treatment. (2)
- Establish rapport, ask permission to address the topic of change, and build trust. (2)

- Elicit, listen to, and acknowledge the aspects of substance use the client enjoys. (2)
- Evoke doubts or concerns in the client about substance use. (2)
- Explore the meaning of the events that brought the client to treatment or the results of previous treatments. (2)
- Obtain the client's perceptions of the problem. (2)
- Offer factual information about the risks of substance use. (2)
- Provide personalized feedback about assessment findings. (2)
- Help a significant other intervene. (2)
- Examine discrepancies between the client's and others' perceptions of the problem behavior. (2)
- Express concern and keep the door open. (2)

The assessment and feedback process can be an important part of the motivational strategy because it informs clients of how their own substance use patterns compare with norms, what specific risks are entailed, and what damage already exists or is likely to occur if changes are not made.

Giving clients personal results from a broad-based and objective assessment, especially if the findings are carefully interpreted and compared with norms or expected values, can be not only informative but also motivating. (1) Providing clients with personalized feedback on the risks associated with *their own* use of a particular substance—especially for their own cultural and gender groups—is a powerful way to develop a sense of *discrepancy* that can motivate change.

Intervening through significant others

Considerable research shows that involvement of family members or significant others (SOs) can help move substance-using persons toward contemplation of change, entry into treatment, involvement and retention in the therapeutic process, and successful recovery. (1) Involving SOs in the early stages of change can greatly enhance a client's commitment to change by addressing the client's substance use in the following ways:

- Providing constructive feedback to the client about the costs and benefits associated with her substance abuse (2)
- Encouraging the resolve of the client to change the negative behavior pattern (2)
- Identifying the client's concrete and emotional obstacles to change (2)
- Alerting the client to social and individual coping resources that lead to a substance-free lifestyle (2)
- Reinforcing the client for employing these social and coping resources to change the substance use behavior (2)

The clinician can engage an SO by asking the client to invite the SO to a treatment session. Explain that the SO will not be asked to monitor the client's substance use but that the SO can perform a valuable role by providing emotional support, identifying problems that might interfere with treatment goals, and participating in activities with the client that do not involve substance use. To strengthen the SO's belief in his capacity to help the client, the clinician can use the following strategies:

- Positively describe the steps used by the SO that have been successful (define "successful" generously). (2)
- Reinforce positive comments made by the SO about the client's current change efforts. (2)
- Discuss future ways in which the client might benefit from the SO's efforts to facilitate change. (2)

Clinicians should use caution when involving an SO in motivational counseling. Although a strong relationship between the SO and the client is necessary, it is not wholly sufficient. The SO must also support a client's substance-free life, and the client must value that support. (1) An SO who is experiencing hardships or emotional problems stemming from the client's substance use may not be a suitable candidate. (1) Such problems can preclude the SO from constructively participating in the counseling sessions, and it may be better to wait until the problems have subsided before including an SO in the client's treatment. (1)

In general, the SO can play a vital role in influencing the client's willingness to change; however, the client must be reminded that the responsibility to change substance use behavior is hers. (2)

Motivational interventions and coerced clients

An increasing number of clients are mandated to obtain treatment by an employer or employee assistance program, the court system, or probation and parole officers. Others are influenced to enter treatment because of legal pressures. The challenge for clinicians is to engage coerced clients in the treatment process. A stable recovery cannot be maintained by external (legal) pressure only; motivation and commitment must come from internal pressure. If you provide interventions appropriate to their stage, coerced clients may become invested in the change process and benefit from the opportunity to consider the consequences of use and the possibility of change—even though that opportunity was not voluntarily chosen. (2)

From contemplation to preparation

Extrinsic and intrinsic motivators should be considered when trying to increase a client's commitment to change and move the client closer to action because these motivators can be examined to enhance decisionmaking, thereby enhancing the client's commitment. Many clients move through the contemplation stage acknowledging only the extrinsic motivators pushing them to change or that brought them to treatment. Help the client discover intrinsic motivators, which typically move the client from contemplating change to acting. (2) In addition

to the standard practices for motivational interviewing (e.g., reflective listening, asking open-ended questions), clinicians can help spur this process of changing extrinsic motivators to intrinsic motivators by doing the following:

- Show curiosity about clients. Because a client's desire to change is seldom limited to substance use, he may find it easier to discuss changing other behaviors. This will help strengthen the therapeutic alliance. (2)
- Reframe a client's negative statement about perceived coercion by re-expressing the statement with a positive spin. (2)

Clinicians can use decisional balancing strategies to help clients thoughtfully consider the positive and negative aspects of their substance use. (1) The ultimate purpose, of course, is to help clients recognize and weigh the negative aspects of substance use so that the scale tips toward beneficial behavior. Techniques to use in decisional balancing exercises include the following:

- Summarize the client's concerns. (2)
- Explore specific pros and cons of substance use behavior. (1)
- Normalize the client's ambivalence. (2)
- Reintroduce feedback from previous assessments. (1)
- Examine the client's understanding of change and expectations of treatment. (1)
- Reexplore the client's values in relation to change. (2)

Throughout this process, emphasize the clients' personal choices and responsibilities for change. The clinician's task is to help clients make choices that are in their best interests. This can be done by exploring and setting goals. Goal-setting is part of the exploring and envisioning activities characteristic of the early and middle preparation stage. The process of talking about and setting goals strengthens commitment to change. (1)

During the preparation stage, the clinician's tasks broaden from using motivational strategies to increase readiness—the goals of precontemplation and contemplation stages—to using these strategies to strengthen a client's commitment and help her make a firm decision to change. At this stage, helping the client develop self-efficacy is important. (2) Self-efficacy is not a global measure, like self-esteem; rather, it is behavior specific. In this case, it is the client's optimism that she can take action to change substance-use behaviors.

From preparation to action

As clients move through the preparation stage, clinicians should be alert for signs of clients' readiness to move into action. There appears to be a limited period of time during which change should be initiated. (2) Clients' recognition of important discrepancies in their lives is too uncomfortable a state to remain in for long, and unless change is begun they can retreat to using defenses such as minimizing or denying to decrease the discomfort. (2) The following can signal a client's readiness to act:

- The client's resistance (i.e., arguing, denying) decreases. (2)
- The client asks fewer questions about the problem. (2)
- The client shows a certain amount of resolve and may be more peaceful, calm, relaxed, unburdened, or settled. (2)
- The client makes direct self-motivational statements reflecting openness to change and optimism. (2)
- The client asks more questions about the change process. (2)
- The client begins to talk about how life might be after a change. (2)
- The client may have begun experimenting with possible change approaches such as going to an Alcoholics Anonymous meeting or stopping substance use for a few days. (2)

Mere vocal fervor about change, however, is not necessarily a sign of dogged determination. Clients who are most vehement in declaring their readiness may be desperately trying to convince themselves, as well as the clinician, of their commitment.

When working with clients in the preparation stage, clinicians should try to

- Clarify the client's own goals and strategies for change. (2)
- Discuss the range of different treatment options and community resources available to meet the client's multiple needs. (2)
- With permission, offer expertise and advice. (2)
- Negotiate a change—or treatment—plan and a behavior contract (2); take into consideration
  - Intensity and amount of help needed
  - Timeframe
  - Available social support, identifying who, where, and when
  - The sequence of smaller goals or steps needed for a successful plan
  - Multiple problems, such as legal, financial, or health concerns
- Consider and lower barriers to change by anticipating possible family, health, system, and other problems. (2)
- Help the client enlist social support (e.g., mentoring groups, churches, recreational centers). (2)
- Explore treatment expectancies and client role. (2)
- Have clients publicly announce their change plans to significant others in their lives. (2)

From action to maintenance

A motivational counseling style has most frequently been used with clients in the precontemplation through preparation stages as they move toward initiating behavioral change. Some clients and clinicians believe that formal, action-oriented substance abuse treatment is a different domain and that motivational strategies are no longer required. This is not true for two reasons. First, clients may still need a surprising amount of support and encouragement to stay with a chosen program or course of treatment. Even after a successful discharge, they may need support and encouragement to maintain the gains they have achieved and to know how to handle recurring crises that may mean a return to problem behaviors. (2) Second, many clients remain ambivalent in the action stage of change or vacillate between some level of contemplation—with associated ambivalence—and continuing action. (2) Moreover, clients who do take action are suddenly faced with the reality of stopping or reducing substance use. This is more difficult than just contemplating action. The first stages of recovery require only thinking about change, which is not as threatening as actually implementing it.

Clients' involvement or participation in treatment can be increased when clinicians

- Develop a nurturing rapport with clients. (2)
- Induct clients into their role in the treatment process. (2)
- Explore what clients expect from treatment and determine discrepancies. (2)
- Prepare clients so that they know there may be some embarrassing, emotionally awkward, and uncomfortable moments but that such moments are a normal part of the recovery process. (2)
- Investigate and resolve barriers to treatment. (2)
- Increase congruence between intrinsic and extrinsic motivation. (2)
- Examine and interpret noncompliant behavior in the context of ambivalence. (2)
- Reach out to demonstrate continuing personal concern and interest to encourage clients to remain in the program. (2)

Clients who are in the action stage can be most effectively helped when clinicians

- Engage clients in treatment and reinforce the importance of remaining in recovery. (2)
- Support a realistic view of change through small steps. (2)
- Acknowledge difficulties for clients in early stages of change. (2)
- Help the client identify high-risk situations through a functional analysis and develop appropriate coping strategies to overcome these. (2)
- Assist the client in finding new reinforcers of positive change. (2)
- Assess whether the client has strong family and social support. (2)

The next challenge that clients and clinicians face is maintaining change. With clients in the maintenance stage, clinicians will be most successful if they can

- Help the client identify and sample substance-free sources of pleasure—i.e., new reinforcers. (1)
- Support lifestyle changes. (2)
- Affirm the client's resolve and self-efficacy. (2)
- Help the client practice and use new coping strategies to avoid a return to substance use. (2)
- Maintain supportive contact. (2)

After clients have planned for stabilization by identifying risky situations, practicing new coping strategies, and finding their sources of support, they still have to build a new lifestyle that will provide sufficient satisfaction and can compete successfully against the lure of substance use. A wide range of life changes ultimately needs to be made if clients are to maintain lasting abstinence. Clinicians can help this change process by using competing reinforcers. (1) A competing reinforcer is anything that clients enjoy that is or can become a healthy alternative to drugs or alcohol as a source of satisfaction.

The essential principle in establishing new sources of positive reinforcement is to get clients involved in generating their own ideas. Clinicians should explore all areas of clients' lives for new reinforcers. Reinforcers should not come from a single source or be of the same type. That way, a setback in one area can be counterbalanced by the availability of positive reinforcement from another area. Since clients have competing motivations, clinicians can help them select reinforcers that will *win out* over substances over time.

Following are a number of potential competing reinforcers that can help clients:

- Doing volunteer work, thus filling time, connecting with socially acceptable friends, and improving their self-efficacy (2)
- Becoming involved in 12–Step-based activities and other self-help groups (2)
- Setting goals to improve their work, education, exercise, and nutrition (2)
- Spending more time with their families and significant others (2)
- Participating in spiritual or cultural activities (2)
- Socializing with nonsubstance-using friends (2)
- Learning new skills or improving in such areas as sports, art, music, and other hobbies (2)

Contingency reinforcement systems, such as voucher programs, have proven to be effective when community support and resources are available. (1) Research has shown that these kinds of reinforcement systems can help to sustain abstinence in drug abusers. The rationale for this type of incentive program is that an appealing external motivator can be used as an immediate and powerful reinforcer to compete with substance use reinforcers. Not all contingent incentives have to have a monetary

value. In many cultures, money is not the most powerful reinforcer.

Measuring Client Motivation

Because motivation is multidimensional, it cannot be easily measured with one instrument or scale. Instead, the Consensus Panel recommends that substance abuse treatment staff use a variety of tools to measure several dimensions of motivation, including (2):

- Self-efficacy
- Importance of change
- Readiness to change
- Decisional balancing
- Motivations for using substances

Integrating Motivational Approaches Into Treatment Programs

One of the principles of current health care management is that the most intensive and expensive treatments should be used only with those with the most serious problems or with those who have not responded to lesser interventions. Motivational interventions can serve many purposes in treatment settings:

- As a means of rapid engagement in the general medical setting to facilitate referral to treatment (2)
- As a first session to increase the likelihood that a client will return and to deliver a useful service if the client does not return (1)
- As an empowering brief consultation when a client is placed on a waiting list, rather than telling a client to wait for treatment (1)
- As a preparation for treatment to increase retention and participation (1)
- To help clients coerced into treatment to move beyond initial feelings of anger and resentment (2)
- To overcome client defensiveness and resistance (2)
- As a stand-alone intervention in settings where there is only brief contact (1)

- As a counseling style used throughout the process of change (1)

Need for Future Research

Motivational interventions are a relatively new, but favorably received, approach to encouraging positive behavioral change. As indicated earlier, motivational interventions have been successfully used with a variety of problems, client populations, and settings, and the methodology appears to be generally applicable, although it was developed primarily with heavy alcohol drinkers and cigarette smokers.

Researchers should consider some of the following questions when planning and developing future research studies (2):

- What are the active ingredients of motivational interventions?
- Can motivational interventions be standardized and taught?
- What types of clients are most amenable to motivational interventions?
- What types of outcomes can be defined and measured?
- What clinician characteristics affect the outcomes of motivational interventions?
- Are stage-matched interventions appropriate?
- How do motivational interventions compare with other substance abuse treatments in terms of cost-effectiveness?
- How do culture and context influence the effectiveness of motivational interventions?
- What kinds of training and support are needed to teach motivational interventions?
- How can motivational interventions be applied successfully to an even broader variety of problems, populations, and settings?

To Which Clients Does This TIP Apply?

Motivational interviewing was originally developed for problem alcohol drinkers in the early stages (precontemplation and contemplation) of readiness for change and was conceived as a way of initiating treatment. However, it soon became apparent that this approach constitutes an intervention in itself. Benefits have been reported with severely substance-dependent populations, polydrug-abusing adolescents, and users of heroin and marijuana. In Project MATCH, the largest clinical trial ever conducted to compare different alcohol treatment methods, a four-session motivational enhancement therapy yielded long-term overall outcomes virtually identical to those of longer outpatient methods. Clients varied widely in problem severity; the vast majority met criteria for alcohol dependence, and they represented a range of cultural backgrounds, particularly Hispanic. It is noteworthy that neither Hispanic nor African-American samples responded differentially to the motivational enhancement therapy approach. In addition, analyses of clinical trials of motivational interviewing that had substantial representation of Hispanic clients found no indication of self-identified ethnicity and socioeconomic status as predictors of outcome. Evidence strongly suggests that motivational interviewing can be applied across cultural and economic differences.

The motivational style of counseling can be useful, not only to instill motivation initially, but throughout the process of treatment in the preparation, action, and maintenance stages as well, with a range of client populations. This is reflected in the following chapters of this TIP.

1 Conceptualizing Motivation And Change

Motivation can be understood not as something that one has but rather as something one does. It involves recognizing a problem, searching for a way to change, and then beginning and sticking with that change strategy. There are, it turns out, many ways to help people move toward such recognition and action.

Miller, 1995

Why do people change? What is motivation? Can individuals' motivation to change their substance-using behavior be modified? Do clinicians have a role in enhancing substance-using clients' motivation for recovery?

Over the past 15 years, considerable research and clinical attention have focused on ways to better motivate substance users to consider, initiate, and continue substance abuse treatment, as well as to stop or reduce their excessive use of alcohol, cigarettes, and drugs, either on their own or with the help of a formal program. A related focus has been on sustaining change and avoiding a recurrence of problem behavior following treatment discharge. This research represents a paradigmatic shift in the addiction field's understanding of the nature of client motivation and the clinician's role in shaping it to promote and maintain positive behavioral change. This shift parallels other recent developments in the addiction field, and the new motivational strategies incorporate or reflect many of these developments. Coupling a new therapeutic style—motivational interviewing—with a transtheoretical stages-of-change model offers a fresh perspective on what clinical strategies may be effective at various points in the recovery process. Motivational interventions resulting from this theoretical construct are promising clinical tools that can be incorporated into all phases of substance abuse treatment as well as many other social and health services settings.

A New Look at Motivation

In substance abuse treatment, clients' motivation to change has often been the focus of clinical interest and frustration. Motivation has been described as a prerequisite for treatment, without which the clinician can do little (Beckman, 1980). Similarly, lack of motivation has been used to explain the failure of individuals to begin, continue, comply with, and succeed in treatment (Appelbaum, 1972; Miller, 1985b). Until recently, motivation was viewed as a static trait or disposition that a client either did or did not have. If a client was not motivated for change, this was viewed as the client's fault. In fact, motivation for treatment connoted an agreement or willingness to go along with a clinician's or program's particular prescription for recovery. A client who seemed amenable to clinical advice or accepted the label of "alcoholic" or "drug addict" was considered to be motivated, whereas one who resisted a diagnosis or refused to adhere to the proffered treatment was deemed unmotivated. Furthermore, motivation was often viewed as the client's responsibility, not the clinician's (Miller and Rollnick, 1991). Although there are reasons why this view developed that will be discussed later, this guideline views motivation from a substantially different perspective.

A New Definition

The motivational approaches described in this TIP are based on the following assumptions about the nature of motivation:

- Motivation is a key to change.
- Motivation is multidimensional.
- Motivation is dynamic and fluctuating.
- Motivation is influenced by social interactions.
- Motivation can be modified.
- Motivation is influenced by the clinician's style.
- The clinician's task is to elicit and enhance motivation.

Motivation is a key to change

The study of motivation is inexorably linked to an understanding of personal change—a concept that has also been scrutinized by modern psychologists and theorists and is the focus of substance abuse treatment. The nature of change and its causes, like motivation, is a complex construct with evolving definitions.

Few of us, for example, take a completely deterministic view of change as an inevitable result of biological forces, yet most of us accept the reality that physical growth and maturation do produce change—the baby begins to walk and the adolescent seems to be driven by hormonal changes. We recognize, too, that social norms and roles can change responses, influencing behaviors as diverse as selecting clothes or joining a gang, although few of us want to think of ourselves as simply conforming to what others expect. Certainly, we believe that reasoning and problem-solving as well as emotional commitment can promote change.

The framework for linking individual change to a new view of motivation stems from what has been termed a *phenomenological* theory of psychology, most familiarly expressed in the writings of Carl Rogers. In this humanistic view, an individual's experience of the core inner *self* is the most important element for personal change and growth—a process of *self-actualization* that prompts goal-directed behavior for enhancing this self (Davidson, 1994). In this context, motivation is redefined as purposeful, intentional, and positive—directed toward the best interests of the self. More specifically, motivation is the probability that a person will enter into, continue, and adhere to a specific change strategy (Miller and Rollnick, 1991).

Motivation is multidimensional

Motivation, in this new meaning, has a number of complex components that will be discussed in subsequent chapters of this TIP. It encompasses the internal urges and desires felt by the client, external pressures and goals that influence the client, perceptions about risks and benefits of behaviors to the self, and cognitive appraisals of the situation.

Motivation is dynamic and fluctuating

Research and experience suggest that motivation is a dynamic state that can fluctuate over time and in relation to different situations, rather than a static personal attribute. Motivation can vacillate between conflicting objectives. Motivation also varies in intensity, faltering in response to doubts and increasing as these are resolved and goals are more clearly envisioned. In this sense, motivation can be an ambivalent, equivocating state or a resolute readiness to act—or not to act.

Motivation is influenced by social interactions

Motivation belongs to one person, yet it can be understood to result from the interactions between the individual and other people or environmental factors (Miller, 1995b). Although internal factors are the basis for change, external factors are the conditions of change. An individual's motivation to change can be strongly influenced by family, friends, emotions, and community support. Lack of community support, such as barriers to health care, employment, and public perception of substance abuse, can also affect an individual's motivation.

Motivation can be modified

Motivation pervades all activities, operating in multiple contexts and at all times. Consequently, motivation is accessible and can be modified or enhanced at many points in the change process. Clients may not have to "hit bottom" or experience terrible, irreparable consequences of their behaviors to become aware of the need for change. Clinicians and others can access and enhance a person's motivation to change well before extensive damage is done to health, relationships, reputation, or self-image (Miller, 1985; Miller et al., 1993).

Although there are substantial differences in what factors influence people's motivation, several types of experiences may have dramatic effects, either increasing or decreasing motivation. Experiences such as the following often prompt people to begin thinking about making changes and to consider what steps are needed:

- *Distress levels* may have a role in increasing the motivation to change or search for a change strategy (Leventhal, 1971; Rogers et al., 1978). For example, many individuals are prompted to change and seek help during or following episodes of severe anxiety or depression.

- *Critical life events* often stimulate the motivation to change. Milestones that prompt change range from spiritual inspiration or religious conversion through traumatic accidents or severe illnesses to deaths of loved ones, being fired, becoming pregnant, or getting married (Sobell et al., 1993b; Tucker et al., 1994).

- *Cognitive evaluation or appraisal,* in which an individual evaluates the impact of substances in his life, can lead to change. This weighing of the pros and cons of substance use accounts for 30 to 60 percent of the changes reported in natural recovery studies (Sobell et al., 1993b).

- *Recognizing negative consequences* and the harm or hurt one has inflicted on others or oneself helps motivate some people to change (Varney et al., 1995). Helping clients see the connection between substance use and adverse consequences to themselves or others is an important motivational strategy.

- *Positive and negative external incentives* also can influence motivation. Supportive and empathic friends, rewards, or coercion of various types may stimulate motivation for change.

Motivation is influenced by the clinician's style

The way you, the clinician, interact with clients has a crucial impact on how they respond and whether treatment is successful. Researchers have found dramatic differences in rates of client dropout or completion among counselors in the same program who are ostensibly using the same techniques (Luborsky et al., 1985). Counselor style may be one of the most important, and most often ignored, variables for predicting client response to an intervention, accounting for more of the variance than client characteristics (Miller and Baca, 1983; Miller et al., 1993). In a review of the literature on counselor characteristics associated with treatment effectiveness for substance users, researchers found that establishing a helping alliance and good interpersonal skills were more important than professional training or experience (Najavits and Weiss, 1994). The most desirable attributes for the counselor mirror those recommended in the general psychological literature and include nonpossessive warmth, friendliness, genuineness, respect, affirmation, and empathy.

A direct comparison of counselor styles suggested that a confrontational and directive approach may precipitate more immediate client resistance and, ultimately, poorer outcomes than a client-centered, supportive, and empathic style that uses reflective listening and gentle persuasion (Miller et al., 1993). In this study, the more a client was confronted, the more alcohol the client drank. Confrontational counseling in this study included challenging the client, disputing, refuting, and using sarcasm.

The clinician's task is to elicit and enhance motivation

Although change is the responsibility of the client and many people change their excessive substance-using behavior on their own without therapeutic intervention (Sobell et al., 1993b), you can enhance your client's motivation for beneficial change at each stage of the change process. Your task is not, however, one of simply teaching, instructing, or dispensing advice. Rather, the clinician assists and encourages clients to recognize a problem behavior (e.g., by encouraging cognitive dissonance), to regard positive change to be in

their best interest, to feel competent to change, to develop a plan for change, to begin taking action, and to continue using strategies that discourage a return to the problem behavior (Miller and Rollnick, 1991). Be sensitive to influences such as your client's cultural background; knowledge or lack thereof can influence your client's motivation.

Why Enhance Motivation?

Research has shown that motivation-enhancing approaches are associated with greater participation in treatment and positive treatment outcomes. Such outcomes include reductions in consumption, increased abstinence rates, social adjustment, and successful referrals to treatment (Landry, 1996; Miller et al., 1995a). A positive attitude toward change and a commitment to change are also associated with positive treatment outcomes (Miller and Tonigan, 1996; Prochaska and DiClemente, 1992).

The benefits of employing motivational enhancement techniques include

- Inspiring motivation to change
- Preparing clients to enter treatment
- Engaging and retaining clients in treatment
- Increasing participation and involvement
- Improving treatment outcomes
- Encouraging a rapid return to treatment if symptoms recur

Changing Perspectives on Addiction and Treatment

Americans have often shown ambivalence toward excessive drug and alcohol use. They have vacillated between viewing offenders as morally corrupt sinners who are the concern of the clergy and the law and seeing them as victims of compulsive craving who should receive medical treatment. After the passage of the Harrison Narcotics Act in 1914, physicians were imprisoned for treating addicts. In the

1920s, compassionate treatment of opiate dependence and withdrawal was available in medical clinics, yet at the same time, equally passionate support of the temperance movement and Prohibition was gaining momentum. These conflicting views were further manifested in public notions of who deserved treatment (e.g., Midwestern farm wives addicted to laudanum) and who did not (e.g., urban African-Americans).

Different views about the nature and etiology of addiction have more recently influenced the development and practice of current treatments for substance abuse. Differing theoretical perspectives have guided the structure and organization of treatment and the services delivered (Institute of Medicine, 1990b). Comparing substance abuse treatment to a swinging pendulum, one writer noted,

> Notions of moral turpitude and incurability have been linked with problems of drug dependence for at least a century. Even now, public and professional attitudes toward alcoholism are an amalgam of contrasting, sometimes seemingly irreconcilable views: The alcoholic is both *sick* and *morally weak*. The attitudes toward those who are dependent on opiates are a similar amalgam, with the element of moral defect in somewhat greater proportion (Jaffee, 1979, p. 9).

Evolving Models of Treatment

The development of a modern treatment system for substance abuse dates only from the late 1960s, with the decriminalization of public drunkenness and the escalation of fears about crime associated with increasing heroin addiction. Nonetheless, the system has rapidly evolved in response to new technologies, research, and changing theories of addiction with associated therapeutic interventions. The six models of addiction described below have competed for attention and guided the application of treatment strategies over the last 30 years.

Moral model

Addiction is viewed by some as a set of behaviors that violate religious, moral, or legal codes of conduct. From this perspective, addiction results from a freely chosen behavior that is immoral, perhaps sinful, and sometimes illegal. It assumes that individuals who choose to misuse substances create suffering for themselves and others and lack self-discipline and self-restraint. Substance misuse and abuse are irresponsible and intentional actions that deserve punishment (Wilbanks, 1989), including arrest and incarceration (Thombs, 1994). Because excessive substance use is seen as the result of a moral choice, change can only come about by an exercise of will power (IOM, 1990b), external punishment, or incarceration.

Medical model

A contrasting view of addiction as a chronic and progressive disease inspired what has come to be called the medical model of treatment, which evolved from earlier forms of disease models that stressed the need for humane treatment and hypothesized a dichotomy between "normals" and "addicts" or "alcoholics." The latter were asserted to differ qualitatively, physiologically, and irreversibly from normal individuals. More recent medical models take a broader "biopsychosocial" view, consonant with a modern understanding of chronic diseases as multiply determined.

Nevertheless, emphasis continues to be placed on physical causes. In this view, genetic factors increase the likelihood for an individual to misuse psychoactive substances or to lose control when using them. Neurochemical changes in the brain resulting from substance use then induce continuing consumption, as does the development of physiological dependence. Treatment in this model is typically delivered in a hospital or medical setting and includes various pharmacological therapies to assist detoxification, symptom reduction, aversion, or maintenance on suitable alternatives.

Responsibility for resolving the problem does not rest with the client, and change can come about only through acknowledging loss of control, adhering to medical prescriptions, and participating in a self-help group (IOM, 1990b).

Spiritual model

The spiritual model of addiction is one of the most influential in America, largely because of such 12-Step fellowships as Alcoholics Anonymous (AA), Cocaine Anonymous, Narcotics Anonymous, and Al-Anon. This model is often confused with the moral and medical models, but its emphasis is quite distinct from these (Miller and Kurtz, 1994). In the original writings of AA, there is discussion of "defects of character" as central to understanding alcoholism, with particular emphasis on issues such as pride versus humility and resentment versus acceptance. In this view, substances are used in an attempt to fill a spiritual emptiness and meaninglessness.

Spiritual models give much less weight to etiology than to the importance of a spiritual path to recovery. Twelve-Step programs emphasize recognizing a Higher Power (often called God in AA) beyond one's self, asking for healing of character, maintaining communication with the Higher Power through prayer and meditation, and seeking to conform one's life to its will. Twelve-Step programs are not wholly "self-help" programs but rather "Higher Power–help" programs. The first of the 12 steps is to recognize that one literally cannot help oneself or find recovery through the power of one's own will. Instead, the path back to health is spiritual, involving surrender of the will to a Higher Power. Clinicians follow various guidelines in supporting their clients' involvement in 12-Step programs (Tonigan et al., 1999).

Twelve-Step programs are rooted in American Protestantism, but other distinctly spiritual models do not rely on Christian or even theistic thought. Transcendental meditation, based on Eastern spiritual practice, has been widely practiced as a method for preventing and recovering from substance abuse problems (Marlatt and Kristeller, 1999). Native American spirituality has been integrated into treatment programs serving Native American populations through the use of sweat lodges and other traditional rituals, such as singing and healing ceremonies. Spiritual models all share a recognition of the limitations of the self and a desire to achieve health through a connection with that which transcends the individual.

Psychological model

In the psychological model of addiction, problematic substance use results from deficits in learning, emotional dysfunction, or psychopathology that can be treated by behaviorally or psychoanalytically oriented dynamic therapies. Sigmund Freud's pioneering work has had a deep and lasting effect on substance abuse treatment. He originated the notion of defense mechanisms (e.g., denial, projection, rationalization), focused on the importance of early childhood experiences, and developed the idea of the unconscious mind. Early psychoanalysis viewed substance abuse disorders as originating from unconscious death wishes and self-destructive tendencies of the id (Thombs, 1994). Substance dependence was believed to be a slow form of suicide (Khantzian, 1980). Other early psychoanalytic writers emphasized the role of oral fixation in substance dependence. A more contemporary psychoanalytic view is that substance use is a symptom of impaired ego functioning—a part of the personality that mediates the demands of the id and the realities of the external world. Another view considers substance abuse disorders as "both developmental and adaptive" (Khantzian et al., 1990).

From this perspective, the use of substances is an attempt to compensate for vulnerabilities in the ego structure. Substance use, then, is motivated by an inability to regulate one's inner life and external behavior. Thus, psychoanalytic treatment assumes that insight obtained through the treatment process results in the strengthening of internal mechanisms, which becomes evident by the establishment of external controls; in other words, the change process shifts from internal (intrapsychic) to external (behavioral, interpersonal). An interesting psychoanalytic parallel to modern motivational theory is found in the writings of Anton Kris, who described the "conflicts of ambivalence" seen in clients that

> May cast a paralyzing inertia not only upon the patient but upon the treatment method. In such instances, patient and analyst, like the driver of an automobile stuck in a snowdrift, must aim at a rocking motion that eventually gathers enough momentum to permit movement in one direction or another (Kris, 1984, p. 224).

Other practitioners view addiction as a symptom of an underlying mental disorder. From this perspective, successful treatment of the primary psychiatric disorder should result in resolution of the substance use problem. However, over the past decade, substantial research and clinical attention have revealed a more complex relationship between psychiatric and substance abuse disorders and symptoms. Specifically, substance use can cause psychiatric symptoms and mimic psychiatric disorders; substance use can prompt or worsen the severity of psychiatric disorders; substance use can mask psychiatric disorders and symptoms; withdrawal from severe substance dependence can precipitate psychiatric symptoms and mimic psychiatric disorders; psychiatric and substance abuse disorders can coexist; and psychiatric disorders can produce behaviors that mimic ones associated with substance use problems (CSAT, 1994b; Landry et al., 1991).

From the perspective of behavioral psychology, substance use is a learned behavior that is repeated in direct relation to the quality, number, and intensity of *reinforcers* that follow each episode of use (McAuliffe and Gordon, 1980). Addiction is based on the principle that people tend to repeat certain behaviors if they are reinforced for engaging in them. Positive reinforcers of substance use depend on the substance used but include powerful effects on the central nervous system. Other social variables, such as peer group acceptance, can also act as positive reinforcers. Negative reinforcers include lessened anxiety and elimination of withdrawal symptoms. A person's experiences and expectations in relation to the effects of selected substances on certain emotions or situations will determine substance-using patterns. Change comes about if the reinforcers are outweighed or replaced by negative consequences, also known as *punishers*, and the client learns to apply strategies for coping with situations that lead to substance use.

Other psychologists have emphasized the role of cognitive processes in addictive behavior. Bandura's concept of self-efficacy—the perceived ability to change or control one's own behavior—has been influential in modern conceptions of addiction (Bandura, 1997). Cognitive therapists have described treatment approaches for modifying pathogenic beliefs that may underlie substance abuse (Beck et al., 1993; Ellis and Velten, 1992).

Sociocultural model

A related, sociocultural perspective on addiction emphasizes the importance of socialization processes and the cultural milieu in developing—and ameliorating—substance abuse disorders. Factors that affect drinking behavior include socioeconomic status, cultural and ethnic beliefs, availability of substances, laws and penalties regulating substance use, the norms and rules of families and other social groups as well as parental and peer expectations, modeling of acceptable behaviors, and the presence or absence of reinforcers. Because substance-related problems are seen as occurring in interactive relations with families, groups, and communities, alterations in policies, laws, and norms are part of the change process. Building new social and family relations, developing social competency and skills, and working within one's cultural infrastructure are important avenues for change in the sociocultural model (IOM, 1990b). From the sociocultural perspective, an often neglected aspect of positive behavioral change is sorting out ethical principles or renewing opportunities for spiritual growth that can ameliorate the guilt, shame, regret, and sadness about the substance-related harm clients may have inflicted on themselves and others.

Composite biopsychosocial–spiritual model

As the conflicts among these competing models of addiction have become evident and as research has confirmed some truth in each model, the addiction field has searched for a single construct to integrate these diverse perspectives (Wallace, 1990). This has led to an emerging biopsychosocial–spiritual framework that recognizes the importance of many interacting influences. Indeed, the current view is that all chronic diseases, whether substance use, cancer, diabetes, or coronary artery disease, are best treated by collaborative and comprehensive approaches that address both biopsychosocial and spiritual components (Borysenko and Borysenko, 1995; Williams and Williams, 1994). This overarching model of addiction retains the proven elements and techniques of each of the preceding models while eliminating some previous—and erroneous—assumptions, which are discussed below.

Myths About Client Traits and Effective Counseling

Although the field is evolving toward a more comprehensive understanding of substance misuse and abuse, earlier views of addiction still persist in parts of our treatment system. Some of these are merely anachronisms; others may actually harm clients. Recent research has shown that some types of interventions that have been historically embedded within treatment approaches in the United States may paradoxically reduce motivation for beneficial change. Other persisting stereotypes also interfere with the establishment of a helping alliance or partnership between the clinician and the client. Among the suppositions about clients and techniques that are being questioned and discarded are those discussed below.

Addiction stems from an addictive personality

Although it is commonly believed that substance abusers possess similar personality traits that make treatment difficult, no distinctive personality traits have been found to predict that an individual will develop a substance abuse disorder. The tendencies of an addictive personality most often cited are denial, projection, poor insight, and poor self-esteem. Research efforts, many of which have focused on clients with alcohol dependence, suggest there is no characteristic personality among substance-dependent individuals (Løberg and Miller, 1986; Miller, 1976; Vaillant, 1995). Rather, research suggests that people with substance abuse problems reflect a broad range of personalities. Nonetheless, the existence of an addictive personality continues to be a popular belief. One reason for this may be that certain similarities of behavior, emotion, cognition, and family dynamics do tend to emerge along the course of a substance abuse disorder. In the course of recovery, these similarities diminish, and people again become more diverse.

Resistance and denial are attributes of addiction

Engaging in denial, rationalization, evasion, defensiveness, manipulation, and resistance are characteristics that are often attributed to substance users. Furthermore, because these responses can be barriers to successful treatment, clinicians and interventions often focus on these issues. Research, however, has not supported the conclusion that substance-dependent persons, as a group, have abnormally robust defense mechanisms.

There are several possible explanations for this belief. The first is selective perception—that is, in retrospect, exceptionally difficult clients are elevated to become *models* of usual responses. Moreover, the terms "denial" and "resistance" are often used to describe lack of compliance or motivation among substance users, whereas the term "motivation" is reserved for such concepts as acceptance and surrender (Kilpatrick et al., 1978; Nir and Cutler, 1978; Taleff, 1997). Thus, clients who disagree with clinicians, who refuse to accept clinicians' diagnoses, and who reject treatment advice are often labeled as unmotivated, in denial, and resistant (Miller, 1985b; Miller and Rollnick, 1991). In other words, the term "denial" can be misused to describe disagreements, misunderstandings, or clinician expectations that differ from clients' personal goals and may reflect countertransference issues (Taleff, 1997).

Another explanation is that behaviors judged as normal in ordinary individuals are labeled as pathological when observed in substance-addicted populations (Orford, 1985). Clinicians and others expect substance users to exhibit pathological—or abnormally strong—defense mechanisms. A third explanation is that treatment procedures actually set up many clients to react defensively. Denial, rationalization, resistance, and arguing, as assertions of personal freedom, are common defense mechanisms that many people use instinctively to protect themselves emotionally (Brehm and Brehm, 1981). When clients are labeled pejoratively as *alcoholic* or *manipulative* or *resistant*, given no voice in selecting treatment goals, or directed authoritatively to do or not to do something, the result is a predictable—and quite normal—response of defiance. Moreover, when clinicians assume that these defenses must be confronted and "broken" by adversarial tactics, treatment can become counterproductive (Taleff, 1997). A strategy of aggressive confrontation is likely to evoke strong resistance and outright denial. Hence, one reason that high levels of denial and resistance are often seen as attributes of substance-dependent individuals as a group is that their normal defense mechanisms are so frequently challenged and aroused by clinical strategies of confrontation. Essentially, this becomes a self-fulfilling prophecy (Jones, 1977).

Confrontation is an effective counseling style

In contemporary treatment, the term "confrontation" has several meanings, referring usually to a type of intervention (a planned confrontation) or to a counseling style (a confrontational session). The term can reflect the assumption that denial and other defense mechanisms must be aggressively "broken through" or "torn down," using therapeutic approaches that can be characterized as authoritarian and adversarial (Taleff, 1997). As just noted, this type of confrontation may promote resistance rather than motivation to change or cooperate. Research suggests that the more frequently clinicians use adversarial confrontational techniques with substance-using clients, the less likely clients will change (Miller et al., 1993), and controlled clinical trials place confrontational approaches among the least effective treatment methods (Miller et al., 1998).

There is, however, a constructive type of therapeutic confrontation. If helping clients confront and assess the reality of their behaviors

What About Confrontation?

For a number of reasons, the treatment field in the United States fell into some rather aggressive, argumentative, "denial-busting" methods for confronting people with alcohol and drug problems. This was guided in part by the belief that substance abuse is accompanied by a particular personality pattern characterized by such rigid defense mechanisms as denial and rationalization. Within this perspective, the clinician must take responsibility for impressing reality on clients, who are thought to be unable to see it on their own. Such confrontation found its way into the popular Minnesota model of treatment and, more particularly, into Synanon (a drug treatment community well known for its group encounter sessions in which participants verbally attacked each other) and other similar therapeutic community programs.

After the 1970s, the treatment field began to move away from such methods. The Hazelden Foundation officially renounced the "tear them down to build them up" approach in 1985, expressing regret that such confrontational approaches had become associated with the Minnesota model. Psychological studies have failed to find any consistent pattern of personality or defense mechanisms associated with substance abuse disorders, and clinical studies have linked poorer outcomes to more confrontational clinicians, groups, and programs (Miller et al., 1995a). Instead, successful outcomes generally have been associated with counselors showing high levels of accurate empathy, as defined by Carl Rogers and described by Najavits and Weiss (Najavits and Weiss, 1994). The Johnson Institute now emphasizes a supportive, compassionate style for conducting family interventions.

I was at first surprised, therefore, when clinicians attending my workshops on motivational interviewing and watching me demonstrate the style, observed, "In a different way, you're very confrontational." This issue comes up in almost every training now. "Gentle confrontation" some call it. This got me thinking about what confrontation really means.

The linguistic roots of the verb "to confront" mean to come face to face. When you think about it that way, confrontation is precisely what we are trying to accomplish: to allow our clients to come face to face with a difficult and often threatening reality, to "let it in" rather than "block it out," and to allow this reality to change them. That makes confrontation a *goal* of counseling rather than a particular *style* or *technique*.

Once you see this—that opening to new information, face to face, is a *goal* of counseling—then the question becomes, "What is the best way to achieve that goal?" Evidence is strong that direct, forceful, aggressive approaches are perhaps the *least* effective way to help people consider new information and change their perceptions. Such confrontation increases the very phenomenon it is supposed to overcome—defensiveness—and decreases the client's likelihood of change (Miller et al., 1993). It is also quite inappropriate in many cultures. Getting in a client's face may work for some, but for most, it is exactly the opposite of what is needed—to come face to face with painful reality and to change.

William R. Miller, Consensus Panel Chair

is a prerequisite for intentional change, clinicians using motivational strategies focus on constructive confrontation as a treatment goal. From this perspective, constructive or therapeutic confrontation is useful in assisting clients to identify and reconnect with their personal goals, to recognize discrepancies between current behavior and desired ideals (Ivey et al., 1997), and to resolve ambivalence about making positive changes.

Changes in the Addictions Field

As the addictions field has matured, it has tried to integrate conflicting theories and approaches to treatment, as well as to incorporate relevant research findings into a single, comprehensive model. Many positive changes have emerged, and the new view of motivation and the associated strategies to enhance client motivation fit into and reflect many of these changes. Some of the new features of treatment that have important implications for applying motivational methods are discussed below.

Focus on Client Competencies And Strengths

Whereas the treatment field has historically focused on the deficits and limitations of clients, there is a greater emphasis today on identifying, enhancing, and using clients' strengths and competencies. This trend parallels the principles of motivational counseling, which affirm the client, emphasize free choice, support and strengthen self-efficacy, and encourage optimism that change can be achieved (see Chapter 4). As with some aspects of the moral model of addiction, the responsibility for recovery again rests squarely on the client; however, the judgmental tone is eliminated.

Individualized and Client-Centered Treatment

In the past, clients frequently received standardized treatment, no matter what their problems or severity of substance dependence. Today, treatment is usually based on a client's individual needs, which are carefully and comprehensively assessed at intake. Research studies have shown that positive treatment outcomes are associated with flexible program policies and a focus on individual client needs (Inciardi et al., 1993). Furthermore, clients are given choices about desirable and suitable treatment options, rather than having treatment prescribed. As noted, motivational approaches emphasize client choice and personal responsibility for change—even outside the treatment system. Motivational strategies elicit personal goals from clients and involve clients in selecting the type of treatment needed or desired from a menu of options.

A Shift Away From Labeling

Historically, a diagnosis or disease defined the client and became a dehumanizing attribute of the individual. In modern medicine, individuals with asthma or a psychosis are seldom referred to—at least face to face—as "the asthmatic" or "the psychotic." Similarly, in the substance use arena, there is a trend to avoid labeling persons with substance abuse disorders as "addicts" or "alcoholics." Clinicians who use a motivational style avoid branding clients with names, especially those who may not agree with the diagnosis or do not see a particular behavior as problematic.

Therapeutic Partnerships For Change

In the past, especially in the medical model, clients passively *received* treatment. Today, treatment usually entails a partnership in which the client and the clinician agree on treatment goals and work together to develop strategies to meet those goals. The client is seen as an active partner in treatment planning. The clinician who uses motivational strategies establishes a therapeutic alliance with the client and elicits goals and change strategies from the client. The client has ultimate responsibility for making changes, with or without the clinician's assistance. Although motivational strategies elicit statements from the client about intentions and plans for change, they also recognize biological reality: the heightened risk associated with a genetic predisposition to substance abuse or dependence and the powerful effect of substances on the brain, both of which can make change exceedingly difficult. In fact, motivational strategies ask the client to consider what they like about substances of choice—the motivations to use—before focusing on the less good or negative consequences, and weighing the value of each.

Use of Empathy, Not Authority and Power

Whereas the traditional treatment provider was seen as a disciplinarian and imbued with the power to recommend client termination for rule infractions, penalties for "dirty" urine, or promotion to a higher phase of treatment for successfully following direction, research now demonstrates that positive treatment outcomes are associated with high levels of clinician empathy reflected in warm and supportive listening (Landry, 1996). Clinician characteristics found to increase a client's motivation include good interpersonal skills, confidence in the therapeutic process, the capacity to meet the client where the client happens to be, and optimism that change is possible (Najavits and Weiss, 1994).

Focus on Earlier Interventions

The formal treatment system, especially in the early days of public funding, primarily served a chronic, hard-core group of clients with severe substance dependence (Pattison et al., 1977). This may be one reason why certain characteristics such as denial became associated with addiction. If these clients did not succeed in treatment, or did not cooperate, they were viewed as unmotivated and were discharged back to the community to "hit bottom"—i.e., suffer severe negative consequences that might motivate them for change.

More recently, a variety of treatment programs have been established to intervene earlier with persons whose drinking or drug use is problematic or potentially risky, but not yet serious. These early intervention efforts range from educational programs (including sentencing review or reduction for people apprehended for driving while intoxicated who participate in such programs) to brief interventions in opportunistic settings, such as hospital emergency departments, clinics, and doctors' offices, that point out the risks of excessive drinking, suggest change, and make referrals to formal treatment programs as necessary.

Some of the most successful of these early intervention programs use motivational strategies to intercede with persons who are not yet aware they have a substance-related problem (see Chapter 2 and the companion forthcoming Treatment Improvement Protocol (TIP), *Brief Interventions and Brief Therapies for Substance Abuse* [CSAT, in press (a)]). This shift in thinking means not only that treatment services are provided when clients first develop a substance use problem but also that clients have not depleted personal resources and can more easily muster sufficient energy and optimism to initiate change. Brief motivationally focused interventions are increasingly being offered in acute and primary health care settings (D'Onofrio et al., 1998; Ockene et al., 1997; Samet et al., 1996).

Focus on Less Intensive Treatments

A corollary of the new emphasis on earlier intervention and individualized care is the provision of less intensive, but equally effective, treatments. When care was standardized, most programs had not only a routine protocol of services but also a fixed length of stay. Twenty-eight days was considered the proper length of time for successful inpatient (usually hospital-based) care in the popular Minnesota model of alcohol treatment. Residential facilities and outpatient clinics also had standard courses of treatment. Research has now demonstrated that shorter, less intensive forms of intervention can be as effective as more intensive therapies (Bien et al., 1993b; IOM, 1990b; Project MATCH Research Group, 1997a). The issue of treatment "intensity" is far too vague, in that it refers to the length, amount, and cost of services provided without reference to the content of those services. The challenge for future research is to identify *what kinds* of intervention demonstrably improve outcomes in an additive fashion. For purposes of this TIP, emphasis has been placed on the fact that even when therapeutic contact is constrained to a relatively brief period, it is still possible to affect client motivation and trigger change.

Impact of Managed Care on Treatment

Changes in health care financing (managed care) have markedly affected the amount of treatment provided, shifting the emphasis from inpatient to outpatient settings and capping the duration of some treatments. Still unknown is the overall impact of these changes on treatment access, quality, outcomes, and cost. In this context, it is important to remember that even within relatively brief treatment contacts, one can be helpful to clients in evoking change through motivational approaches. Brief motivational interventions can also be an effective way for intervening earlier in the development of substance abuse while severity and complexity of problems are lower (Obert et al., 1997).

Recognition of a Continuum of Substance Abuse Problems

Formerly, substance misuse, particularly the *disease* of alcoholism, was viewed as a progressive condition that, if left untreated, would inevitably lead to full-blown dependence and, likely, an early death. Currently, clinicians recognize that substance abuse disorders exist along a continuum from risky or problematic use through varying types of abuse to dependence that meets diagnostic criteria in the *Diagnostic and Statistical Manual of Mental Disorders*, 4th Edition (DSM –IV) (American Psychiatric Association [APA], 1994). Moreover, progression toward increasing severity is not automatic. Many individuals never progress beyond risky consumption, and others cycle back and forth through periods of abstinence, excessive use, and dependence. Recovery from substance dependence is seen as a multidimensional process that differs among people and changes over time within the same person (IOM, 1990a, 1990b). Motivational strategies can be effectively applied to persons in any stage of substance use through dependence. The crucial variable, as will be seen, is not the severity of the substance use pattern, but the client's readiness for change.

Recognition of Multiple Substance Abuse

Practitioners have come to recognize not only that substance-related disorders vary in intensity but also that most involve more than one substance. For example, a recent study reported that in the United States, just over 25 percent of the general adult population smoke cigarettes, whereas 80 to 90 percent of adults with alcohol use disorders are smokers (Wetter et al., 1998). Formerly, alcohol and drug treatment programs were completely separated by ideology and policy, even though most individuals with substance abuse disorders also drink heavily and many persons who drink excessively also experiment with substances, including prescribed medications that can be substituted for alcohol or that alleviate withdrawal symptoms. Although many treatment programs properly specialize in serving a particular type of client for whom their therapies are appropriate (e.g., methadone maintenance programs for opioid-using clients), most now also treat secondary substance use and psychological problems or at least identify these and make referrals as necessary (Brown et al., 1995, 1999). Here, too, motivational approaches involve clients in choosing goals and negotiating priorities.

Acceptance of New Treatment Goals

In the past, addiction treatment, at least for clients having trouble with alcohol, was considered successful only if the client became abstinent and never returned to substance use following discharge—a goal that proved difficult to achieve (Brownell et al., 1986; Polich et al., 1981). The focus of treatment was almost entirely to have the client stop using and to start understanding the nature of her addiction. Today, treatment goals include a broad range of biopsychosocial measures, such as reduction in substance use, improvement in health and psychosocial functioning, improvement in employment stability, and reduction in criminal justice activity. Recovery itself is multifaceted, and gains made toward recovery can appear in one aspect of a client's life, but not another; achieving the goal of abstinence does not necessarily translate into improved life functioning for the client. Treatment outcomes include interim, incremental, and even temporary steps toward ultimate goals. Motivational strategies incorporate these ideas and help clients select and work toward the goals of most importance to them, including reducing substance use to less harmful levels, even though abstinence may become an ultimate goal if cutting back does not work. Harm reduction (e.g., reducing the intensity of use and high-risk behavior, substituting a less risky substance) can be an important goal in early treatment (APA, 1995). The client is encouraged to focus on personal values and goals, including spiritual aspirations and repair of marital and other important interpersonal relationships. Goals are set within a more holistic context, and

significant others are often included in the motivational sessions.

Integration of Substance Abuse Treatment With Other Disciplines

Historically, the substance abuse treatment system was often isolated from mainstream health care, partly because medical professionals had little training in this area and did not recognize or know what to do with substance users whom they saw in practice settings. Welfare offices, courts, jails, emergency departments, and mental health clinics also were not prepared to respond appropriately to substance misuse. Today there is a strong movement to perceive addiction treatment in the context of public health and to recognize its impact on numerous other service systems. Thanks to the cross-training of professionals and an increase in jointly administered programs, other systems are identifying substance users and either making referrals for them or providing appropriate treatment services (e.g., substance abuse treatment within the criminal justice system, special services for clients who have both substance abuse disorders and mental health disorders). Motivational interventions have been tested and found to be effective in most of these opportunistic settings. Although substance users originally come in for other services, they can be identified and often motivated to reduce use or become abstinent through carefully designed brief interventions (see Chapter 2 and the forthcoming TIP, *Brief Interventions and Brief Therapies for Substance Abuse* [CSAT, in press (a)]). If broadly applied, these brief interventions will tie the addiction treatment system more closely to other service networks through referrals of persons who, after a brief intervention, cannot control their harmful use of substances either on their own or with the limited help of a nonspecialist.

A Transtheoretical Model Of the Stages of Change

As noted at the beginning of this chapter, motivation and personal change are inescapably linked. In addition to developing a new understanding of motivation, substantial addiction research has focused on the determinants and mechanisms of personal change. By understanding better how people change without professional assistance, researchers and clinicians have become better able to develop and apply interventions to facilitate changes in clients' maladaptive and unhealthy behaviors.

Natural Change

The shift in thinking about motivation includes the notion that change is more a process than an outcome (Sobell et al., 1993b; Tucker et al., 1994). Change occurs in the natural environment, among all people, in relation to many behaviors, and without professional intervention. This is also true of positive behavioral changes related to substance use, which often occur without therapeutic intervention or self-help groups. There is well-documented evidence of self-directed or natural recovery from excessive, problematic abuse of alcohol, cigarettes, and drugs (Blomqvist, 1996; Chen and Kandel, 1995; Orleans et al., 1991; Sobell and Sobell, 1998). One of the best-documented studies of this natural recovery process is the longitudinal followup of returning veterans from the Vietnam War (Robins et al., 1974). Although a substantial number of these soldiers became addicted to heroin during their tours of duty in Vietnam, only 5 percent continued to be addicted a year after returning home, and only 12 percent began to use heroin again within the first 3 years—most for only a short time. Although a few of these veterans benefited from short-term detoxification programs, most did not enter formal treatment programs and

apparently recovered on their own. Recovery from substance dependence also can occur with very limited treatment and, in the longer run, through a maturation process (Brecht et al., 1990; Strang et al., 1997). Recognizing the processes involved in natural recovery and self-directed change helps illuminate how changes related to substance use can be precipitated and stimulated by enhancing motivation.

Figure 1-1 illustrates two kinds of natural changes: common and substance-related. Everyone must make decisions about important life changes such as marriage or divorce or buying a house. Sometimes, individuals consult a counselor or other specialist to help with these ordinary decisions, but usually people decide on such changes without professional assistance. Natural change related to substance use also entails decisions to increase, decrease, or stop substance use. Some of the decisions are responses to critical life events, others reflect different kinds of external pressures, and still others seem to be motivated by an appraisal of personal values.

It is important to note that natural changes related to substance use can go in either direction. In response to an impending divorce, for example, one individual may begin to drink heavily whereas another may reduce or stop using alcohol. People who use psychoactive substances thus can and do make many choices regarding consumption patterns without professional intervention.

Stages of Change

Theorists have developed various models to illustrate how behavioral change happens. In one perspective, external consequences and restrictions are largely responsible for moving individuals to change their substance use behaviors. In another model, intrinsic motivations are responsible for initiating or ending substance use behaviors. Some researchers believe that motivation is better

---

Figure 1-1

Examples of Natural Changes

Common Natural Changes	Natural Changes in Substance Use
■ Going to college	■ Experimenting with substances during high school
■ Getting married	■ Stopping drinking after an automobile accident
■ Getting divorced	■ Reducing alcohol use after college
■ Changing jobs	■ Stopping substance use prior to pregnancy
■ Joining the Army	■ Increasing alcohol use during a divorce
■ Taking a vacation	■ Decreasing cigarette use after a price increase
■ Moving	■ Quitting marijuana smoking before looking for employment
■ Buying a home	■ Refraining from drinking with some friends
■ Having a baby	■ Reducing consumption following a physician's advice
■ Retiring	

---

described as a continuum of readiness than as separate stages of change (Bandura, 1997; Sutton, 1996). This hypothesis is also supported by motivational research involving serious substance abuse of illicit drugs (Simpson and Joe, 1993).

The change process has been conceptualized as a sequence of stages through which people typically progress as they think about, initiate, and maintain new behaviors (Prochaska and DiClemente, 1984). This model emerged from an examination of 18 psychological and behavioral theories about how change occurs, including components that compose a biopsychosocial framework for understanding addiction. In this sense, the model is "transtheoretical" (IOM, 1990b).

This model also reflects how change occurs outside of therapeutic environments. The authors applied this template to individuals who modified behaviors related to smoking, drinking, eating, exercising, parenting, and marital communications on their own, without professional intervention. When natural self-change was compared with therapeutic interventions, many similarities were noticed, leading these investigators to describe the occurrence of change in steps or stages. They

observed that people who make behavioral changes on their own or under professional guidance first "move from being unaware or unwilling to do anything about the problem to considering the possibility of change, then to becoming determined and prepared to make the change, and finally to taking action and sustaining or maintaining that change over time" (DiClemente, 1991, p. 191).

As a clinician, you can be helpful at any point in the process of change by using appropriate motivational strategies that are specific to the change stage of the individual. Chapters 4 through 7 of this TIP use the stages-of-change model to organize and conceptualize ways in which you can enhance clients' motivation to progress to the next change stage. In this context, the stages of change represent a series of tasks for both you and your clients (Miller and Heather, 1998).

The stages of change can be visualized as a wheel with four to six parts, depending on how specifically the process is broken down (Prochaska and DiClemente, 1984). For this TIP, the wheel (Figure 1-2) has five parts, with a final exit to enduring recovery. It is important to note that the change process is cyclical, and individuals typically move back and forth

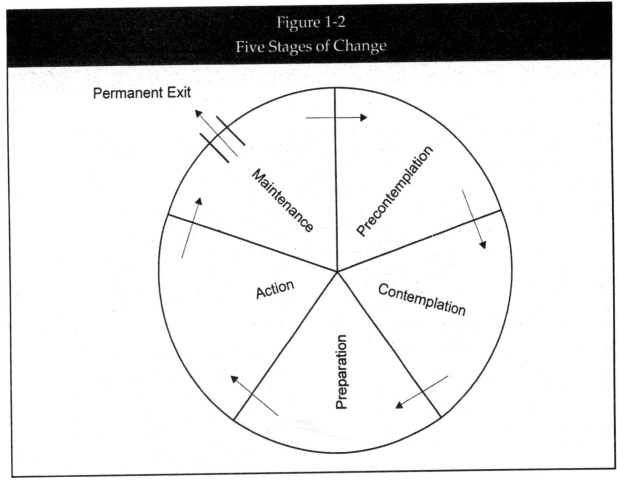

Figure 1-2
Five Stages of Change

between the stages and cycle through the stages at different rates. In one individual, this movement through the stages can vary in relation to different behaviors or objectives. Individuals can move through stages quickly. Sometimes, they move so rapidly that it is difficult to pinpoint where they are because change is a dynamic process. It is not uncommon, however, for individuals to linger in the early stages.

For most substance-using individuals, progress through the stages of change is circular or spiral in nature, not linear. In this model, recurrence is a normal event because many clients cycle through the different stages several times before achieving stable change. The five stages and the issue of recurrence are described below.

Precontemplation

During the precontemplation stage, substance-using persons are not considering change and do not intend to change behaviors in the foreseeable future. They may be partly or completely unaware that a problem exists, that they have to make changes, and that they may need help in this endeavor. Alternatively, they may be unwilling or too discouraged to change their behavior. Individuals in this stage usually have not experienced adverse consequences or crises because of their substance use and often are not convinced that their pattern of use is problematic or even risky.

Contemplation

As these individuals become aware that a problem exists, they begin to perceive that there may be cause for concern and reasons to change. Typically, they are ambivalent, simultaneously seeing reasons to change and reasons not to change. Individuals in this stage are still using substances, but they are considering the possibility of stopping or cutting back in the near future. At this point, they may seek relevant information, reevaluate their substance use behavior, or seek help to support the possibility of changing behavior. They typically weigh the positive and negative aspects of making a change. It is not uncommon for individuals to remain in this stage for extended periods, often for years, vacillating between wanting and not wanting to change.

Preparation

When an individual perceives that the envisioned advantages of change and adverse consequences of substance use outweigh any positive features of continuing use at the same level and maintaining the status quo, the decisional balance tips in favor of change. Once instigation to change occurs, an individual enters the preparation stage, during which commitment is strengthened. Preparation entails more specific planning for change, such as making choices about whether treatment is needed and, if so, what kind. Preparation also entails an examination of one's perceived capabilities—or self-efficacy—for change. Individuals in the preparation stage are still using substances, but typically they intend to stop using very soon. They may have already attempted to reduce or stop use on their own or may be experimenting now with ways to quit or cut back (DiClemente and Prochaska, 1998). They begin to set goals for themselves and make

commitments to stop using, even telling close associates or significant others about their plans.

Action

Individuals in the action stage choose a strategy for change and begin to pursue it. At this stage, clients are actively modifying their habits and environment. They are making drastic lifestyle changes and may be faced with particularly challenging situations and the physiological effects of withdrawal. Clients may begin to reevaluate their own self-image as they move from excessive or hazardous use to nonuse or safe use. For many, the action stage can last from 3 to 6 months following termination or reduction of substance use. For some, it is a honeymoon period before they face more daunting and longstanding challenges.

Maintenance

During the maintenance stage, efforts are made to sustain the gains achieved during the action stage. Maintenance is the stage at which people work to sustain sobriety and prevent recurrence (Marlatt and Gordon, 1985). Extra precautions may be necessary to keep from reverting to problematic behaviors. Individuals learn how to detect and guard against dangerous situations and other triggers that may cause them to use substances again. In most cases, individuals attempting long-term behavior change do return to use at least once and revert to an earlier stage (Prochaska et al., 1992). Recurrence of symptoms can be viewed as part of the learning process. Knowledge about the personal cues or

---

Decisionmaking

Decisionmaking has been conceptualized as a balance sheet of potential gains and losses (Janis and Mann, 1977). These two decisional measures—the pros and the cons—have become critical constructs in the transtheoretical model of change stages. The weights given to the pros and cons—or positive and negative aspects of continuing use and of change itself—vary according to personal values and the individual's stage of change. During the contemplation stage, the pros and cons tend to balance—or cancel each other out. When the preparation stage is reached, the pros for changing the behavior outweigh the cons, and the decisional balance tips toward a commitment to change.

dangerous situations that contribute to recurrence is useful information for future change attempts. Maintenance requires prolonged behavioral change—by remaining abstinent or moderating consumption to acceptable, targeted levels—and continued vigilance for a minimum of 6 months to several years, depending on the target behavior (Prochaska and DiClemente, 1992).

Recurrence

Most people do not immediately sustain the new changes they are attempting to make, and a return to substance use after a period of abstinence is the rule rather than the exception (Brownell et al., 1986; Prochaska and DiClemente, 1992). These experiences contribute information that can facilitate or hinder subsequent progression through the stages of change. Recurrence, often referred to as relapse, is the event that triggers the individual's return to earlier stages of change and recycling through the process. Individuals may learn that certain goals are unrealistic, certain strategies are ineffective, or certain environments are not conducive to successful change. Most substance users will require several revolutions through the stages of change to achieve successful recovery (DiClemente and Scott, 1997). After a return to substance use, clients usually revert to an earlier change stage—not always to maintenance or action, but more often to some level of contemplation. They may even become precontemplators again, temporarily unwilling or unable to try to change soon. As will be described in the following chapters, resuming substance use and returning to a previous stage of change should not be considered a failure and need not become a disastrous or prolonged recurrence. A recurrence of symptoms does not necessarily mean that a client has abandoned a commitment to change.

Triggers to Change

The multidimensional nature of motivation is captured, in part, in the popular phrase that a person is *ready, willing,* and *able* to change. This expression highlights three critical elements of motivation—but in reverse order from that in which motivation typically evolves. *Ability* refers to the extent to which the person has the necessary skills, resources, and confidence (self-efficacy) to carry out a change. One can be able to change, but not willing. The *willing* component involves the importance a person places on changing—how much a change is wanted or desired. (Note that it is possible to feel willing yet unable to change.) However, even willingness and ability are not always enough. You probably can think of examples of people who are willing and able to change, but not yet ready to change. The *ready* component represents a final step in which the person finally decides to change a particular behavior. Being willing and able but not ready can often be explained by the relative importance of this change compared with other priorities in the person's life. To instill motivation for change is to help the client become ready, willing, and able. As discussed in later chapters, your clinical approach can be guided by deciding which of these three needs bolstering.

To Whom Does This TIP Apply?

To which client populations is material covered in this TIP applicable? Motivational interviewing was originally developed to work with problem alcohol drinkers at early stages (precontemplation and contemplation) of readiness for change and was conceived as a way of initiating treatment (Miller, 1983; Miller et al., 1988). It soon became apparent, however, that this brief counseling approach constitutes an intervention in itself. Problem alcohol drinkers in the community who were given motivational interventions seldom initiated treatment but did show large decreases in their drinking (Heather et al., 1996b; Marlatt et al., 1998; Miller et al., 1993; Senft et al., 1997). In the largest clinical trial ever conducted to compare different alcohol treatment methods, a four-session motivational enhancement therapy yielded long-term overall outcomes virtually identical to those of longer outpatient methods (Project MATCH Research Group, 1998a), and the motivational approach was differentially beneficial with angry clients (Project MATCH Research Group, 1997a). The MATCH population consisted of treatment-seeking clients who varied widely in problem severity, the vast majority of whom met criteria for alcohol dependence. Clients represented a range of cultural backgrounds, particularly Hispanic. It is noteworthy that neither Hispanic nor African-American samples responded differentially to the motivational enhancement therapy approach.

Moreover, analyses of clinical trials of motivational interviewing that have included substantial representation of Hispanic clients (Brown and Miller, 1993; Miller et al., 1988, 1993) have found no indication of self-identified ethnicity and socioeconomic status as predictors of outcome. A motivational interviewing trial addressing weight and diabetes management among women, 41 percent of whom were African-American, demonstrated positive results (Smith et al., 1997). Evidence strongly suggests that motivational interviewing can be applied across cultural and economic differences.

While motivational counseling appears to be sufficient for some clients, for others it can be combined with additional therapeutic methods. With more severely dependent drinkers, a motivational interviewing session at the outset of treatment has been found to double the rate of abstinence following private inpatient treatment (Brown and Miller, 1993) and

Veterans Affairs outpatient programs for substance abuse treatment (Bien et al., 1993a). Benefits have been reported with other severely dependent populations (e.g., Allsop et al., 1997). Polydrug-abusing adolescents stayed in outpatient treatment nearly three times longer and showed substantially lower substance use and consequences after treatment when they had received a motivational interview at intake (Aubrey, 1998). Similar additive benefits have been reported in treating problems with heroin (Saunders et al., 1995), marijuana (Stephens et al., 1994), weight control and diabetes management (Smith et al., 1997; Trigwell et al., 1997), and cardiovascular rehabilitation (Scales, 1998). It is clear, therefore, that the motivational approach described in this TIP can be combined beneficially with other forms of treatment and can be applied with problems beyond substance abuse alone.

The motivational style of counseling, therefore, can be useful, not only to instill motivation initially, but throughout the process of treatment in the preparation, action, and maintenance stages as well. This is reflected in subsequent chapters of this TIP. Whether motivational interviewing will be *sufficient* to trigger change in a given case is difficult to predict. Sometimes motivational counseling may be all that is needed. Sometimes it is only a beginning. A stepped care approach, described in Chapter 9, is one in which the amount of care provided is adjusted to the needs of the individual. If lasting change follows after motivational interviewing alone, who can be dissatisfied? Often more is needed. However brief or extensive the service provided, the evidence indicates that you are most likely to help your clients change their substance use by maintaining an empathic motivational style. It is a matter of staying with and supporting each client until together you find what works.

Summary

Linking the new view of motivation, the strategies found to enhance it, and the stages-of-change model, along with an understanding of what causes change, can create an innovative approach to helping substance-using clients. This approach provokes less resistance and encourages clients to progress at their own pace toward deciding about, planning, making, and sustaining positive behavioral change.

In this treatment model, described in the next chapter, motivation is seen as a dynamic state that can be modified or enhanced by the clinician. Motivational enhancement has evolved, while various myths about clients and what constitutes effective counseling have been dispelled. The notion of the addictive personality has lost credence, and many clinicians have discarded the use of a confrontational style. Other factors in contemporary counseling practices have encouraged the development and implementation of motivational interventions. Increasingly, counseling has become optimistic, focusing on clients' strengths, and client centered. Counseling relationships are more likely to rely on empathy, rather than authority, to involve the client in treatment. Less intensive treatments have also become more common in the era of managed care.

Motivation is what propels substance users to make changes in their lives. It guides clients through several stages of change that are typical of people thinking about, initiating, and maintaining new behaviors. When applied to substance abuse treatment, motivational interventions can help clients move from not even considering changing their behavior to being ready, willing, and able to do so.

2 Motivation and Intervention

Using the transtheoretical perspective...seeks to assist clients in moving from the early stages of change...to determination or action. It uses stage-specific strategies to foster a commitment to take action for change...[and it] assists clients to convince themselves that change is necessary.

Noonan and Moyers, 1997

Motivational intervention is broadly defined as any clinical strategy designed to enhance client motivation for change. It can include counseling, client assessment, multiple sessions, or a 30-minute brief intervention. This chapter examines the elements of effective motivational approaches and supporting research. Motivational strategies are then correlated with the stages-of-change model (a framework that is discussed in Chapter 1 and elaborated on in later chapters) to highlight approaches that are appropriate to specific stages. Recommendations are presented for providing motivational interventions that are responsive and sensitive to differing cultural and diagnostic needs, as well as to different settings and formats. This chapter concludes with a description of an increasingly accepted type of intervention known as a brief intervention, which is useful outside of traditional substance abuse treatment settings. For a broader discussion of brief interventions and therapies, refer to the forthcoming TIP, *Brief Interventions and Brief Therapies for Substance Abuse* (CSAT, in press [a]).

Elements of Effective Motivational Interventions

To understand what prompts a person to reduce or eliminate substance use, investigators have searched for the critical components—the most important and common elements that inspire positive change—of effective interventions. The following are important elements of current motivational approaches:

- The FRAMES approach
- Decisional balance exercises
- Discrepancies between personal goals and current behavior
- Flexible pacing
- Personal contact with clients not in treatment

These elements are described in the following subsections.

XVIII

FRAMES Approach

Six elements have been identified that were present in brief clinical trials, and the acronym FRAMES was coined to summarize them (Miller and Sanchez, 1994). These elements are defined as the following:

- *Feedback* regarding personal risk or impairment is given to the client following assessment of substance use patterns and associated problems.
- *Responsibility* for change is placed squarely and explicitly on the client (and with respect for the client's right to make choices for himself).
- *Advice* about changing—reducing or stopping—substance use is clearly given to the client by the clinician in a nonjudgmental manner.
- *Menus* of self-directed change options and treatment alternatives are offered to the client.
- *Empathic* counseling—showing warmth, respect, and understanding—is emphasized.
- *Self-efficacy* or optimistic empowerment is engendered in the client to encourage change.

Figure 2-1 lists 32 trials and their FRAME components, as reviewed by Bien and colleagues (Bien et al., 1993b). Since the FRAMES construct was developed, further clinical research and experience have expanded on and refined elements of this motivational model. These components have been combined in different ways and tested in diverse settings and cultural contexts. Consequently, additional building blocks or tools are now available that can be tailored to meet your clients' needs.

Feedback

The literature describing successful motivational interventions confirms the persuasiveness of personal, individualized feedback (Bien et al., 1993b; Edwards et al., 1977; Kristenson et al., 1983). Providing constructive, nonconfrontational feedback about a client's degree and type of impairment based on information from structured and objective assessments is particularly valuable (Miller et al., 1988). This type of feedback usually compares a client's scores or ratings on standard tests or instruments with normative data from a general population or from groups in treatment (for examples, see Figures 4-1 and 4-2).

Figure 2-1							
Specific FRAMES Components of 32 Evaluated Brief Trials							
Author(s)	**Feedback**	**Responsibility**	**Advice**	**Menu**	**Empathy**	**Self-Efficacy**	**Outcome**
Anderson and Scott, 1992*	Yes	Yes	Yes	Yes	Yes	Yes	Brief > No counseling
Babor and Grant, 1992*	Yes	Yes	Yes	Manual	Yes	Yes	Brief > No counseling
Bien, 1992*	Yes	Yes	Yes	No	Yes	Yes	Brief > No counseling
Brown and Miller, 1992*	Yes	Yes	Yes	No	Yes	Yes	Brief > No counseling
Carpenter et al., 1985*	Yes	No	Yes	No	No	No	Brief = Extended cnslg
Chapman and Huygens, 1988*	Yes	Yes	Yes	Yes	No	Yes	Brief = IPT = OPT
Chick et al., 1985*	Yes	Yes	Yes	No	Yes	Yes	Brief > No counseling
Chick et al., 1988*	No	Yes	Yes	No	No	No	Brief < Extended motivational cnslg
Daniels et al., 1992	Yes	No	Yes	Manual	No	No	Advice + Manual = No advice
Drummond et al., 1990	Yes	No	Yes	No	No	No	Brief = OPT

Figure 2-1 (continued)							
Specific FRAMES Components of 32 Evaluated Brief Trials							
Author(s)	**Feedback**	**Responsi-bility**	**Advice**	**Menu**	**Empathy**	**Self-Efficacy**	**Outcome**
Edwards et al., 1977	Yes	Yes	Yes	No	Yes	Yes	Brief = OPT/IPT
Elvy et al., 1988	Yes	No	Yes	No	No	No	Brief > No counseling
Harris and Miller, 1990*	No	Yes	Yes	Manual	Yes	Yes	Brief = Extended > No Rx
Heather et al., 1986*	Yes	Yes	Manual	Manual	No	No	Manual > No manual
Heather et al., 1987*	Yes	Yes	Yes	Manual	No	No	Brief = No counseling
Heather et al., 1990*	Yes	Yes	Yes	Manual	No	No	Manual > No manual
Kristenson et al., 1983	Yes	Yes	Yes	No	Yes	Yes	Brief > No counseling
Kuchipudl et al., 1990	Yes	No	Yes	Yes	No	No	Brief = No counseling
Maheswaran et al., 1992	Yes	No	Yes	No	No	No	Brief > No counseling
Miller and Taylor, 1980*	No	Yes	Yes	Manual	Yes	Yes	Brief = Behavioral cnslg
Miller et al., 1980*	No	Yes	Yes	Manual	Yes	Yes	Brief = Behavioral cnslg
Miller et al., 1981*	No	Yes	Yes	Manual	Yes	Yes	Brief = Behavioral cnslg
Miller et al., 1988*	Yes	Yes	Yes	Yes	Yes	Yes	Brief > No counseling
Miller et al., 1993*	Yes	Yes	Yes	Yes	Yes	Yes	Brief > No counseling
Persson and Magnusson, 1989*	Yes	Yes	Yes	No	Yes	Yes	Brief > No counseling
Robertson et al., 1986*	Yes	Yes	Yes	Yes	Yes	Yes	Brief < Behavioral cnslg
Romelsjo et al., 1989*	Yes	Yes	Yes	No	Yes	Yes	Brief = OPT treatment
Sannibale, 1988*	Yes	Yes	Yes	No	Yes	Yes	Brief = OPT treatment
Scott and Anderson, 1990*	Yes	Yes	Yes	Yes	Yes	Yes	Brief = No counseling
Skutle & Berg, 1987*	No	Yes	Yes	Yes+ Manual	Yes	Yes	Brief = Behavioral cnslg
Wallace et al., 1988*	Yes	Yes	Yes	Manual	Yes	Yes	Brief > No counseling
Zweben et al., 1988	Yes	Yes	Yes	Yes	No	Yes	Brief = Conjoint therapy
Percentage w/FRAMES components	81	81	100	59	63	69	

* Additional information obtained from study authors.

Abbreviations: Manual: manual-guided therapy; IPT: inpatient treatment setting; OPT: outpatient treatment setting; cnslg: counseling; > : more effective than; < : not as effective as; = : as effective as.

Source: Bien et al., 1993b; Miller et al., 1995c.

Assessments may include measures related to substance consumption patterns, substance-related problems, physical health, risk factors including a family history of substance use or affective disorders, and various medical tests (Miller et al., 1995c). (Assessments and feedback are described in more detail in Chapter 4.) A respectful manner when delivering feedback to your client is crucial. A confrontational or judgmental approach may leave the client unreceptive.

Do not present feedback as evidence that can be used against the client. Rather, offer the information in a straightforward, respectful way, using easy-to-understand and culturally appropriate language. The point is to present information in a manner that helps the client recognize the existence of a substance use problem and the need for change. Reflective listening and an empathic style help the client understand the feedback, interpret the meaning, gain a new perspective about the personal impact of substance use, express concern, and begin to consider change.

Not all clients respond in the same way to feedback. One person may be alarmed to find that she drinks much more in a given week than comparable peers but be unconcerned about potential health risks. Another may be concerned about potential health risks at this level of drinking. Still another may not be impressed by such aspects of substance use as the amount of money spent on substances, possible impotence, or the level of impairment— especially with regard to driving ability— caused by even low blood alcohol concentrations (BACs). Personalized feedback can be applied to other lifestyle issues as well, and can be used throughout treatment. Feedback about improvements is especially valuable as a method of reinforcing progress.

Responsibility

Individuals have the choice of continuing their behavior or changing. A motivational approach allows clients to be active rather than passive by insisting that they choose their treatment and take responsibility for changing. Do not impose views or goals on clients; instead, ask clients for permission to talk about substance use and invite them to consider information. If clients are free to choose, they feel less need to resist or dismiss your ideas. Some clinicians begin an intervention by stating clearly that they will not ask the client to do anything he is unwilling to do but will try nevertheless to negotiate a common agenda in regard to treatment goals. When clients realize they are responsible for the change process, they feel empowered and more invested in it. This results in better outcomes (Deci, 1975, 1980). When clients make their own choices, you will be less frustrated and more satisfied because the client is doing the work. Indeed, clients are the best experts about their own needs.

Advice

The simple act of giving gentle advice can promote positive behavioral change. As already discussed, research shows that short sessions in which you offer suggestions can be effective in changing behaviors such as smoking, drinking alcohol, and other substance use (Drummond et al., 1990; Edwards et al., 1977; Miller and Taylor, 1980; Sannibale, 1988; Wallace et al., 1988). As with feedback, the *manner* in which you advise

---

A Realistic Model of Change: Advice to Clients

Throughout the treatment process, it is important to give clients permission to talk about their problems with substance use. During these kinds of dialogs, I often point out some of the realities of the recovery process:

- Most change does not occur overnight.
- Change is best viewed as a gradual process with occasional setbacks, much like hiking up a bumpy hill.
- Difficulties and setbacks can be reframed as learning experiences, not failures.

Linda C. Sobell, Consensus Panel Member

The PIES Approach

In World War I, military psychiatrists first realized that motivational interventions, done at the right time, could return a great number of dysfunctionally stressed soldiers to duty. The method could be put into an easily remembered acronym: PIES.

- *Proximity:* Provide treatment near the place of duty; don't evacuate to a hospital.
- *Immediacy:* Intervene and treat as soon as the problem is noticed.
- *Expectancy:* Expect the intervention to be successful and return the person to duty.
- *Simplicity:* Simply listening, showing empathy, and demonstrating understanding works best.

Highlight the fact the person is normal while the situation is abnormal and that the person will recover with rest and nourishment. No prolonged or complex therapy was needed for the great majority of cases. Evacuation to higher echelons of care was reserved for the low percentage of individuals who did not respond to this straightforward approach.

Kenneth J. Hoffman, Field Reviewer

clients determines how the advice will be used. It is better not to *tell* people what to do— *suggesting* yields better results. A motivational approach to offering advice may be either directive (making a suggestion) or educational (explaining information). Educational advice is based on credible scientific evidence supported in the literature. Facts that relate to the client's conditions, such as BAC levels at the time of an accident or safe drinking limits recommended by the National Institute on Alcohol Abuse and Alcoholism, can be presented in a nonthreatening way. Thoughtfully address the client's behavior by saying, "Can I tell you what I've seen in the past in these situations?" or, "Let me explain something to you about tolerance."

Such questions provide a nondirective opportunity to share your knowledge about substance use in a gentle and respectful manner. If the client requests direction, redirect her questions in order to clarify what is wanted rather than giving advice immediately. Any advice you give should be simple, not overwhelming, and matched to the client's level of understanding and readiness, the urgency of the situation, and her culture. (In some cultures, a more directive approach is required to adequately convey the importance of the advice or situation; in other cultures, a directive style is considered rude and intrusive.) This style of giving advice requires patience. The timing of any advice is also important, relying on your ability to "hear"—in the broad sense—what the client is requesting and willing to receive.

Options

Compliance with change strategies is enhanced when clients choose—or perceive that they can choose—from a menu of options. Thus, motivation for participating in treatment is heightened by giving clients choices regarding treatment goals and types of services needed. Offering a menu of options helps decrease dropout rates and resistance to treatment and increases overall treatment effectiveness (Costello, 1975; Parker et al., 1979). As you describe alternative approaches to treatment or change that are appropriate for your clients, provide accurate information about each option and a best guess about the implications of choosing one particular path. Elicit from your clients what they think is effective or what has worked for them in the past. Providing a menu of options is consistent with the motivational principle that clients must choose and take responsibility for their choices. Your role is to enhance your clients' ability to make informed choices. When clients make independent decisions, they are likely to be more committed to them. This concept is further discussed in Chapter 6.

Empathic counseling

Empathy is not specific to motivational interventions but rather applies to many types of therapies (Rogers, 1959; Truax and Carkhuff, 1967). Empathy during counseling has been interpreted in terms of such therapist characteristics as warmth, respect, caring, commitment, and active interest (Miller and Rollnick, 1991). Empathy usually entails reflective listening—listening attentively to each client statement and reflecting it back in different words so that the client knows you understand the meaning.

The client does most of the talking when a clinician uses an empathic style. It is your responsibility to create a safe environment that encourages a free flow of information from the client. Your implied message to the client is "I see where you are, and I'm not judgmental. Where would you like to go from here?" The assumption is that, with empathic support, a client will naturally move in a healthy direction. Let this process unfold, rather than direct or interrupt it. Although an empathic style appears easy to adopt, it actually requires careful training and significant effort on your part. This style can be particularly effective with clients who seem angry, resistant, or defensive.

Self-efficacy

To succeed in changing, clients must believe they are capable of undertaking specific tasks and must have the necessary skills and confidence (Bandura, 1989; Marlatt and Gordon, 1985). One of your most important roles is to foster hope and optimism by reinforcing your clients' beliefs in their own capacities and capabilities (Yahne and Miller, 1999). This role is more likely to be successful if you believe in your client's ability to change (Leake and King, 1977). You can help clients identify how they

have successfully coped with problems in the past by asking, "How did you get from where you were to where you are now?" Once you identify strengths, you can help clients build on past successes. It is important to affirm the small steps that are taken and reinforce any positive changes. The importance of self-efficacy is discussed again in Chapters 3 and 5.

Decisional Balance Exercises

The concept of exploring the pros and cons—or benefits and disadvantages—of change is not new and is well documented in the literature (Colten and Janis, 1982; Janis and Mann, 1977). Individuals naturally explore the pros and cons of any major life choices such as changing jobs or getting married. In the context of recovery from substance use, the client weighs the pros and cons of changing versus not changing substance-using behavior. You assist this process by asking your client to articulate the good and less good aspects of using substances and then list them on a sheet of paper. This process is usually called *decisional balancing* and is further described in Chapters 5 and 8. The purpose of exploring the pros and cons of a substance use problem is to tip the scales toward a decision for positive change.

The actual number of reasons a client lists on each side of a decisional balance sheet is not as important as the weight—or personal value—of each one. For example, a 20-year-old smoker might not put as much weight on getting lung cancer as an older man, but he might be very concerned that his diminished lung capacity interferes with playing tennis or basketball.

Discrepancies Between Goals and Current Behavior

One way to enhance motivation for change is to help clients recognize a *discrepancy* or gap between their future goals and their current behavior. You might clarify this discrepancy by asking, "How does your drinking fit in with having a happy family and a stable job?" When an individual sees that present actions conflict with important personal goals such as health, success, or family happiness, change is more likely to occur (Miller and Rollnick, 1991). This concept is expanded in Chapters 3 and 5.

Flexible Pacing

Every client moves through the stages of change at her own pace. Some will cycle back and forth numerous times between, for example, contemplating change and making a commitment to do so. Others seem stuck in an ambivalent state for a long time. A few are ready to get started and take action immediately. Therefore, assess your client's readiness for change. By determining where the individual has been and is now within the stages of change, you can better facilitate the change process.

The concept of pacing requires that you meet your clients at their levels and use as much or as little time as is necessary with the essential tasks of each stage of change. For example, with some clients, you may have to schedule frequent sessions at the beginning of treatment and fewer later. In other cases, you might suggest a "therapeutic vacation" for a client who has to take a break before continuing a particularly difficult aspect of recovery. If you push clients at a faster pace than they are ready to take, the therapeutic alliance may break down.

Personal Contact With Clients Not In Treatment

Motivational interventions can include simple activities designed to enhance continuity of contact between you and your client and strengthen your relationship. Such activities can include personal handwritten letters or telephone calls from you to your client. Research has shown that these simple motivation-enhancing interventions are effective for encouraging clients to return for another

clinical consultation, to return to treatment following a missed appointment, to stay involved in treatment, and to increase adherence (Intagliata, 1976; Koumans and Muller, 1965; Nirenberg et al., 1980; Panepinto and Higgins, 1969). This concept is discussed in Chapter 7.

Motivational Intervention And the Stages of Change

Clients need and use different kinds of motivational support according to which stage of change they are in and into what stage they are moving. If you try to use strategies appropriate to a stage other than the one the client is in, the result could be treatment resistance or noncompliance. For example, if your client is at the contemplation stage, weighing the pros and cons of change versus continued substance use, and you pursue change strategies appropriate to the action stage, your client will predictably resist. The simple reason for this reaction is that you have taken the positive (change) side of the argument, leaving the client to argue the other (no change) side; this results in a standoff.

To consider change, individuals at the precontemplation stage must have their awareness raised. To resolve their ambivalence, clients in the contemplation stage require help choosing positive change over their current situation. Clients in the preparation stage need help identifying potential change strategies and choosing the most appropriate one for their circumstances. Clients in the action stage (the stage at which most formal treatment occurs) need help to carry out and comply with the change strategies. During the maintenance stage, clients may have to develop new skills for maintaining recovery and a lifestyle without substance use. Moreover, if clients resume their substance use, they can be assisted to recover as quickly as possible to resume the change process.

Figure 2-2 provides examples of appropriate motivational strategies you can use at each stage of change. Of course, these are not the only ways to enhance motivation for beneficial change. Chapter 3 describes some of the fundamental principles of motivational interviewing that apply to all stages. Chapters 4 through 7 describe in more detail the motivational strategies that are most appropriate for encouraging progression to each new change stage. Chapters 4 and 8 present some tools to help you recognize clients' readiness to change in terms of their current stage.

Catalysts for Change

In the search for common processes—integrative models—of personal growth and change across psychotherapies and behavioral approaches, Prochaska (Prochaska, 1979) initially isolated the core approaches of many therapeutic systems and further developed these in a factor analytic study (Davidson, 1994; Prochaska and DiClemente, 1983). These fundamental processes represent cognitive, affective, behavioral, and environmental factors influencing change as they appear in major systems of therapy (DiClemente and Scott, 1997). These change catalysts are derived from studies examining smoking cessation, alcohol abstinence, general psychotherapeutic problems, weight loss, and exercise adoption (Prochaska et al., 1992b). For each of the 10 catalysts, several different interventions can be used to encourage change. Figure 2-3 describes these catalysts for change and illustrates a few interventions often used for each.

Typically, cognitive–experiential processes are used early in the cycle (i.e., contemplation, preparation), and behavioral processes are critical for the later stages (i.e., action, maintenance) (Prochaska and Goldstein, 1991).

Figure 2-4 suggests which catalysts are most appropriate for each change stage. To avoid confusion for both the client and clinician, only those catalysts that are best supported or most logical are recommended for a particular stage; this does not imply, however, that the other catalysts are irrelevant.

Special Applications of Motivational Interventions

The principles underlying motivational enhancement have been applied across cultures, to different types of problems, in various treatment settings, and with many different populations. The research literature suggests that motivational interventions are associated with a variety of successful outcomes, including facilitation of referrals for treatment, reduction or termination of substance use, and increased participation in and compliance with specialized treatment (Bien et al., 1993b; Noonan and Moyers, 1997). Motivational interventions have been tested in at least 15 countries, including Canada, England, Scotland, Wales, the Netherlands, Australia, Sweden, Bulgaria, Costa Rica, Kenya, Zimbabwe, Mexico, Norway, the former Soviet Union, and the United States (Bien et al., 1993; Miller and Rollnick, 1991). Motivational strategies have been used primarily with problem alcohol drinkers and cigarette smokers, but also have yielded encouraging results in marijuana and opiate users with serious substance-related problems (Bernstein et al., 1997a; Miller and Rollnick, 1991; Noonan and Moyers, 1997; Sobell et al., 1995).

Special applications of motivational approaches have been or are currently being explored with diabetic patients, for pain management, in coronary heart disease rehabilitation, for HIV risk reduction, with sex offenders, with pregnant alcohol drinkers, with severely alcohol-impaired veterans, with persons who have eating disorders, and with

	Figure 2-2
	Appropriate Motivational Strategies for Each Stage of Change
Client's Stage of Change	**Appropriate Motivational Strategies for the Clinician**

Precontemplation
 	
The client is not yet considering change or is unwilling or unable to change.
	■ Establish rapport, ask permission, and build trust.
	■ Raise doubts or concerns in the client about substance-using patterns by
	  ♦ Exploring the meaning of events that brought the client to treatment or the results of previous treatments
	  ♦ Eliciting the client's perceptions of the problem
	  ♦ Offering factual information about the risks of substance use
	  ♦ Providing personalized feedback about assessment findings
	  ♦ Exploring the pros and cons of substance use
	  ♦ Helping a significant other intervene
	  ♦ Examining discrepancies between the client's and others' perceptions of the problem behavior
	■ Express concern and keep the door open.

Contemplation
 	
The client acknowledges concerns and is considering the possibility of change but is ambivalent and uncertain.
	■ Normalize ambivalence.
	■ Help the client "tip the decisional balance scales" toward change by
	  ♦ Eliciting and weighing pros and cons of substance use and change
	  ♦ Changing extrinsic to intrinsic motivation
	  ♦ Examining the client's personal values in relation to change
	  ♦ Emphasizing the client's free choice, responsibility, and self-efficacy for change
	■ Elicit self-motivational statements of intent and commitment from the client.
	■ Elicit ideas regarding the client's perceived self-efficacy and expectations regarding treatment.
	■ Summarize self-motivational statements.

Preparation The client is committed to and planning to make a change in the near future but is still considering what to do.	■ Clarify the client's own goals and strategies for change. ■ Offer a menu of options for change or treatment. ■ With permission, offer expertise and advice. ■ Negotiate a change—or treatment—plan and behavior contract. ■ Consider and lower barriers to change. ■ Help the client enlist social support. ■ Explore treatment expectancies and the client's role.

Figure 2-2 (continued) Appropriate Motivational Strategies for Each Stage of Change	
Client's Stage of Change	**Appropriate Motivational Strategies for the Clinician**
Preparation (continued)	■ Elicit from the client what has worked in the past either for him or others whom he knows. ■ Assist the client to negotiate finances, child care, work, transportation, or other potential barriers. ■ Have the client publicly announce plans to change.
Action The client is actively taking steps to change but has not yet reached a stable state.	■ Engage the client in treatment and reinforce the importance of remaining in recovery. ■ Support a realistic view of change through small steps. ■ Acknowledge difficulties for the client in early stages of change. ■ Help the client identify high-risk situations through a functional analysis and develop appropriate coping strategies to overcome these. ■ Assist the client in finding new reinforcers of positive change. ■ Help the client assess whether she has strong family and social support.
Maintenance The client has achieved initial goals such as abstinence and is now working to maintain gains.	■ Help the client identify and sample drug-free sources of pleasure (i.e., new reinforcers). ■ Support lifestyle changes. ■ Affirm the client's resolve and self-efficacy. ■ Help the client practice and use new coping strategies to avoid a return to use. ■ Maintain supportive contact (e.g., explain to the client that you are available to talk between sessions). ■ Develop a "fire escape" plan if the client resumes substance use. ■ Review long-term goals with the client.
Recurrence The client has experienced a recurrence of symptoms and must now cope with consequences and decide what to do next.	■ Help the client reenter the change cycle and commend any willingness to reconsider positive change. ■ Explore the meaning and reality of the recurrence as a learning opportunity. ■ Assist the client in finding alternative coping strategies. ■ Maintain supportive contact.

individuals with coexisting substance use and psychiatric disorders (Carey, 1996; Noonan and Moyers, 1997; Ziedonis and Fisher, 1996). Populations that have been responsive to motivational interventions include persons arrested for driving under the influence and other nonviolent offenders, adolescents (Colby et al., 1998), older adults, employees, married

---

Figure 2-3
Ten Effective Catalysts for Change

1. **Consciousness raising** is increasing information about the problem. Interventions could include observations, interpretations, and bibliotherapy.

2. **Self-reevaluation** involves assessing how one feels and thinks about oneself with respect to problem behaviors. Interventions could include clarifying values and challenging beliefs or expectations.

3. **Self-liberation** means choosing and committing to act or believing in ability to change. Interventions could include commitment-enhancing techniques, decisionmaking therapy, and New Year's resolutions.

4. **Counterconditioning** involves substituting coping alternatives for anxiety caused by substance-related behaviors. Interventions could include relaxation training, desensitization, assertion, and positive self-statements.

5. **Stimulus control** means avoiding or countering stimuli that elicit problem behaviors. Interventions could include avoiding high-risk cues and removing substances from one's environment.

6. **Reinforcement management** is rewarding oneself or being rewarded by others for making changes. Interventions could include contingency contracts and overt and covert reinforcement.

7. **Helping relationships** are created by being open and trusting about problems with people who care. Interventions could include self-help groups, social support, or a therapeutic relationship.

8. **Emotional arousal and dramatic relief** involve experiencing and expressing feelings about one's problems and solutions to them. Interventions could include role-playing and psychodrama.

9. **Environmental reevaluation** is the process of assessing how one's problems affect the personal and physical environment. Interventions could include empathy training and documentaries.

10. **Social liberation** involves increasing alternatives for nonproblematic behavior. Interventions could include advocating for the rights of the oppressed and policy interventions.

Source: Adapted from DiClemente and Scott, 1997.

---

couples, opioid-dependent clients receiving methadone maintenance, and victims and perpetrators of domestic violence (Bernstein et al., 1997a; Miller and Rollnick, 1991; Noonan and Moyers, 1997). The literature also describes successful use of these motivational techniques in primary care facilities (Daley et al., 1998), hospital emergency departments (Bernstein et al., 1997a; D'Onofrio et al., 1998), traditional inpatient and outpatient substance abuse treatment environments, drug courts, and community prevention efforts. These interventions have been used with individuals, couples, groups, and in face-to-face sessions or through mailed materials (Miller and Rollnick, 1991; Sobell and Sobell, 1998). The simplicity and universality of the concepts underlying motivational interventions permit broad application and offer great potential to reach clients with many types of problems and in many different cultures or settings.

Responding to Differing Needs

Clients in treatment for substance abuse differ in ethnic and racial backgrounds, socioeconomic status, education, gender, age, sexual orientation, type and severity of substance use problems, and psychological health. As noted

Figure 2-4	
Catalysts and the Stages of Change	
Stage of Change	**Catalysts**
Precontemplation	■ Consciousness raising ■ Environmental reevaluation ■ Emotional arousal and dramatic relief
Contemplation	■ Self-reevaluation ■ Emotional arousal and dramatic relief ■ Environmental reevaluation
Preparation	■ Self-liberation ■ Counterconditioning ■ Helping relationships
Action	■ Counterconditioning ■ Stimulus control ■ Reinforcement management ■ Helping relationships ■ Self-liberation
Maintenance	■ Helping relationships ■ Environmental reevaluation ■ Self-liberation ■ Reinforcement management

above, research and experience suggest that the change process is the same or similar across different populations. Thus, the principles and mechanisms of enhancing motivation to change seem to be broadly applicable. Nonetheless, there may be important differences among populations and cultural contexts regarding the expression of motivation for change and the importance of critical life events. Hence, be familiar with the populations with whom you expect to establish therapeutic relationships and use your clients as teachers regarding their own culture.

Because motivational strategies emphasize the client's responsibility to voice personal goals and values as well as to select among options for change, a sensitive clinician will understand and, ideally, respond in a nonjudgmental way to cultural differences. Cultural differences might be reflected in the value of health, the meaning

of time, the stigma of heavy drinking, or responsibilities to community and family. Try to understand the client's perspective rather than impose mainstream values or make quick judgments. This requires knowledge of the influences that promote or sustain substance use among different populations. Motivation-enhancing strategies should be congruent with clients' cultural and social principles, standards, and expectations. For example, older adults often struggle with loss of status and personal identity when they retire, and they may not know how to occupy their leisure time. Help such retired clients understand their need for new activities and how their use of substances is a coping mechanism. Similarly, when you try to enhance motivation for change in adolescents, consider how peers influence their behaviors and values and how families may limit their emerging autonomy.

Cultural Appropriateness

In my practice with persons who have different world views, I've made a number of observations on the ways in which culture influences the change process. I try to pay attention to cultural effects on a person's style of receiving and processing information, making decisions, pacing, and being ready to act. The more clients are assimilated into the surrounding culture, the more likely they are to process information, respond, and make choices that are congruent with mainstream beliefs and styles. The responsibility for being aware of different cultural value systems lies with the practitioner, not the client being treated.

More specifically, the manner in which a person communicates, verbally and nonverbally, is often directly related to culture. One young Native American stated on initial contact that he "might not be able to come back because his shoes were too tight." This was his way of saying he had no money.

However, ethnicity doesn't always determine the culture or values one chooses to live by. For example, white Americans may adopt Eastern world views and value systems. Further, an advanced education doesn't necessarily indicate the degree of assimilation or acculturation. Asian-Americans or African-Americans who are well educated may choose to live according to their traditional cultural value system and process information for change accordingly.

Culture is a powerful contributor to defining one's identity. Not having a healthy ethnic sense of self affects all stages of the change process. As Maslow wrote, to have a strong sense of self, you have to be powerful in the areas of being, knowing, doing, and having. Ethnic Americans who have been raised in environments that isolate them from their own cultures may not have accurate information about their ethnicity and may not develop a healthy ethnic sense of self.

I believe clinicians who use motivational enhancement therapy need to know different cultural value systems and be culturally sensitive. If in doubt of the client's beliefs, explore them with the client. Acknowledging and honoring differing cultural world views greatly influence both motivational style and therapeutic outcome.

Rosalyn Harris-Offutt, Consensus Panel Member

In addition to understanding and using a special population's values to encourage change, identify how those values may present potential barriers to change. Some clients will identify strongly with cultural or religious traditions and work diligently to gain the respect of elders or other group leaders; others find membership or participation in groups of this type an anathema. Some populations are willing to involve family members in counseling; others find this disrespectful, if not disgraceful. The label "alcoholic" is proudly and voluntarily adopted by members of AA but viewed as dehumanizing by others. The message is simple: Know and be sensitive to the concerns and values of your clients.

Another sensitive area is matching the client with the clinician. Although the literature suggests that warmth, empathy, and genuine respect are more important in building a therapeutic partnership than professional training or experience (Najavits and Weiss, 1994), nevertheless, programs can identify those clinicians who may be optimally suited because of cultural identification, language, or other similarities of background, to work with clients from specific populations. Programs will find it useful to develop a network of bilingual clinicians or interpreters who can communicate with non–English-speaking clients.

Finally, know what personal and material resources are available to your clients and be sensitive to issues of poverty, social isolation, and recent losses. In particular, recognize that access to financial and social resources is an important part of the motivation for and process of change. Prolonged poverty and lack of resources make change more difficult, both because many alternatives are not possible and because despair can be pervasive. It is a challenge to affirm self-efficacy and stimulate hope and optimism in clients who lack material resources and have suffered the effects of discrimination. The facts of the situation should be firmly acknowledged. Nevertheless, clients' capacity for endurance and personal growth in the face of dire circumstances can be respected and affirmed and then drawn on as a strength in attempting positive change.

Brief Interventions

Over the last two decades, there has been a growing trend worldwide to view substance-related problems in a much broader context than diagnosable abuse and dependence syndromes. The recognition that persons with substance-related problems compose a much larger group—and pose a serious and costly public health threat—than the smaller number of persons needing traditional, specialized treatment is not always reflected in the organization and availability of treatment services. As part of a movement toward early identification of hazardous drinking patterns and the development of effective and low-cost methods to ameliorate this widespread problem, brief interventions have been initiated and evaluated, primarily in the United Kingdom (Institute of Medicine, 1990a) and Canada but also in many other nations. (For a greater discussion of brief intervention and brief therapy, refer to the forthcoming TIP, *Brief Interventions and Brief Therapies for Substance Abuse* [CSAT, in press (a)].) They have been tried in the United States and elsewhere with

great success, although they have not been widely adopted outside research settings (Drummond, 1997; Kahan et al., 1995). The impetus to expand the use of this shorter form of treatment is a response to

- The need for a broader base of treatment and prevention components to serve all segments of the population who have minimal to severe substance-related problems and consumption patterns
- The need for cost-effective interventions that will not further deplete public coffers and will also satisfy cost-containment policies in an era of managed health care (although research indicates that intensive treatment for nicotine dependence is more cost effective [Agency for Health Care Policy and Research, 1996])
- A growing body of research findings that consistently demonstrate the efficacy of brief interventions relative to no intervention

Uses of Brief Interventions

Brief interventions for substance-using individuals are applied most often outside traditional treatment settings (in what are often referred to as *opportunistic* settings), where clients are not seeking help for a substance abuse disorder but have come, for example, to seek medical attention, to pick up a welfare check, or to respond to a court summons. These settings provide an opportunity to meet and engage with individuals with substance abuse disorders "where they are at." In these situations, persons seeking services may be routinely screened for substance-related problems or asked about their consumption patterns. (For more on how this can work in one such setting, see TIP 24, *A Guide to Substance Abuse Services for Primary Care Clinicians* [CSAT, 1997].) Those found to have risky or excessive patterns of substance use or related problems receive a brief intervention of one or more sessions, each lasting a few minutes to an hour.

Brief Intervention in the Emergency Department

When I apply a motivational interviewing style in my practice of emergency medicine, I experience considerable professional satisfaction. Honestly, it's a struggle to let go of the need to be the expert in charge. It helps to recognize that the person I'm talking with in these medical encounters is also an expert—an expert in her own lifestyle, needs, and choices.

After learning about the FRAMES principles in 1987, I tried them once or twice, and they worked, so I tried them again and again. This is not to say that I don't fall back to old ways and sometimes ask someone, "Do you want to go to detox?" But more often than not, I try to ask permission to discuss each individual's substance use. I ask patients to help me to understand what they enjoy about using substances, and then what they enjoy less about it. Patients often tell me they like to get high because it helps them relax and forget their problems and it's a part of their social life. But they say they don't like getting sick from drugs. They don't like their family avoiding them or having car accidents or having chest pains after using crack. I listen attentively and reflect back what I understood each person to have said, summarize, and ask, "Where does this leave you?" I also inquire about how ready they are to change their substance use on a scale of 1 to 10. If someone is low on the scale, I inquire about what it will take to move forward. If someone is high on the scale, indicating readiness to change, I ask what this person thinks would work for him to change his substance use.

If a patient expresses an interest in treatment, I explore the pros and cons of different choices. An emergency department specialist in substance use disorders then works with the person to find placement in a program and, if needed, provides a transportation voucher. This systematic approach, which incorporates motivational interviewing principles, is helpful to me in our hectic practice setting. It's not only ethically sound, based as it is on respect for the individual's autonomy, but it's less time consuming and frustrating. Each person does the work for him- or herself by naming the problem and identifying possible solutions. My role is to facilitate that process.

Ed Bernstein, Consensus Panel Member

Urgent care may involve just one brief encounter, with possible referral to other services. These brief interventions are usually conducted by professionals from the service area where the person seeks services, not by substance abuse treatment specialists. The purpose of a brief intervention is usually to counsel individuals about hazardous substance use patterns and to advise them to limit or stop their consumption altogether, depending on the circumstances. If the initial intervention does not result in substantial improvement, the professional can make a referral for additional specialized substance abuse treatment. A brief intervention also can explore the pros and cons of entering treatment and present a menu of options for treatment, as well as facilitate contact with the treatment system.

Brief interventions have been used effectively within substance abuse treatment settings with persons seeking assistance but placed on waiting lists, as a motivational prelude to engagement and participation in more intensive treatment, and as a first attempt to facilitate behavior change with little additional clinical attention. A series of brief interventions can constitute brief therapy, a treatment strategy that applies therapeutic techniques specifically oriented toward a limited length of treatment, making it particularly useful for certain populations (e.g., older adults, adolescents).

3 Motivational Interviewing as a Counseling Style

Motivational interviewing is a way of being with a client, not just a set of techniques for doing counseling.

Miller and Rollnick, 1991

Motivational interviewing is a technique in which you become a helper in the change process and express acceptance of your client. It is a way to interact with substance-using clients, not merely as an adjunct to other therapeutic approaches, and a style of counseling that can help resolve the ambivalence that prevents clients from realizing personal goals. Motivational interviewing builds on Carl Rogers' optimistic and humanistic theories about people's capabilities for exercising free choice and changing through a process of self-actualization. The therapeutic relationship for both Rogerian and motivational interviewers is a democratic partnership. Your role in motivational interviewing is directive, with a goal of eliciting self-motivational statements and behavioral change from the client in addition to creating client discrepancy to enhance motivation for positive change (Davidson, 1994; Miller and Rollnick, 1991). Essentially, motivational interviewing activates the capability for beneficial change that everyone possesses (Rollnick and Miller, 1995). Although some people can continue change on their own, others require more formal treatment and support over

the long journey of recovery. Even for clients with low readiness, motivational interviewing serves as a vital prelude to later therapeutic work.

Motivational interviewing is a counseling style based on the following assumptions:

- Ambivalence about substance use (and change) is normal and constitutes an important motivational obstacle in recovery.
- Ambivalence can be resolved by working with your client's intrinsic motivations and values.
- The alliance between you and your client is a collaborative partnership to which you each bring important expertise.
- An empathic, supportive, yet directive, counseling style provides conditions under which change can occur. (Direct argument and aggressive confrontation may tend to increase client defensiveness and reduce the likelihood of behavioral change.)

This chapter briefly discusses ambivalence and its role in client motivation. Five basic principles of motivational interviewing are then presented to address ambivalence and to facilitate the change process. Opening strategies to use with clients in the early stages of treatment are offered as well. The chapter concludes with a summary of a 1997 review by Noonan and Moyers that studied the effectiveness of motivational interviewing.

Ambivalence

Individuals with substance abuse disorders are usually aware of the dangers of their substance-using behavior but continue to use substances anyway. They may want to stop using substances, but at the same time they do not want to. They enter treatment programs but claim their problems are not all that serious. These disparate feelings can be characterized as ambivalence, and they are natural, regardless of the client's state of readiness. It is important to understand and accept your client's ambivalence because ambivalence is often the central problem—and lack of motivation can be a manifestation of this ambivalence (Miller and Rollnick, 1991). If you interpret ambivalence as

denial or resistance, friction between you and your client tends to occur.

The motivational interviewing style facilitates exploration of stage-specific motivational conflicts that can potentially hinder further progress. However, each dilemma also offers an opportunity to use the motivational style to help your client explore and resolve opposing attitudes. Examples of how these conflicts might be expressed at different stages of change are provided in Figure 3-1.

Five Principles of Motivational Interviewing

In their book, *Motivational Interviewing: Preparing People To Change Addictive Behavior*, Miller and Rollnick wrote,

> [M]otivational interviewing has been *practical* in focus.... The strategies of motivational

Figure 3-1 Stage-Specific Motivational Conflicts	
Stage of Change	**Client Conflict**
Precontemplation	I don't see how my cocaine use warrants concern, but I hope that by agreeing to talk about it, my wife will feel reassured.
Contemplation	I can picture how quitting heroin would improve my self-esteem, but I can't imagine never shooting up again.
Preparation	I'm feeling good about setting a quit date, but I'm wondering if I have the courage to follow through.
Action	Staying clean for the past 3 weeks really makes me feel good, but part of me wants to celebrate by getting loaded.
Maintenance	These recent months of abstinence have made me feel that I'm progressing toward recovery, but I'm still wondering whether abstinence is really necessary.

interviewing are more persuasive than coercive, more supportive than argumentative. The motivational interviewer must proceed with a strong sense of purpose, clear strategies and skills for pursuing that purpose, and a sense of timing to intervene in particular ways at incisive moments (Miller and Rollnick, 1991, pp. 51–52).

The clinician practices motivational interviewing with five general principles in mind:

1. Express empathy through reflective listening.
2. Develop discrepancy between clients' goals or values and their current behavior.
3. Avoid argument and direct confrontation.
4. Adjust to client resistance rather than opposing it directly.
5. Support self-efficacy and optimism.

Express Empathy

Empathy "is a specifiable and learnable skill for *understanding* another's meaning through the use of reflective listening….It requires sharp attention to each new client statement, and the continual generation of hypotheses as to the underlying meaning" (Miller and Rollnick, 1991, p. 20). An empathic style

- Communicates respect for and acceptance of clients and their feelings
- Encourages a nonjudgmental, collaborative relationship
- Allows you to be a supportive and knowledgeable consultant
- Sincerely compliments rather than denigrates
- Listens rather than tells

- Gently persuades, with the understanding that the decision to change is the client's
- Provides support throughout the recovery process

Empathic motivational interviewing establishes a safe and open environment that is conducive to examining issues and eliciting personal reasons and methods for change. A fundamental component of motivational interviewing is understanding each client's unique perspective, feelings, and values. Your attitude should be one of acceptance, but not necessarily approval or agreement, recognizing that ambivalence about change is to be expected. Motivational interviewing is most successful when a trusting relationship is established between you and your client.

Although empathy is the foundation of a motivational counseling style, it "should not be confused with the meaning of empathy as *identification* with the client or the sharing of common past experiences. In fact, a recent personal history of the same problem area…may compromise a counselor's ability to provide the critical conditions of change" (Miller and Rollnick, 1991, p. 5). The key component to expressing empathy is reflective listening.

If you are not listening reflectively but are instead imposing direction and judgment, you are creating barriers that impair the therapeutic relationship (Miller and Rollnick, 1991). The client will most likely react by stopping, diverting, or changing direction. Twelve examples of such nonempathic responses have been identified (Gordon, 1970):

Expressing Empathy

- Acceptance facilitates change.
- Skillful reflective listening is fundamental to expressing empathy.
- Ambivalence is normal.

Source: Miller and Rollnick, 1991. Reprinted with permission.

Expressing Empathy With Native American Clients

For many traditional Native American groups, expressing empathy begins with the introduction. Native Americans generally expect the clinician to be aware of and practice the culturally accepted norms for introducing oneself and showing respect. For example, when first meeting a Navajo, the person often is expected to say his name, clan relationship or ethnic origin, and place of origin. Physical contact is kept to a minimum, except for a brief handshake, which may be no more than a soft touch of the palms.

Ray Daw, Consensus Panel Member

---

1. *Ordering or directing.* Direction is given with a voice of authority. The speaker may be in a position of power (e.g., parent, employer) or the words may simply be phrased and spoken in an authoritarian manner.

2. *Warning or threatening.* These messages are similar to ordering but they carry an overt or covert threat of impending negative consequences if the advice or direction is not followed. The threat may be one the clinician will carry out or simply a prediction of a negative outcome if the client doesn't comply—for example, "If you don't listen to me, you'll be sorry."

3. *Giving advice, making suggestions, or providing solutions prematurely or when unsolicited.* The message recommends a course of action based on the clinician's knowledge and personal experience. These recommendations often begin with phrases such as, "What I would do is…."

4. *Persuading with logic, arguing, or lecturing.* The underlying assumption of these messages is that the client has not reasoned through the problem adequately and needs help to do so.

5. *Moralizing, preaching, or telling clients their duty.* These statements contain such words as "should" or "ought" to convey moral instructions.

6. *Judging, criticizing, disagreeing, or blaming.* These messages imply that something is wrong with the client or with what the client has said. Even simple disagreement may be interpreted as critical.

7. *Agreeing, approving, or praising.* Surprisingly, praise or approval also can be an obstacle if the message sanctions or implies agreement with whatever the client has said. Unsolicited approval can interrupt the communication process and can imply an uneven relationship between the speaker and the listener. Reflective listening does not require agreement.

8. *Shaming, ridiculing, labeling, or name-calling.* These messages express overt disapproval and intent to correct a specific behavior or attitude.

9. *Interpreting or analyzing.* Clinicians are frequently and easily tempted to impose their own interpretations on a client's statement and to find some hidden, analytical meaning. Interpretive statements might imply that the clinician knows what the client's *real* problem is.

10. *Reassuring, sympathizing, or consoling.* Clinicians often want to make the client feel better by offering consolation. Such reassurance can interrupt the flow of communication and interfere with careful listening.

11. *Questioning or probing.* Clinicians often mistake questioning for good listening. Although the clinician may ask questions to learn more about the client, the underlying message is that the clinician might find the right answer to all the client's problems if enough questions are asked. In fact, intensive questioning can interfere with the spontaneous flow of communication and

---

Expressing Empathy With African-American Clients

One way I empathize with African-American clients is, first and foremost, to be a genuine person (not just a counselor or clinician). The client may begin the relationship asking questions about you the person, not the professional, in an attempt to locate you in the world. It's as if the client's internal dialog says, "As you try to understand me, by what pathways, perspectives, life experiences, and values are you coming to that understanding of me?" Typical questions my African-American clients have asked me are

- Are you Christian?
- Where are you from?
- What part of town do you live in?
- Who are your folks?
- Are you married?

All of these are reasonable questions that work to establish a real, not contrived, relationship with the clinician. As part of a democratic partnership, the client has a right and, in some instances, a cultural expectation to know about the helper.

On another level, African-Americans are a very spiritual people. This spirituality is expressed and practiced in ways that supersede religious affiliations. Young people pat their chests and say, "I feel you," as a way to describe this sense of empathy. Understanding and working with this can enhance the clinician's expression of empathy. In other words, the therapeutic alliance between the client and clinician can be deepened, permitting another level of empathic connection that some might call an intuitive understanding and others a spiritual connection to the client. What emerges is a therapeutic alliance—a spiritual connection—that goes beyond what mere words can say. The more clinicians express that side of themselves, whether they call it intuition or spirituality, the more intense the empathic connection the African-American client will feel.

Cheryl Grills, Consensus Panel Member

---

divert it in directions of interest to the clinician rather than the client.

12. *Withdrawing, distracting, humoring, or changing the subject.* Although humor may represent an attempt to take the client's mind off emotional subjects or threatening problems, it also can be a distraction that diverts communication and implies that the client's statements are unimportant.

Ethnic and cultural differences must be considered when expressing empathy because they influence how both you and your client interpret verbal and nonverbal communications.

Develop Discrepancy

Motivation for change is enhanced when clients perceive discrepancies between their current situation and their hopes for the future. Your task is to help focus your client's attention on how current behavior differs from ideal or desired behavior. Discrepancy is initially highlighted by raising your clients' awareness of the negative personal, familial, or community consequences of a problem behavior and helping them confront the substance use that contributed to the consequences. Although helping a client perceive discrepancy can be difficult, carefully chosen and strategic reflecting can underscore incongruities.

Developing Discrepancy

- Developing awareness of consequences helps clients examine their behavior.
- A discrepancy between present behavior and important goals motivates change.
- The client should present the arguments for change.

Source: Miller and Rollnick, 1991.

Separate the behavior from the person and help your client explore how important personal goals (e.g., good health, marital happiness, financial success) are being undermined by current substance use patterns. This requires you to listen carefully to your client's statements about values and connections to community, family, and church. If the client shows concern about the effects of personal behavior, highlight this concern to heighten the client's perception and acknowledgment of discrepancy.

Once a client begins to understand how the consequences or potential consequences of current behavior conflict with significant personal values, amplify and focus on this discordance until the client can articulate consistent concern and commitment to change.

One useful tactic for helping a client perceive discrepancy is sometimes called the "Columbo approach" (Kanfer and Schefft, 1988). This approach is particularly useful with a client who prefers to be in control. Essentially, the clinician

The Columbo Approach

Sometimes I use what I refer to as the Columbo approach to develop discrepancy with clients. In the old "Columbo" TV series, Peter Falk played a detective who had a sense of what had really occurred but used a somewhat bumbling, unassuming Socratic style of querying his prime suspect, strategically posing questions and making reflections to piece together a picture of what really happened. As the pieces began to fall into place, the object of Columbo's investigation would often reveal the real story.

Using the Columbo approach, the clinician plays the role of a detective who is trying to solve a mystery but is having a difficult time because the clues don't add up. The "Columbo clinician" engages the client in solving the mystery:

Example #1: "Hmm. Help me figure this out. You've told me that keeping custody of your daughter and being a good parent are the most important things to you now. How does your heroin use fit in with that?"

Example #2: "So, sometimes when you drink during the week, you can't get out of bed to get to work. Last month, you missed 5 days. But you enjoy your work, and doing well in your job is very important to you."

In both cases, the clinician expresses confusion, which allows the client to take over and explain how these conflicting desires fit together.

The value of the Columbo approach is that it forces clients, rather than clinicians, to grapple with discrepancies and attempt to resolve them. This approach reinforces the notion that clients are the experts on their own behavior and values. They truly are the only ones who can resolve the discrepancy. If the clinician attempts to do this instead of the client, however, the clinician risks making the wrong interpretation, rushing to her own conclusions rather than listening to the client's perspective, and perhaps most important, making the client a passive rather than an active participant in the process.

Cheryl Grills, Consensus Panel Member

expresses understanding and continuously seeks clarification of the client's problems but appears unable to perceive any solution. A stance of uncertainty or confusion can motivate the client to take control of the situation by offering a solution to the clinician (Van Bilsen, 1991).

Tools other than talking can be used to reveal discrepancy. For example, show a video and then discuss it with the client, allowing the client to make the connection to his own situation. Juxtaposing different media messages or images that are meaningful to a client can also be effective. This strategy may be particularly effective for adolescents because it provides stimulation for discussion and reaction.

You can help your client perceive discrepancy on a number of different levels, from physical to spiritual, and in different domains, from attitudinal to behavioral. To do this, it is useful to understand not only what an individual values but also what the community values. For example, substance use might conflict with the client's personal identity and values; it might conflict with the values of the larger community; it might conflict with spiritual or religious beliefs; or it might conflict with the values of the client's family members. Thus, discrepancy can be made clear by contrasting substance-using behavior with the importance the clients ascribe to their relationships with family, religious groups, and the community.

The client's cultural background can affect perceptions of discrepancy. For example, African-Americans may regard addiction as "chemical slavery," which may conflict with their ethnic pride and desire to overcome a collective history of oppression. Moreover, African-Americans may be more strongly influenced than white Americans by the expressed values of a larger religious or spiritual community. In a recent focus group study with adolescents, African-American youths were much more likely than other youths to view cigarette smoking as conflicting with their ethnic pride (Luke, 1998). They pointed to this conflict as an important reason not to smoke.

Avoid Argument

You may occasionally be tempted to argue with a client who is unsure about changing or unwilling to change, especially if the client is hostile, defiant, or provocative. However, trying to convince a client that a problem exists or that change is needed could precipitate even more resistance. If you try to prove a point, the client predictably takes the opposite side. Arguments with the client can rapidly degenerate into a power struggle and do not enhance motivation for beneficial change. When it is the client, not you, who voices arguments for change, progress can be made. The goal is to "walk" with clients (i.e., accompany clients through treatment), not "drag" them along (i.e., direct clients' treatment).

A common area of argument is the client's unwillingness to accept a label such as "alcoholic" or "drug abuser." Miller and Rollnick stated that

> [T]here is no particular reason why the therapist should badger clients to accept a label, or exert great persuasive effort in this direction. Accusing clients of being *in denial* or

---

Avoiding Arguments

- Arguments are counterproductive.
- Defending breeds defensiveness.
- Resistance is a signal to change strategies.
- Labeling is unnecessary.

Source: Miller and Rollnick, 1991. Reprinted with permission.

resistant or *addicted* is more likely to increase their resistance than to instill motivation for change. We advocate starting with clients wherever they are, and altering their self-perceptions, not by arguing about labels, but through substantially more effective means (Miller and Rollnick, 1991, p. 59).

Although this conflicts with some clinicians' belief that clients must be persuaded to self-label, the approach advocated in the "Big Book" of Alcoholics Anonymous (AA) is that labels are not to be imposed (AA, 1976). Rather, it is a personal decision of each individual.

Roll With Resistance

Resistance is a legitimate concern for the clinician because it is predictive of poor treatment outcomes and lack of involvement in the therapeutic process. One view of resistance is that the client is behaving defiantly. Another, perhaps more constructive, viewpoint is that resistance is a signal that the client views the situation differently. This requires you to understand your client's perspective and proceed from there. Resistance is a signal to you to change direction or listen more carefully. Resistance actually offers you an opportunity to respond in a new, perhaps surprising, way and to take advantage of the situation without being confrontational.

Adjusting to resistance is similar to avoiding argument in that it offers another chance to express empathy by remaining nonjudgmental and respectful, encouraging the client to talk and stay involved. Try to avoid evoking resistance whenever possible, and divert or deflect the energy the client is investing in resistance toward positive change.

How do you recognize resistance? Figure 3-2 depicts four common behaviors that indicate that a client is resisting treatment. How do you avoid arguing and, instead, adapt to resistance? Miller and colleagues have identified and provided examples of at least seven ways to react appropriately to client resistance (Miller and Rollnick, 1991; Miller et al., 1992). These are described below.

Simple reflection

The simplest approach to responding to resistance is with nonresistance, by repeating the client's statement in a neutral form. This acknowledges and validates what the client has said and can elicit an opposite response.

Client: I don't plan to quit drinking anytime soon.

Clinician: You don't think that abstinence would work for you right now.

Amplified reflection

Another strategy is to reflect the client's statement in an exaggerated form—to state it in a more extreme way but without sarcasm. This can move the client toward positive change rather than resistance.

Client: I don't know why my wife is worried about this. I don't drink any more than any of my friends.

Clinician: So your wife is worrying needlessly.

Double-sided reflection

A third strategy entails acknowledging what the client has said but then also stating contrary things she has said in the past. This requires the use of information that the client has offered previously, although perhaps not in the same session.

Client: I know you want me to give up drinking completely, but I'm not going to do that!

Clinician: You can see that there are some real problems here, but you're not willing to think about quitting altogether.

Figure 3-2
Four Types of Client Resistance

Arguing

The client contests the accuracy, expertise, or integrity of the clinician.

- *Challenging.* The client directly challenges the accuracy of what the clinician has said.
- *Discounting.* The client questions the clinician's personal authority and expertise.
- *Hostility.* The client expresses direct hostility toward the clinician.

Interrupting

The client breaks in and interrupts the clinician in a defensive manner.

- *Talking over.* The client speaks while the clinician is still talking, without waiting for an appropriate pause or silence.
- *Cutting off.* The client breaks in with words obviously intended to cut the clinician off (e.g., "Now wait a minute. I've heard about enough").

Denying

The client expresses unwillingness to recognize problems, cooperate, accept responsibility, or take advice.

- *Blaming.* The client blames other people for problems.
- *Disagreeing.* The client disagrees with a suggestion that the clinician has made, offering no constructive alternative. This includes the familiar "Yes, but...," which explains what is wrong with suggestions that are made.
- *Excusing.* The client makes excuses for his behavior.
- *Claiming impunity.* The client claims that she is not in any danger (e.g., from drinking).
- *Minimizing.* The client suggests that the clinician is exaggerating risks or dangers and that it really isn't so bad.
- *Pessimism.* The client makes statements about himself or others that are pessimistic, defeatist, or negative in tone.
- *Reluctance.* The client expresses reservations and reluctance about information or advice given.
- *Unwillingness to change.* The client expresses a lack of desire or an unwillingness to change.

Ignoring

The client shows evidence of ignoring or not following the clinician.

- *Inattention.* The client's response indicates that she has not been paying attention to the clinician.
- *Nonanswer.* In answering a clinician's query, the client gives a response that is not an answer to the question.
- *No response.* The client gives no audible verbal or clear nonverbal reply to the clinician's query.
- *Sidetracking.* The client changes the direction of the conversation that the clinician has been pursuing.

Source: Miller and Rollnick, 1991. Adapted from a behavior coding system by Chamberlain et al., 1984. Reprinted with permission.

Shifting focus

You can defuse resistance by helping the client shift focus away from obstacles and barriers. This method offers an opportunity to affirm your client's personal choice regarding the conduct of his own life.

Client: I can't stop smoking reefer when all my friends are doing it.

Clinician: You're way ahead of me. We're still exploring your concerns about whether you can get into college. We're not ready yet to decide how marijuana fits into your goals.

Agreement with a twist

A subtle strategy is to agree with the client, but with a slight twist or change of direction that propels the discussion forward.

Client: Why are you and my wife so stuck on my drinking? What about all *her* problems? You'd drink, too, if your family were nagging you all the time.

Clinician: You've got a good point there, and that's important. There is a bigger picture here, and maybe I haven't been paying enough attention to that. It's not as simple as one person's drinking. I agree with you that we shouldn't be trying to place blame here. Drinking problems like these do involve the whole family.

Reframing

A good strategy to use when a client denies personal problems is reframing—offering a new and positive interpretation of negative information provided by the client. Reframing "acknowledges the validity of the client's raw observations, but offers a new meaning…for them" (Miller and Rollnick, 1991, p. 107).

Client: My husband is always nagging me about my drinking—always calling me an alcoholic. It really bugs me.

Clinician: It sounds like he really cares about you and is concerned, although he expresses it in a way that makes you angry. Maybe we can help him learn how to tell you he loves you and is worried about you in a more positive and acceptable way.

In another example, the concept of relative tolerance to alcohol provides a good opportunity for reframing with problem drinkers (Miller and Rollnick, 1991). Many heavy drinkers believe they are not alcoholics because they can "hold their liquor." When you explain that tolerance is a risk factor and a warning signal, not a source of pride, you can change your client's perspective about the meaning of feeling no effects. Thus, reframing is not only educational but sheds new light on the client's experience of alcohol.

Siding with the negative

One more strategy for adapting to client resistance is to "side with the negative"—to take up the negative voice in the discussion. This is not "reverse psychology," nor does it involve the ethical quandaries of prescribing more of the symptom, as in a "therapeutic paradox." Typically, siding with the negative is stating

---

Rolling With Resistance

- Momentum can be used to good advantage.
- Perceptions can be shifted.
- New perspectives are invited but not imposed.
- The client is a valuable resource in finding solutions to problems.

Source: Miller and Rollnick, 1991. Reprinted with permission.

what the client has already said while arguing against change, perhaps as an amplified reflection. If your client is ambivalent, your taking the negative side of the argument evokes a "Yes, but..." from the client, who then expresses the other (positive) side. Be cautious, however, in using this too early in treatment or with depressed clients.

Client: Well, I know some people think I drink too much, and I may be damaging my liver, but I still don't believe I'm an alcoholic or in need of treatment.

Clinician: We've spent considerable time now going over your positive feelings and concerns about your drinking, but you still don't think you are ready or want to change your drinking patterns. Maybe changing would be too difficult for you, especially if you really want to stay the same. Anyway, I'm not sure you believe you could change even if you wanted to.

Support Self-Efficacy

Many clients do not have a well-developed sense of self-efficacy and find it difficult to believe that they can begin or maintain behavioral change. Improving self-efficacy requires eliciting and supporting hope, optimism, and the feasibility of accomplishing change. This requires you to recognize the client's strengths and bring these to the forefront whenever possible. Unless a client believes change is possible, the perceived discrepancy between the desire for change and feelings of hopelessness about accomplishing change is likely to result in rationalizations or denial in order to reduce discomfort. Because self-efficacy is a critical component of behavior change, it is crucial that you as the clinician also believe in your clients' capacity to reach their goals.

Discussing treatment or change options that might still be attractive to clients is usually helpful, even though they may have dropped out of other treatment programs or returned to substance use after a period of being substance free. It is also helpful to talk about how persons in similar situations have successfully changed their behavior. Other clients can serve as role models and offer encouragement. Nonetheless, clients must ultimately come to believe that change is their responsibility and that long-term success begins with a single step forward. The AA motto, "one day at a time," may help clients focus and embark on the immediate and small changes that they believe are feasible.

Education can increase clients' sense of self-efficacy. Credible, understandable, and accurate information helps clients understand how substance use progresses to abuse or dependency. Making the biology of addiction and the medical effects of substance use relevant to the clients' experience may alleviate shame and guilt and instill hope that recovery can be achieved by using appropriate methods and tools. A process that initially feels overwhelming and hopeless can be broken down into achievable small steps toward recovery.

Five Opening Strategies For Early Sessions

Clinicians who adopt motivational interviewing as a preferred style have found that the five strategies discussed below are particularly useful in the early stages of treatment. They are based on the five principles described in the previous section: express empathy, develop discrepancy, avoid argument, adjust to rather than oppose client resistance, and support self-efficacy. Helping clients address their natural ambivalence is a good starting point. These opening strategies ensure your support for your client and help the client explore ambivalence in

Self-Efficacy
■ Belief in the possibility of change is an important motivator.
■ The client is responsible for choosing and carrying out personal change.
■ There is hope in the range of alternative approaches available.
Source: Miller and Rollnick, 1991. Reprinted with permission.

a safe setting. The first four strategies, which are derived from client-centered counseling, help clients explore their ambivalence and reasons for change. The fifth strategy is specific to motivational interviewing and integrates and guides the other four.

In early treatment sessions, determine your client's readiness to change or stage of change (see Chapters 1, 4, and 8). Be careful to avoid focusing prematurely on a particular stage of change or assuming the client is at a particular stage because of the setting where you meet. As already noted, using strategies inappropriate for a particular change stage or forming an inaccurate perception regarding the client's wants or needs could be harmful. Therefore, try not to identify the goals of counseling until you have sufficiently explored the client's readiness.

Ask Open-Ended Questions

Asking open-ended questions helps you understand your clients' point of view and elicits their feelings about a given topic or situation. Open-ended questions facilitate dialog; they cannot be answered with a single word or phrase and do not require any particular response. They are a means to solicit additional information in a neutral way. Open-ended questions encourage the client to do most of the talking, help you avoid making premature judgments, and keep communication moving forward (see Figure 3-3).

Listen Reflectively

Reflective listening, a fundamental component of motivational interviewing, is a challenging skill in which you demonstrate that you have accurately heard and understood a client's communication by restating its meaning. That is, you hazard a guess about what the client intended to convey and express this in a responsive statement, not a question. "Reflective listening is a way of checking rather than assuming that you *know* what is meant" (Miller and Rollnick, 1991, p. 75).

Reflective listening strengthens the empathic relationship between the clinician and the client and encourages further exploration of problems and feelings. This form of communication is particularly appropriate for early stages of counseling. Reflective listening helps the client by providing a synthesis of content and process. It reduces the likelihood of resistance, encourages the client to keep talking, communicates respect, cements the therapeutic alliance, clarifies exactly what the client means, and reinforces motivation (Miller et al., 1992).

This process has a tremendous amount of flexibility, and you can use reflective listening to reinforce your client's positive ideas (Miller et al., 1992). The following dialog gives some examples of clinician's responses that illustrate effective reflective listening. Essentially, true reflective listening requires continuous alert tracking of the client's verbal and nonverbal responses and their possible meanings, formulation of reflections at the appropriate level of complexity, and ongoing adjustment of hypotheses.

Clinician: What else concerns you about your drinking?

Client: Well, I'm not sure I'm *concerned* about it, but I do wonder sometimes if I'm drinking too much.

Figure 3-3 How To Ask Open-Ended Questions	
Closed Question	**Open Question**
So you are here because you are concerned about your use of alcohol, correct?	Tell me, what is it that brings you here today?
How many children do you have?	Tell me about your family.
Do you agree that it would be a good idea for you to go through detoxification?	What do you think about the possibility of going through detoxification?
First, I'd like you to tell me some about your marijuana use. On a typical day, how much do you smoke?	Tell me about your marijuana use during a typical week.
Do you like to smoke?	What are some of the things you like about smoking?
How has your drug use been this week, compared to last: more, less, or about the same?	What has your drug use been like during the past week?
Do you think you use amphetamines too often?	In what ways are you concerned about your use of amphetamines?
How long ago did you have your last drink?	Tell me about the last time you had a drink.
Are you sure that your probation officer told you that it's only cocaine he is concerned about in your urine screens?	Now what exactly are the conditions that your probation officer wants you to follow?
When do you plan to quit drinking?	So what do you think you want to do about your drinking?

Clinician: Too much for…?

Client: For my own good, I guess. I mean it's not like it's really serious, but sometimes when I wake up in the morning I feel really awful, and I can't think straight most of the morning.

Clinician: It messes up your thinking, your concentration.

Client: Yes, and sometimes I have trouble remembering things.

Clinician: And you wonder if that might be because you're drinking too much?

Client: Well, I know it is sometimes.

Clinician: You're pretty sure about that. But maybe there's more….

Client: Yeah, even when I'm not drinking, sometimes I mix things up, and I wonder about that.

Clinician: Wonder if…?

Client: If alcohol's pickling my brain, I guess.

Clinician: You think that can happen to people, maybe to you.

Client: Well, can't it? I've heard that alcohol kills brain cells.

Clinician: Um-hmm. I can see why that would worry you.

Client: But I don't think I'm an alcoholic or anything.

Clinician: You don't think you're that bad off, but you do wonder if maybe you're overdoing it and damaging yourself in the process.

Client: Yeah.

Clinician: Kind of a scary thought. What else worries you?

Summarize

Most clinicians find it useful to periodically summarize what has occurred in a counseling session. Summarizing consists of distilling the essence of what a client has expressed and communicating it back. "Summaries reinforce what has been said, show that you have been listening carefully, and prepare the client to move on" (Miller and Rollnick, 1991, p. 78). A summary that links the client's positive and negative feelings about substance use can facilitate an understanding of initial ambivalence and promote the perception of discrepancy. Summarizing is also a good way to begin and end each counseling session and to provide a natural bridge when the client is transitioning between stages of change.

Summarizing also serves strategic purposes. In presenting a summary, you can select what information should be included and what can be minimized or left out. Correction of a summary by the client should be invited, and this often leads to further comments and discussion. Summarizing helps clients consider their own responses and contemplate their own experience. It also gives you and your client an opportunity to notice what might have been overlooked as well as incorrectly stated.

Affirm

When it is done sincerely, affirming your client supports and promotes self-efficacy. More broadly, your affirmation acknowledges the difficulties the client has experienced. By affirming, you are saying, "I hear; I understand," and validating the client's experiences and feelings. Affirming helps clients feel confident about marshaling their inner resources to take action and change behavior. Emphasizing their past experiences that demonstrate strength, success, or power can prevent discouragement. For some clients, such as many African-Americans, affirmation has a spiritual context. Affirming their inner guiding spirit and their faith may help resolve their ambivalence. Several examples of affirming statements (Miller and Rollnick, 1991) follow:

- I appreciate how hard it must have been for you to decide to come here. You took a big step.
- I think it's great that you want to do something about this problem.
- That must have been very difficult for you.
- You're certainly a resourceful person to have been able to live with the problem this long and not fall apart.
- That's a good suggestion.
- It must be difficult for you to accept a day-to-day life so full of stress. I must say, if I were in your position, I would also find that difficult.

Elicit Self-Motivational Statements

Engaging the client in the process of change is the fundamental task of motivational interviewing. Rather than identifying the problem and promoting ways to solve it, your task is to help the client recognize how life might be better and choose ways to make it so.

Remember that your role is to entice the client to voice personal concerns and intentions, not to convince him that a transformation is necessary. Successful motivational interviewing requires that clients, not the clinician, ultimately argue for change and persuade themselves that they want to and can improve. One signal that the client's ambivalence and resistance are diminishing is the self-motivational statement.

Four types of motivational statements can be identified (Miller and Rollnick, 1991):

- Cognitive recognition of the problem (e.g., "I guess this is more serious than I thought.")

- Affective expression of concern about the perceived problem (e.g., "I'm really worried about what is happening to me.")
- A direct or implicit intention to change behavior (e.g., "I've got to do something about this.")
- Optimism about one's ability to change (e.g., "I know that if I try, I can really do it.")

Figure 3-4 illustrates how you can differentiate a self-motivational statement from a countermotivational assertion. You can reinforce your client's self-motivational statements by reflecting them, nodding, or making approving facial expressions and affirming statements. Encourage clients to continue exploring the possibility of change. This can be done by asking for an elaboration, explicit examples, or more details about remaining concerns. Questions beginning with "What else" are effective ways to invite further amplification. Sometimes asking clients to identify the extremes of the problem (e.g., "What are you most concerned about?") helps to

enhance their motivation. Another effective approach is to ask clients to envision what they would like for the future. From there, clients may be able to begin establishing specific goals.

Figure 3-5 provides a useful list of questions you can ask to elicit self-motivational statements from the client.

Effectiveness of Motivational Interviewing

A recent review of 11 clinical trials of motivational interviewing concluded that this is a "useful clinical intervention…[and] appears to be an effective, efficient, and adaptive therapeutic style worthy of further development, application, and research" (Noonan and Moyers, 1997, p. 8). Motivational interviewing is a counseling approach that more closely reflects the principles of motivational enhancement than the variety of brief interventions reviewed in Chapter 2, and it also

Figure 3-4
How To Recognize Self-Motivational Statements

Self-Motivational Statements	Countermotivational Assertions
I guess this has been affecting me more than I realized.	I don't have any problem with marijuana.
Sometimes when I've been using, I just can't think or concentrate.	When I'm high, I'm more relaxed and creative.
I guess I wonder if I've been pickling my brain.	I can drink all night and never get drunk.
I feel terrible about how my drinking has hurt my family.	I'm not the one with the problem.
I don't know what to do, but something has to change.	No way am I giving up coke.
Tell me what I would need to do if I went into treatment.	I'm not going into a hospital.
I think I could become clean and sober if I decided to.	I've tried to quit, and I just can't do it.
If I really put my mind to something, I can do it.	I have so much else going on right now that I can't think about quitting.

Figure 3-5
Sample Questions To Evoke Self-Motivational Statements

Problem Recognition

- What things make you think that this is a problem?
- What difficulties have you had in relation to your drug use?
- In what ways do you think you or other people have been harmed by your drinking?
- In what ways has this been a problem for you?
- How has your use of tranquilizers stopped you from doing what you want to do?

Concern

- What is there about your drinking that you or other people might see as reasons for concern?
- What worries you about your drug use? What can you imagine happening to you?
- How much does this concern you?
- In what ways does this concern you?
- What do you think will happen if you don't make a change?

Intention to Change

- The fact that you're here indicates that at least part of you thinks it's time to do something.
- What are the reasons you see for making a change?
- What makes you think that you may need to make a change?
- If you were 100 percent successful and things worked out exactly as you would like, what would be different?
- What things make you think that you should keep on drinking the way you have been? And what about the other side? What makes you think it's time for a change?
- I can see that you're feeling stuck at the moment. What's going to have to change?

Optimism

- What makes you think that if you decide to make a change, you could do it?
- What encourages you that you can change if you want to?
- What do you think would work for you, if you needed to change?

Source: Miller and Rollnick, 1991. Reprinted with permission.

links these basic precepts to the stages-of-change model.

Of the 11 studies reviewed, 9 found motivational interviewing more effective than no treatment, standard care, extended treatment, or being on a waiting list before receiving the intervention. Two of the 11 studies did not support the effectiveness of motivational interviewing, although the reviewers suggested that the *spirit* of this approach may not have been followed because the providers delivered advice in an authoritarian manner and may not

have been adequately trained (Noonan and Moyers, 1997). Moreover, one study had a high dropout rate. Two studies supported the efficacy of motivational interviewing as a stand-alone intervention for self-identified concerned drinkers who were provided feedback about their drinking patterns but received no additional clinical attention. Three trials confirmed the usefulness of motivational interviewing as an enhancement to traditional treatment, five supported the effectiveness of motivational interviewing in reducing substance-using patterns of patients appearing in medical settings for other health-related conditions, and one trial compared a brief motivational intervention favorably with a more extensive alternative treatment for marijuana users.

Motivational Interviewing and Managed Care

In addition to its effectiveness, motivational interviewing is beneficial in that it can easily be applied in a managed care setting, where issues of cost containment are of great concern. Motivational interviewing approaches are particularly well suited to managed care in the following ways:

- **Low cost**. Motivational interviewing was designed from the outset to be a brief intervention and is normally delivered in two to four outpatient sessions.
- **Efficacy**. There is strong evidence that motivational interviewing triggers change in high-risk lifestyle behaviors.
- **Effectiveness**. Large effects from brief motivational counseling have held up across a wide variety of real-life clinical settings.

- **Mobilizing client resources**. Motivational interviewing focuses on mobilizing the client's own resources for change.
- **Compatibility with health care delivery**. Motivational interviewing does not assume a long-term client–therapist relationship. Even a single session has been found to invoke behavior change, and motivational interviewing can be delivered within the context of larger health care delivery systems.
- **Emphasizing client motivation**. Client motivation is a strong predictor of change, and this approach puts primary emphasis on first building client motivation for change. Thus, even if clients do not stay for a long course of treatment (as is often the case with substance abuse), they have been given something that is likely to help them within the first few sessions.
- **Enhancing adherence**. Motivational interviewing is also a sensible prelude to other health care interventions because it has been shown to increase adherence, which in turn improves treatment outcomes.

4 From Precontemplation to Contemplation: Building Readiness

There is a myth...in dealing with serious health-related addictive...problems, that more is always better. More education, more intense treatment, more confrontation will necessarily produce more change. Nowhere is this less true than with precontemplators. More intensity will often produce fewer results with this group. So it is particularly important to use careful motivational strategies, rather than to mount high-intensity programs...that will be ignored by those uninterested in changing the...problem behavior.... We cannot make precontemplators change, but we can help motivate them to move to contemplation.

DiClemente, 1991

Before people enter treatment for substance use or quit or moderate substance use on their own, they may have been alerted by a crisis or series of escalating incidents that their current consumption pattern is an issue—at least to someone else. If a significant other or a family member describes their substance-using behavior as problematic, substance users may react with surprise, hostility, denial, disbelief, or—occasionally—with acceptance. According to the stages-of-change model (presented in Chapter 1), those who are not yet concerned about current consumption patterns, or considering change, are in the precontemplation stage—no matter how much and how frequently they imbibe or how serious their substance use-

related problems are. Moreover, these substance users may remain in a precontemplation or early contemplation stage for years, rarely or possibly never thinking about change. Epidemiological studies indicate that only 5 to 10 percent of persons with active substance abuse disorders are in treatment or self-help groups at any one time (Stanton, 1997). One study estimated that at least 80 percent of persons with substance abuse disorders are currently in a precontemplation or contemplation stage (DiClemente and Prochaska, 1998).

Many scenarios present an opportunity for the clinician to help someone who is abusing or dependent on a substance to start on a pathway toward change—to move from precontemplation to contemplation. By definition, no one at the precontemplation stage willingly walks into a substance abuse treatment program without some reservations, but people who are at this stage are sent to or bring themselves to treatment programs. The following situations might result in a call to a treatment facility by a substance user or by a person making a referral that could involve someone at this stage:

- A college coach refers an athlete for treatment after he tests positive for cocaine.
- A wife is desperate about her husband's drinking and insists she will file for divorce unless he seeks treatment.
- A tenant is displaced from a Federal housing project for substance use.
- A driver is referred for treatment by the court for driving while intoxicated.
- A woman tests positive for substances during a prenatal visit to a public health clinic.
- An employer sends an employee whose job performance has deteriorated to the company's employee assistance program, and she is subsequently referred for substance abuse treatment.
- A physician in an emergency department treats a driver involved in a serious auto accident and discovers alcohol in his system.
- A family physician finds physical symptoms in a patient that indicate alcohol dependence and suggests treatment.
- A mother whose children have been taken into custody by a child protective services agency because they are neglected is told she cannot get them back until she stops using substances and seeks treatment.

In each of these situations, those with an important relationship to the substance users have stated that the substance use is risky, dangerous, aberrant, or harmful to self or others. The substance users' responses depend, in part,

on their perception of the circumstances as well as the manner in which the facts are presented. They will be better motivated to moderate their substance use or to abstain (either solely through their own efforts or with the help of a treatment program), if these key persons offer relevant information in a supportive and empathic manner, rather than being judgmental, dismissive, or confrontational. Substance users often respond to overt persuasion with some form of resistance (Rollnick et al., 1992a).

This chapter discusses a variety of proven techniques and gentle tactics that you, the clinician in a treatment facility, can use to raise the topic with people not thinking of change, to create client doubt about the commonly held belief that substance abuse is "harmless" and to lead to client conviction that substance-abuse is having, or will in the future have, significant negative results. An assessment and feedback process is an important part of the motivational strategy, informing your clients about how their personal substance use patterns compare with norms, what specific risks are entailed, and what damage already exists or is likely to occur if changes are not made. Many clinicians have succeeded in helping significant others act as mediators and use appropriate motivational strategies for intervening with close relations who are substance users. This chapter also discusses the following strategies for helping those in the precontemplation stage build their readiness to change: unilateral family therapy, the community reinforcement approach, and community reinforcement approach to family training. Constructive means of encouraging those clients mandated to enter treatment are described in this chapter as well.

Raising the Topic

You may find it difficult to believe that some persons entering treatment are unaware that their substance use is dangerous or causing

---

Liver Transplantation: Precontemplation to Contemplation

The client in precontemplation can appear in surprising medical settings. It is not uncommon for me to find myself sitting across from a patient with end-stage liver disease being evaluated for a liver transplant. From a medical perspective, the etiology of the patient's liver disease appears to be alcoholic hepatitis, which led to cirrhosis. A variety of other laboratory and collateral information further supports a history of years of heavy alcohol consumption. The diagnosis of alcohol dependence is not only supported by the medical information but also is given greater clarity when the patient's family indicates years of heavy drinking despite intensely negative consequences, such as being charged with driving while intoxicated and marital stress related to the drinking. Yet, despite what might seem to be an overwhelming amount of evidence, the patient himself, for a variety of dynamic and motivational reasons, cannot see himself as having a problem with alcohol. The patient may feel guilty that he caused his liver damage and think he doesn't deserve this life-saving intervention. Or he may be fearful that if he examines his alcohol use too closely and shares his history he may not be considered for transplantation at all. He may even have already been told that if he is actively drinking he will not be listed for transplantation.

It is particularly important at this point for me as a clinician not to be surprised or judgmental about the patient's reluctance to see his problematic relationship with alcohol. The simple fact is that he has never connected his health problems with his use of alcohol. To confront the patient with the overwhelming evidence about his problem drinking only makes him more defensive, reinforces his denial, and intensifies his feelings of guilt and shame.

During the assessment, I will take every opportunity to connect with the patient's history and current situation without excessive self-disclosure. Being particularly sensitive to what the patient needs and what he fears, I will help support the therapeutic alliance by asking him to share the positive side of his alcohol and drug use thus acknowledging that from his perspective, his use has utility.

In a situation such as this, it is not uncommon for me, after completing a thorough assessment, to provide the patient with a medical perspective on alcohol dependence. I will talk about the variance in brain chemistry, reward systems, issues of tolerance, genetic variables, and different enzymatic responses to alcohol, as well as other biological processes that support addictive disease, depending on the patient's educational background and medical understanding. I may go into considerable detail. If the patient is less sophisticated, I will use analogies to other, more familiar diseases such as diabetes mellitus. As the patient asks questions, he begins to paint a new picture of addictive disease that allows him to see himself in that picture. By tailoring the presentation to each patient and encouraging questions throughout, I provide him and his family, if present, with important information about the biological factors supporting alcohol dependence. This knowledge often leads to self-diagnosis.

This psychoeducational reframing gives the client a different perspective on his relationship with alcohol, taking away some of the guilt and shame that was based on a more moralistic understanding of the disease. The very act of self-diagnosis is a movement from precontemplation to contemplation. It can be accomplished by a simple cognitive reframe within the context of a thorough and caring assessment completed in a professional, yet genuinely compassionate manner.

Jeffrey M. Georgi, Consensus Panel Member

---

problems. It is tempting to assume that the client with obvious clinical signs of intense and long-term alcohol use must be contemplating or ready for change. However, such assumptions may be wrong. The new client could be at any point in the severity continuum (from mild problem use to more severe dependence), could have few or many associated health or social problems, and could be at any stage of readiness to change. The strategies you use for beginning a therapeutic dialog should be guided by your assessment of the client's motivation and readiness.

In opening sessions it is important to

- Establish rapport and trust
- Explore events that precipitated treatment entry
- Commend clients for coming

These recommendations are discussed further below.

Establish Rapport and Trust

Before you raise the topic of change with people who are not thinking about it, establish rapport and trust. The challenge is to create a safe and supportive environment in which the client can feel comfortable about engaging in authentic dialog. One way to foster rapport is first to ask the client for permission to address the topic of change; this shows respect for the client's autonomy.

Next, tell the client something about how you or your program operates and how you and the client could work together. This is the time to state how long the session will last and what you expect to accomplish both now and over a specified time. Try not to overwhelm the new client at this point with all the rules and regulations of the program. Do specify what assessments or other formal arrangements will be needed, if appropriate. If there are confidentiality issues (discussed in more detail later in this chapter), these should be introduced early in the session. It is critical that you inform the client which information will be kept private, which can be released with permission, and which must be sent back to a referring agency.

Because you are using a motivational approach, explain that you will not tell the client what to do or how and whether to change. Rather, you will be asking the client to do most of the talking—giving her perspective about both what is happening and how she feels about it. You can also invite comments about what the client expects or hopes to achieve.

Then ask the client to tell you why she has come or mention what you know about the reasons, and ask for the client's version or elaboration (Miller and Rollnick, 1991). If the client seems particularly hesitant or defensive, one strategy is to choose a topic of likely interest to the client that can be linked to substance use. A clue to such an interest might be provided by the referral source or can be ascertained by asking if the client has any stresses such as illness, marital discord, or overwork. This can lead naturally into questions such as "How does your use of…fit into this?" or "How does your use of…affect your health?" Avoid referring to the client's "problem" or "substance abuse," because this may not reflect her perspective about her substance use (Rollnick et al., 1992a). You are trying to understand the context in which substances are used and this client's readiness to change. Of course, if you discover that she is contemplating or committed to change, you can move immediately to strategies more appropriate to later change stages (see Chapters 5 and 6).

An important point to state at the first session is whether or not you will work with a client who is obviously inebriated or high on drugs at the counseling sessions. You are not likely to receive accurate and reliable information from someone who has recently ingested a mind-altering substance (Sobell et al., 1994). Many programs administer breath tests for alcohol or urine tests for drugs and reschedule counseling sessions if substances are detected at a specified level or if a client appears to be under the influence (Miller et al., 1992).

Explore the Events That Precipitated Treatment Entry

The emotional state in which the client comes to treatment is an important part of the *gestalt* or context in which counseling begins. Clients referred to treatment will exhibit a range of emotions associated with the experiences that brought them to counseling—an arrest, a confrontation with a spouse or employer, or a health crisis. People enter treatment shaken, angry, withdrawn, ashamed, terrified, or relieved—often experiencing a combination of feelings. Strong emotions can block change if you, the counselor, do not acknowledge them through reflective listening. The situation that led an individual to treatment can increase *or* decrease defensiveness about change.

It is important that your initial dialog be grounded in the client's recent experience and that you take advantage of the opportunities provided to increase motivation. For example, an athlete is likely to be concerned about his continued participation in sports, as well as athletic performance; the employee may want to keep her job; and the driver is probably worried about the possibility of losing his driving license, going to jail, or injuring someone. The pregnant woman wants a healthy child; the neglectful mother probably wants to regain custody of her children; and the concerned husband needs specific guidance on convincing his wife to enter treatment.

However, clients sometimes blame the referring source or someone else for coercing them into counseling. The implication is often that this individual or agency does not view the situation accurately. To find ways to motivate change, ascertain what the client sees and believes is true. For example, if the client's wife has insisted he come and the client denies any problem, you might ask, "What kind of things seem to bother her?" Or, "What do you think makes her believe there is a problem associated with your drinking?" If the wife's perceptions are inconsistent with the client's, you may suggest that the wife come to treatment so that differences can be better understood. Similarly, you may have to review and confirm a referring agency's account or the physical evidence forwarded by a physician to help you to introduce alternative viewpoints to the client in nonthreatening ways. If the client thinks a probation officer is the problem, you can ask, "Why do you think your probation officer believes you have a problem?" This enables the client to express the problem from the perspective of the referring party. It also provides you with an opportunity to encourage the client to acknowledge any truth in the other party's account (Rollnick et al., 1992a).

In opening sessions, remember to use all the strategies described in Chapter 3: Ask open-ended questions, listen reflectively, affirm, summarize, and elicit self-motivational statements (Miller and Rollnick, 1991).

Commend Clients for Coming

Clients referred for treatment may feel they have little control in the process. Some will expect to be criticized or blamed; some will expect you can cure them. Others will hope that counseling can solve all their problems without too much effort. Whatever their expectations, affirm their courage in coming by saying, "I'm impressed you made the effort to get here." Praising their demonstration of responsibility increases their confidence that change is possible. You also can intimate that coming to counseling shows that they have some investment in the topic and an interest in change. For example, you can commend a client's decision to come to treatment rather than risk losing custody of her child by saying, "You must care very much about your child." Such affirmations subtly indicate to clients that they are capable of making good choices in their own best interest.

Gentle Strategies To Use With the Precontemplator

Once you have found a way to engage the client, the following strategies are useful for increasing the client's readiness to change and encouraging contemplation.

Agree on Direction

In helping the client who is not yet thinking seriously of change, it is important to plan your strategies carefully and negotiate a pathway that is acceptable to the client. Some are agreeable to one option but not another. You honor your role as a clinician by being straightforward about the fact that you are promoting positive change. It also may be appropriate to give advice based on your own experience and concern. However, do ask whether the client wants to hear what you have to say. For example, "I'd like to tell you about what we could do here. Would that be all right?" Whenever you express a different viewpoint from that of the client, make clear that you intend to be supportive—not authoritative or confrontational. The client still has the choice about whether to heed your advice or agree to a plan. It is not necessary at this early stage in the process to agree on treatment goals.

Types of precontemplators

Persons with addictive behaviors who are not yet contemplating change can be grouped into four categories (DiClemente, 1991). Each category offers you guidance about appropriate strategies for moving clients forward:

- *Reluctant precontemplators* lack sufficient knowledge about the dimensions of the problem, or the personal impact it can have, to think change is necessary. They often respond to sensitive feedback about how substance use is actually affecting their lives.
- *Rebellious precontemplators* are afraid of losing control over their lives and have a large investment in their substance of choice. Your challenge is to help them shift this energy into making more positive choices for themselves rather than rebelling against what they perceive as coercion. Emphasizing personal control can work well with this type of client.
- *Resigned precontemplators* feel hopeless about change and overwhelmed by the energy required. They probably have been in treatment many times before or have tried repeatedly to quit on their own to no avail. This group must regain hope and optimism about their capacity for change. This can sometimes be accomplished by exploring specific barriers that impede new beginnings.
- *Rationalizing precontemplators* have all the answers. Substance use may be a problem for others but not for them, because the odds are against their being at risk. Double-sided reflection, rather than reasoned argument, seems the most effective strategy for this type of client. Acknowledge what the client says, but add any qualms the client may have expressed earlier (see Chapter 3).

Assess Readiness To Change

When you meet the client for the first time, ascertain her readiness to change. This will determine what intervention strategies are likely to be successful. There are several ways to assess a client's readiness to change. Two common methods are described below (see Chapter 8 for other instruments to assess readiness to change).

Readiness Ruler

The simplest way to assess the client's willingness to change is to use a Readiness Ruler (see Chapter 8 and Figure 8-2) or a 1 to 10 scale, on which the lower numbers represent no thoughts about change and the higher numbers represent specific plans or attempts to change. Ask the client to indicate a best answer on the ruler to the question, "How important is it for you to change?" or, "How confident are you that you could change if you decided to?" Precontemplators will be at the lower end of the scale, generally between 0 and 3. You can then ask, "What would it take for you to move from an x (lower number) to a y (higher number)?"

Keep in mind that these numerical assessments are not fixed, nor are they always linear. The client moves forward or backward across stages or jumps from one part of the continuum to another, in either direction and at various times. Your role is to facilitate movement in a positive direction.

Description of a typical day

Another, less direct, way to assess readiness for change, as well as to build rapport and encourage clients to talk about substance use patterns in a nonpathological framework, is to ask them to describe a typical day (Rollnick et al., 1992a). This approach also helps you understand the context of the client's substance use. For example, it may reveal how much of each day is spent trying to earn a living and how little is left to spend with loved ones. By eliciting information about both behaviors and feelings, you can learn much about what substance use means to the client and how difficult—or simple—it may be to give it up. Substance use is the most cohesive element in some clients' lives, literally providing an identity. For others it is powerful biological and chemical changes in the body that drive continued use. Alcohol and drugs mask deep emotional wounds for some, lubricate friendships for others, and offer excitement to still others.

Start by telling the client, "Let's spend the next few minutes going through a typical day or session of...use, from beginning to end. Let's start at the beginning." Clinicians experienced in using this strategy suggest avoiding any reference to "problems" or "concerns" as the exercise is introduced. Follow the client through the sequence of events for an entire day,

focusing on both behaviors and feelings. Keep asking, "What happens?" Pace your questions carefully, and do not interject your own hypotheses about problems or why certain events transpired. Let clients use their own words and ask for clarification only when you do not understand particular jargon or if something is missing.

Provide Information About the Effects and Risks of Substance Use

Provide basic information about substance use early in the treatment process if clients have not been exposed to drug and alcohol education before and seem interested. Tell clients directly, "Let me tell you a little bit about the effects of..." or ask them to explain what they know about the effects or risks of the substance of choice. To stay on neutral ground, illustrate what happens to any user of the substance, rather than referring just to the client. Also, state what *experts* have found, not what *you* think happens. As you provide information, ask, "What do you make of all this?" (Rollnick et al., 1992a).

It is sometimes helpful to describe the addiction process in biological terms to persons who are substance dependent and worried that they are crazy. Understanding facts about addiction can increase hope as well as readiness to change. For example, "When you first start using substances, it provides a pleasurable sensation. As you keep using substances, your mind begins to believe that you need these substances in the same way you need life-sustaining things like food—that you need them to survive. You're not stronger than this process, but you can be smarter, and you can regain your independence from substances."

Similarly, people who have driven under the influence of alcohol may be surprised to learn how few drinks constitute legal intoxication and how drinking at these levels affects their responses. A young woman hoping to have children may not understand how substances can diminish fertility and potentially harm the fetus even before she knows she is pregnant. A client may not realize how alcohol interacts with other medications he is taking for depression or hypertension.

Use Motivational Language in Written Materials

Remember that the effective strategies for increasing motivation in face-to-face contacts also apply to written language. Brochures, flyers, educational materials, and advertisements can influence a client to think about change. However, judgmental language is just as off-putting in these contexts as it is in therapy. For example, such words as "abuse" or "denial" may be turnoffs. All literature on the counseling services you provide should be written with motivation in mind. If your brochure starts with a long list of rules, the client may be scared away rather than encouraged to come in for treatment. Review written materials from the viewpoint of the prospective client and keep in mind your role as a partner in a change process for which the client must take ultimate responsibility.

Create Doubt and Evoke Concern

As clients move beyond a precontemplation stage and become aware of or acknowledge some problems in relation to their substance use, change becomes an increased possibility. Such clients become more aware of conflict and feel greater ambivalence (Miller and Rollnick, 1991). The major strategy for moving clients from a precontemplation to a contemplation stage is to raise doubts in them about the harmlessness of their substance use patterns and to evoke concerns that *all is not well* after all.

One way to foster concern in the client is to explore the *good* and *less good* aspects of substance use. Start with the client's perceptions about the possible "benefits" of

alcohol or drugs and move on a continuum to less beneficial aspects rather than setting up a dichotomy of *bad things* or *problems* associated with substance use. If you limit the discussion to negative aspects of substance use, the client could end up defending the substance use while you become the advocate for unwanted change. In addition, the client may not be ready to perceive any harmful effects of substance use. By showing that you understand why the client values alcohol or drugs, you set the stage for a more open acknowledgment of emerging problems. For example, you might ask, "Help me to understand what you like about your drinking. What do you enjoy about it?" Then move on to ask, "What do you like less about drinking?" The client who cannot recognize any of the less good things related to substance use is probably not ready to consider change and may need more information. After this exploration, summarize the interchange in personal language so that the client can clearly hear any ambivalence that is developing: "So, using...helps you relax, you enjoy doing...with friends, and...also helps when you are really angry. On the other hand, you say you sometimes resent all the money you are spending, and it's hard for you to get to work on Mondays" (Rollnick et al., 1992a). Chapter 5 provides additional guidance on working with ambivalence.

You can also move clients toward the contemplation stage by having them consider the many ways in which substance use can affect life experiences. For example, you might ask, "How is your substance use affecting your studies? How is your drinking affecting your family life?" As you explore the effects of substance use in the individual's life, use balanced reflective listening: "Help me understand. You've been saying you see no need to change, and you also are concerned about losing your family. I don't see how this fits together. It must be confusing for you."

Assessment and Feedback Process

Most treatment programs require that clients complete assessment questionnaires and interviews as part of the intake process. Sometimes these are administered all at once, which places a significant burden on the client and poses an obstacle to entering treatment. The program may request that the client go to one or more locations to complete the assessment, requiring the investment of considerable time and energy. Although the treatment counselor may conduct intake evaluations, assessments often are administered by someone the client does not know and may not see or be involved with again. Too often, programs do not use the results of intake evaluations for treatment planning but, rather, to confirm a diagnosis or to rule out physical or emotional problems that it cannot treat.

More and more programs, however, now emphasize comprehensive evaluations along a number of dimensions that will help clinicians tailor care to individual needs and set priorities for treatment. The domains assessed usually depend on the types of clients treated and the kinds of services offered. For example, an inner-city substance abuse treatment program will probably have more interest in an applicant's criminal history, employment skills, housing arrangements, and HIV test results than an outpatient evening program for alcohol-abusing middle class professionals.

Clinicians also have discovered that giving clients personal results from a broad-based and objective assessment, especially if the findings are carefully interpreted and compared with norms or expected values, can be not only informative but also motivating (Miller and Rollnick, 1991; Miller and Sovereign, 1989; Miller et al., 1992; Sobell et al., 1996b). This is particularly true for clients who misuse or abuse alcohol because there are social norms for alcohol use, and numerous research studies show levels beyond which consumption is risky in terms of specific health problems or physical reactions. The data are not so extensive for illegal drugs, although a similar approach has been used with marijuana users (Stephens et al., 1994). Providing clients with personalized feedback on the risks associated with their *own* use of a particular substance and how their consumption pattern compares to norms— especially for their own cultural and gender groups—is a powerful way to develop a sense of discrepancy that can motivate change. When clients hear about their evaluation results and understand the risks and consequences, many come face to face with the considerable gap between where they are and where their values lie.

Preparation for an Assessment

Findings from an assessment can most readily become part of the therapeutic process if the client understands the practical value of objective information and believes the results will be helpful. Hence, you would most appropriately schedule formal assessments after the client has had at least one session with you so that you can lay the groundwork and determine the client's readiness for change and potential responsiveness to personalized feedback. You then can explain what types of tests or questionnaires will be administered and what information these will reveal. You can also estimate how long this usually takes and give any other necessary instructions. If the client is not considering change and has not acknowledged any concerns or problems with substance use, you can agree that there might not be a problem but that the evaluation is designed to ascertain exactly what is happening. Just like a medical examination, the assessment can pinpoint places where there are—or may be—concerns and where some change might be considered.

Content of an Assessment

A variety of instruments and procedures may be used to evaluate clients. Eight major domains considered comprehensive in scope for assessing clients with primarily alcohol-related problems have been suggested (Miller and Rollnick, 1991). These eight domains are highlighted below.

Substance use patterns

The primary domain for assessment is drug and alcohol use, including the typical quantity currently consumed; frequency of use; mode of use (e.g., injection); and history of initiation, escalation, previous treatment, and last use. The questions should cover all legal substances (including prescription medications and nicotine) and illegal drugs. The Consensus Panel strongly recommends that you assess smoking patterns because of the well-documented link between alcohol and nicotine use (Hurt et al., 1996). It is estimated that 80 to 90 percent of all people with alcohol problems in the United States smoke cigarettes, compared with around 25 percent of the general adult population (Wetter et al., 1998). Furthermore, tobacco-related diseases have been found to be the leading cause of death in patients who have been treated for substance use (Hurt et al., 1996). Examining your client's total pattern of substance use is essential to avoid substituting one harmful dependence for another. Since alcohol and drugs often are used in combination, it is important that you gain full information about which drugs are used, how they are used, and how they may interact.

This information can be gathered by a variety of methods, including questionnaires, structured interviews that calculate averages by constructing a typical week of substance use and variations from this, day-by-day reconstructions guided by a calendar and prompted memory, or client self-monitoring with a daily diary or Alcohol Timeline Followback for a selected

period of time (Miller et al., 1992; Sobell and Sobell, 1995a). TIP 24, *A Guide to Substance Abuse Services for Primary Care Clinicians* (CSAT, 1997), provides more screening and assessment instruments.

Dependence syndrome

A related dimension for assessment is substance dependence, using criteria specified in the *Diagnostic and Statistical Manual of Mental Disorders*, 4th Edition (DSM-IV) (American Psychiatric Association, 1994). The usual elements probed are the development of tolerance demonstrated by the need for increased amounts of the substance to achieve the same effects; manifestation of characteristic withdrawal symptoms if the substance is stopped abruptly (e.g., amnesic events—blackouts, alcohol withdrawal, and delirium tremens); pursuing the substance at the expense of usual daily activities and despite serious consequences to health and safety; consumption of more of the substance and over a more prolonged time than intended; devoting excessive time to pursuit of the substance or recovery from use; and persistent and unsuccessful attempts to cut down or stop use. It is important that you know the severity of your client's dependence to plan possible medical treatment and as an important indicator of outcome (Miller and Rollnick, 1991). Structured interview questions, such as those from the Structured Clinical Interview for DSM-IV, may yield a more reliable and defensible diagnosis.

Life functioning problems

Identification of problems occurring in an individual's life, whether related to substance use or not, can point to other difficulties that require direct and immediate intervention. These could range from marital problems to domestic violence, unemployment, criminal charges, and financial crises. Screening instruments such as the Michigan Alcohol

Screening Test (MAST), and CAGE are not good measures of current life problems, in part because they mix together a variety of dimensions (e.g., help seeking, pathological use, dependence, and negative consequences). Instruments specifically designed to assess substance-related problems are preferable. (For a review, see Allen and Columbus, 1995; Miller et al., 1995b.)

Functional analysis

A functional analysis probes the situations surrounding drug and alcohol use. Specifically, it examines the relationships among stimuli that trigger use and consequences that follow. This type of analysis provides important clues regarding the meaning of the behavior to the client, as well as possible motivators and barriers to change. See Chapter 7 for more information on functional analysis.

Biomedical effects

Unfortunately, drug and alcohol use do not have predictable effects on physical health because of the wide variability of individual response. Although there are a variety of biomedical measures of the impact of alcohol, such as blood chemistries and blood pressure screening, no conclusive diagnostic test or set of tests can verify a substance abuse disorder (Eastwood and Avunduk, 1994). However, certain indicators can lead you to become suspicious of excessive drug or alcohol use. Elevations in blood pressure or in certain enzymes, such a gamma-glutamyltransferase, aspartate aminotransferase, and alanine aminotransferase, are examples (Eastwood and Avunduk, 1994). A host of physiological concerns is associated with abusive use of alcohol and drugs. Almost all systems within the body can be affected.

Neuropsychological effects

Impaired memory and other cognitive effects may be either temporary or permanent consequences of alcohol and drug use. Although tests in this domain can be expensive

and are not routinely ordered, feedback about impairment on such measures can provide a potent motivational boost because such information is novel and not available to the person from ordinary daily experience (Miller and Rollnick, 1991). However, because the impairment detected by the assessment may have preceded the substance use, use caution when providing feedback. (For reviews of appropriate tests, see Miller, 1985a, and Miller and Saucedo, 1983.) More information on how to screen and assess both physical and cognitive disabilities that might be mistaken for the results of substance use can be found in TIP 29, *Substance Use Disorder Treatment for People With Physical and Cognitive Disabilities* (CSAT, 1998).

Family history

Because risk for substance abuse and dependence is, in part, influenced by genetic factors, a complete family history of relatives on both sides who have experienced substance-related problems or affective disorders, antisocial personality disorder, or attention deficit/hyperactivity disorder can be illuminating. Predisposition toward substance-related problems does not predict a consequence of a substance abuse disorder, but risk can be an important warning signal and a motivator for clients to choose consciously to be free from addictive substances.

Other psychological problems

Abuse of alcohol and drugs is frequently associated with additional psychological problems, including depression, anxiety disorders, antisocial personality, sexual problems, and social skills deficits (Miller and Rollnick, 1991). Because symptoms of intoxication or withdrawal from some drugs and alcohol can mimic or mask symptoms of some psychological problems, it is important that a client remain abstinent for some time before psychological testing is conducted. Some psychological disorders respond well to different types of prescription medications, and it should be determined whether your client has a coexisting disorder and can benefit from simultaneous treatment of both disabilities. If you are not trained to assess clients for coexisting psychological disorders, and if your program is not staffed to handle such assessments or treatment, you should refer your clients to appropriate mental health programs or clinicians for assessment. For more information on assessing clients who have both a substance abuse disorder and an additional psychological problem, see TIP 9, *Assessment and Treatment of Patients With Coexisting Mental Illness and Alcohol and Other Drug Abuse* (CSAT, 1994b).

Personalize and Interpret Feedback About Assessment Results

The presentation and discussion of assessment results can be pivotal for enhancing motivation; thus, structure this session thoughtfully and establish rapport before providing your clients with individual scores from the tests and questionnaires that were administered. First, express appreciation for clients' efforts in providing the information. Ask if there were any difficulties. Inasmuch as answering questions or filling out forms can be revealing in itself, clients may already have a new perception about the role of substances in their lives. You can raise this point by asking, "Sometimes people learn surprising things as they complete an assessment. What were your reactions to the testing?" Make clear that you may need their help to interpret the findings accurately. Encourage them to ask questions: "I'm going to be giving you a lot of information. Please stop me if you don't understand something or want more explanation. We have plenty of time today or in another session, if need be." You may also want to stress the objectivity of the instruments used and give a bit of background, if appropriate, about how they are standardized and how widely they are used. It is also helpful

to provide a written summary so that clients can have a copy.

It is helpful in providing feedback to compare clients' personal scores with normative data or other interpretive information. Clients must understand, for example, that their usual drinking level is above the normal range and that this is predictive of long-term risk for such negative consequences as stroke, liver cirrhosis, breast cancer for women, and all cancers for men (see Figure 4-1). Both the score and the interpretive explanation are important; neither is interesting or motivational in itself. The realization that, for instance, a high score of 23 on the Alcohol Use Disorders Identification Test (AUDIT) indicates heavy—and problematic—drinking can raise questions for clients about what they previously thought was normal behavior (see Figure 4-2). The AUDIT is reproduced in Appendix B.

Although clients are often already given handouts that contain extensive information, even minimal data should be presented in written form with accompanying explanations. Also, use a motivational style in presenting the information. Do not pressure clients to accept a diagnosis or offer unsolicited opinions about what a result might mean. Instead, preface explanations with such statements as, "I don't know whether this will concern you, but..." or "I don't know what you will make of this result, but...." Let them form their own conclusions, but help them along by asking, "What do you make of this?" or, "How do you feel about this?" When soliciting clients' reactions, watch for nonverbal cues such as scowls, frowns, or even tears. Reflect these in statements such as, "I guess this must be difficult for you to accept because it confirms what your wife has been saying" or, "This must be scary" or, "I can see you are having a hard time believing all this" (Miller and Rollnick, 1991).

Finally, summarize the results, including risks and problems that have emerged, clients'

Figure 4-1
Where Does Your Drinking Fit In?: Health Risks

HEALTH RISKS

Does your current drinking place you at risk for health problems? The arrow in each graph shows the chances you're taking. You must decide how much drinking is too risky for you.

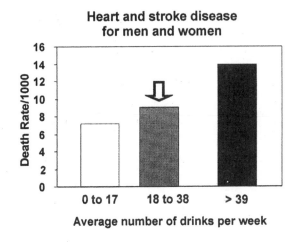

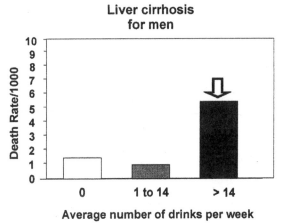

Your average is:
25 drinks/week

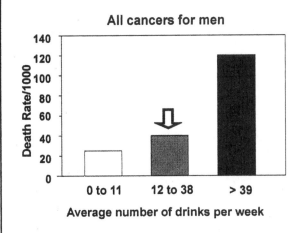

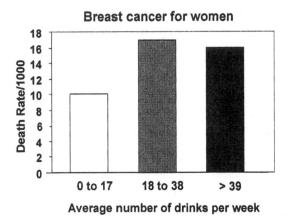

Source: Sobell et al., 1996b.

Figure 4-2
Where Does Your Drinking Fit In?: AUDIT Score

AUDIT SCORE

The AUDIT questionnaire was developed by the World Health Organization to evaluate a person's use of alcohol. Your AUDIT score shows whether your drinking should be considered a problem. Higher scores typically reflect more serious problems.

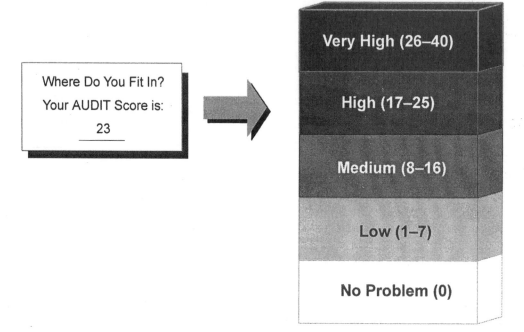

ALCOHOL-RELATED CONSEQUENCES

The various alcohol-related problems you reported are checked (✓) below. When people stop or reduce heavy drinking these consequences will often decrease or disappear.

> **Your Consequences When Drinking:**
>
> Physical health problems   ✓ Verbally abusive or physically aggressive
> ✓ Blackouts or memory problems   ✓ Work/educational problems
> Emotional problems   Legal problems
> ✓ Relationship problems   Financial problems

Source: Sobell et al., 1996b.

reactions, and any self-motivational statements that the feedback has prompted. Then ask clients to add to or correct your summary.

When presented in a motivational style, assessment data alone can move clients toward a new way of thinking about substance use and its consequences. If they still have difficulty accepting assessment results and maintain that consumption levels are not unusual, you can try the "Columbo approach" (see Chapter 3): "I'm confused. When we were talking earlier, there didn't seem to be a problem. But these results suggest there is a problem, and these are usually considered pretty reliable tests. What do you make of this?"

One good example of a format and description of the feedback process can be found in the Personal Feedback Report developed for Project MATCH (Miller et al., 1995c), reproduced in Appendix B. Another is the summary report, *Where Does Your Drinking Fit In?* (Sobell et al., 1996b) (parts of which are given in Figures 4-1 and 4-2), given to individuals who participate in Guided Self-Change—an assessment and feedback program developed for excessive drinkers who do not view their alcohol consumption as serious enough to warrant formal treatment but do agree to a checkup. The materials are intended to foster self-change by encouraging drinkers to view their alcohol use from a new perspective (Sobell and Sobell, 1998).

For practitioners working in situations that do not allow an extensive drinking assessment, a free, personalized alcohol feedback program is available for use on the Internet. Three researchers (Drs. Cunningham, Humphries, and Koski-Jannes) have developed a program based on the materials used in the *Project MATCH Personal Feedback Report* (Miller et al., 1995c) and the *Where Does Your Drinking Fit In?* report (Sobell et al., 1996b). This program can be accessed on the Web site of the Addiction Research Foundation, a division of the Centre

for Addiction and Mental Health in Toronto, Canada: www.arf.org. The respondent fills out a brief, 21-question survey about her drinking and submits the data. A personalized feedback report is returned that compares the respondent's drinking to others of the same age, gender, and country of origin (for people living in the United States or Canada). While brief, the feedback program is a useful tool for practitioners to use.

Providing feedback—on clients' level of alcohol or drug use compared with norms, health hazards associated with their level of use, costs of use at the current level, and similar facts—is sometimes sufficient to move precontemplators through a fairly rapid change process without further need for counseling and guidance. Feedback provided in a motivational style also enhances commitment to change and improves treatment outcomes. For example, one study in which persons admitted to a residential treatment center received assessment feedback and a motivational interview found these clients to be more involved in treatment, as perceived by clinicians, than a control group and to have twice the normal rate of abstinence at followup (Brown and Miller, 1993).

Intervene Through Significant Others

Considerable research shows that involvement of significant others (SOs) can help move substance users to contemplation of change, entry into treatment, retention and involvement in the therapeutic process, and successful recovery. An SO can play a vital role in enhancing an individual's commitment to change by addressing a client's substance use in the following ways:

■ Providing constructive feedback to the client about the costs and benefits associated with his substance use behavior

---

Involving a Significant Other in the Change Process

I have found that actively involving an SO such as a spouse, relative, or friend in motivational counseling can really help facilitate a client's commitment to change. The SO can provide constructive input while the client is struggling with ambivalence about changing the addictive behavior. Feedback from the SO can help raise the client's awareness of the negative consequences of substance use. At the same time, the SO can provide the requisite support in sustaining the client's commitment to change.

Before involving the SO, I routinely determine whether the SO has a positive relationship with the client and a genuine investment in contributing to the change process. SOs with strong ties to the client and an interest in helping the client change the substance-using behavior can make a valuable contribution toward change; those who lack these qualities can interfere with this process. Therefore, before involving the SO, I assess the interactions between the client and the SO. I am particularly interested in determining whether motivational statements made by the client are supported by the SO.

Following this brief assessment, I employ a variety of commitment-enhancing strategies with the SO to help him facilitate the motivational process. I try to ask questions that will promote optimism on the part of the SO with regard to the client's ability to change. For example, I may ask the SO the following questions:

- Have you noticed what efforts Jack has made to change his drinking?
- What has been most helpful to you in helping Jack deal with the drinking?
- What is different now that leads you to feel better about Jack's ability to change?

By using techniques such as eliciting self-motivational statements from the client, the SO can become a cofacilitator in the change process.

Allen Zweben, Consensus Panel Member

- Encouraging the resolve of the client to change the negative behavior pattern
- Identifying the concrete and emotional obstacles to change
- Alerting the client to social and individual coping resources that lead to a substance-free lifestyle
- Reinforcing the client for using these social and coping resources to change the substance use behavior

Several recognized methods of involving SOs in motivational interventions are discussed in this section: involving them in counseling, in a face-to-face intervention, in family therapy, or as part of a community reinforcement approach.

Significant Others and Motivational Counseling

In general, the SO helps to mobilize the client's inner resources to generate, implement, and sustain actions that subsequently lead to a lifestyle that does not involve substance use. The SO is expected to move the client toward generating her own solutions for change. Nevertheless, it is important to remember that the ultimate responsibility for change lies with the client.

An SO is typically a spouse, live-in partner, or other family member but can be any person who has maintained a close personal relationship with the client. Although a strong relationship is necessary, it is not sufficient for involving an SO in motivational counseling. Evidence indicates that a suitable candidate for

SO-involved treatment is an individual who supports a client's substance-free life and whose support is highly valued by the client (Longabaugh et al., 1993).

Orient the client to SO-involved treatment

Ask a client about inviting an SO to a treatment session. Inform him that an SO can play a crucial role in addressing his substance use by providing emotional support, identifying problems that might interfere with treatment goals, and participating in activities that do not involve substances, such as attending church together. Explain that the SO is not asked to monitor the client's substance use since the ultimate responsibility for change is the client's. The SO's role is entirely supportive, and the decisions and choices belong entirely to the client. Review confidentiality issues and tell the client that information shared between the partners should not be discussed with others outside of the sessions unless agreed on by both parties. Some settings may require a written statement giving permission for the SO to participate.

Create a comfortable, supportive, and optimistic treatment environment

In the initial SO-involved session, compliment the SO and client for their willingness to work collaboratively and constructively on changing the client's substance use pattern. Reiterate the rationale for asking the SO to participate and explain the roles and responsibilities of each of the partners, reminding them that the client is ultimately responsible for changing. Also, it is essential to instill a sense of optimism in the SO about her own ability to effect change in the client. Often, SOs enter treatment feeling frustrated or disappointed; many do not understand the chronicity of the problem or the phases of recurrence and recovery, leading to increased frustration. As a result, the SO may

feel helpless about her ability to influence the change process. To strengthen the SO's belief about her capacity to help, you can use the following strategies:

- Positively connote the steps used by the SO which have been successful, and define successful generously.
- Reinforce positive comments made by the SO about the client's current change efforts.
- Discuss future ways in which the client might benefit the SO's efforts to facilitate change.

The overall goal at this point is to empower the SO in helping the client change.

Provide constructive feedback

In motivational counseling sessions, a positive movement toward change often occurs after the SO has had an opportunity to point out that continuing a current pattern of substance use could potentially interfere with sustaining a highly valued relationship. A client is particularly susceptible to an SO's input because it can potentially lead to loss of or harm to important relationships. Explain to the client that the benefits of substance use cannot be obtained without increasing the social costs. The benefits might include enhancing pleasurable activities or coping resources; the costs entail loss of or harm to highly valued relationships. Consequently, the client may feel a state of disequilibrium over his continued substance use. To reduce the dissonance, the client must make a decision about stopping his substance use. In this context, the SO's feedback becomes a major vehicle for activating the change process.

For this reason, ask the SO to be more involved in the counseling; for example, by sharing relevant information about precipitants and consequences of the client's substance use problem and working collaboratively with the client to find strategies for change. Such information must be communicated in a constructive manner. This is accomplished by focusing the discussion on the consequences or harm resulting from the drinking or drug use (e.g., family disruption) rather than on the client herself (e.g., "She is a bad person because of her drinking"). The feedback from the SO can cause a shift in the client's decisional balance.

Maintain a therapeutic alliance

Special efforts should be made to strengthen ties between the SO and client, especially if the SO is a spouse. Having strong family ties is considered an active ingredient in sustaining a client's commitment to change (Zweben, 1991). Explore with the couple various activities that can contribute to improving the quality of the marital relationship, such as vacationing and dining out without the children. For some SOs, carrying out these tasks might become a cause of concern, especially if the client has a history of disrupting the household while using substances. The SO may be afraid that the client will once again destabilize the family situation if he is given major responsibilities in the home. (Such a concern may be realistic if the client has had an unstable pattern of recovery.) The counselor must acknowledge these concerns, normalize them, and develop an incremental plan for handling these new arrangements. A step-by-step approach should be introduced, including a procedure for handling recurrence if it occurs. This may prevent family members from feeling overwhelmed by the magnitude of the tasks involved in reintegrating the client into the household.

Problematic SOs

Despite proper screening, some SOs demonstrate little or no commitment to change. These SOs repeatedly miss treatment sessions, cancel appointments without rebooking, arrive late, and in general, display a negative attitude toward the client. Some interact negatively with the client, offering few constructive remarks without excessive prompting by the counselor.

Others refuse to participate in substance-free activities. It is important to deal with these SOs before they pose serious problems in treatment. In such circumstances, consider the following:

- Gently remind the SO about the purposes of SO-involved treatment—namely, to offer emotional support, to provide constructive feedback, to reinforce incentives for change, and in general, to work collaboratively with the client to change the substance using behavior.

- Some SOs may be unaware of the anxiety they are feeling about the client's ability and willingness to change, which in turn could account for the negative feelings being expressed to the client. In such circumstances, address these underlying concerns of the SO. Using such techniques as reflective listening, normalizing, clarifying, and summarizing, you can help the SO explore the underlying reasons for her negative reactions to the client. This strategy gives the SO an opportunity to vent her anxieties about the client. Otherwise the SO may continue to respond negatively (i.e., "act out" the anxiety) to the client in the sessions. These issues are usually addressed in an individual session with the SO.

- If the above approaches do not work, consider limiting the SO's role to mainly information sharing. Inform the SO only about the proposed treatment plan for the client, such as attending self-help groups, taking medications, and completing specific tasks such as finding new employment. These matters could be covered in a single session with the option of adding another appointment if warranted. No attempt is made to involve the SO in reinforcing or decisionmaking activities related to changing the substance use behavior. For SOs requiring or requesting additional help, a referral to individual counseling or a community support group such as Al-Anon may be in order. This can help the SO distance herself from the client's problems and prevent her from undermining the therapeutic process.

Research support

Studies of brief motivational counseling have suggested that SO participation (mainly the spouse's) can be an important factor contributing to the effectiveness of the intervention (Longabaugh et al., 1993; Sisson and Azrin, 1986; Zweben et al., 1988). Beginning with the work of Edwards, SO-involved brief motivational counseling has been found to be just as effective or more effective than more extensive conventional treatment approaches across a number of outcome measures, such as drinking and related problems (Edwards et al., 1977; Holder et al., 1991; Zweben and Barrett, 1993). All the studies were conducted with individuals having alcohol-related problems. Nonetheless, given the favorable outcomes found in the above studies and positive experiences reported by practitioners who have used the model with clients using other substances, consideration should be given to adding an SO-involved component to motivational counseling approaches with individuals having a variety of substance abuse problems. This can help augment the potency of the intervention with certain clients, namely those individuals who have strong positive ties with their families.

However, the relative contributions of different components of brief motivational counseling (such as therapist empathy, feedback and advice, and bibliotherapy) to enhancing client motivation have not yet been determined (Zweben and Fleming, in press); it may be that such factors as therapist empathy could play a more salient role than SO involvement in effecting motivational change. Future research will have to further explore the relative contribution of the SO involvement component compared to the other treatment components (e.g., therapist empathy) in facilitating change.

The Johnson Intervention

Since its introduction in the 1960s, the approach developed by the Johnson Institute has been modified from a confrontational technique to a much less harsh strategy with numerous permutations (Stanton, 1997). The Johnson Intervention is a well-known technique in which family members and others from the user's social network, after considerable formal training and rehearsal, confront the substance user in a clinician's presence. They take turns telling the user how substance use has affected them, urge the user to seek help, and specify what consequences will occur if change—usually treatment entry—does not happen. An element of surprise is usually part of the plan. The basic assumptions outlined by the originator of this method are as follows (Johnson, 1973):

- Meaningful, influential persons present the user with facts or personal information.
- The data presented must be specific and descriptive of actual events or conditions, not opinions.
- The tone of the confrontation should not be judgmental but reflect concern.
- The evidence presented should be tied directly to drinking or other substance use and given in some detail.
- The goal is that the substance user will see and accept enough facts to acknowledge the need for help.
- The user should be offered appropriate and available choices of treatment so that dignity is retained and decisionmaking capabilities are respected.

Although the approach was originally applied to referrals for inpatient care (e.g., 28-day, Minnesota model programs), it has subsequently been used by outpatient facilities.

However, it has not been extensively evaluated, and the little research reflects a small number of participants. A recent study of people seeking help from a treatment center found that those who had experienced a Johnson Intervention were more likely to enter treatment than were those who were there as a result of coercion (e.g., by judge, employer, public assistance) or voluntary referral (Loneck et al., 1996a, 1996b). A major problem, however, is that as many as 75 percent of families who begin counseling for a Johnson Intervention find it unacceptable or, for other reasons, fail to go through with the family confrontation meeting (Liepman et al., 1989). Families who complete a confrontation thus represent a minority, and it is among these families that 80 percent or more of drinkers enter treatment. It also has been reported that those who enter treatment after a Johnson Intervention are more likely to have a recurrence of drinking and symptoms, relative to those entering treatment through other referral sources (Loneck et al., 1996b).

Unilateral Family Therapy

In unilateral family therapy (UFT), a counselor helps a cooperative, nonusing spouse identify and capitalize on opportunities to encourage the substance-using partner to change. This approach assumes the user's spouse is "a vital and potentially crucial point of leverage who may be the main or only rehabilitative influence accessible to the therapist" (Thomas and Ager, 1993). Different forms of unilateral family therapy are currently being used by clinicians, as described below.

The Thomas and Ager Approach to UFT

This approach includes descriptions of three foci of intervention for UFT for alcohol use disorders:

- *An individual focus* increases the coping skills of the nonusing spouse and helps him find specific ways to address the drinking problem.
- *An interactive focus* helps the spouse improve marital and family functioning by reducing both ineffective tactics of interaction with the substance-using partner (such as nagging or pouring out liquor) and enabling behaviors (such as buying alcohol).
- *A third-party focus* entails preparing the spouse and other family members to conduct interventions that may motivate the person who drinks to seek treatment, stop drinking, or both (Thomas and Ager, 1993).

As practiced by Thomas and associates, UFT has three phases. The first phase, requiring three to eight weekly sessions, prepares the spouse to assume a role in rehabilitation. The spouse is educated on the effects of alcohol; monitors the extent and timing of the partner's drinking; learns how to enhance the marital relationship by trying out reinforcing, enjoyable behaviors when the person is not drinking; eliminates or modifies old and ineffective drinking control behaviors; and reduces enabling behaviors.

The second phase, lasting 5 to 18 weeks, involves assessing the suitability and feasibility of different types of user-directed interventions that are tailored to the special characteristics of the resistant drinker, then conducting either nonconfrontational interventions (e.g., sobriety support or examination by a physician for alcohol abuse) or more systematic, well-rehearsed confrontations or requests in the presence of the clinician. The interventions are marked by their firm and compassionate tone. Followup interventions can occur if the drinker does not follow through on her commitment.

The third phase, which entails three to six weekly sessions, focuses on maintaining spouse and partner gains. The nondrinking spouse receives help in adjusting to the partner's sobriety—or reduced drinking—and learns to play a positive and appropriate role in deterring renewed or increased drinking (Thomas and Ager, 1993).

Two studies of this approach to UFT indicate that the coping skills of participating spouses were improved, as indicated by reductions in associated life distress and psychopathology; the marital relationship was enriched, as indicated by measures of spousal happiness and adjustment; and the drinking persons who had mediating spouses also entered treatment and moderated drinking or became abstinent more frequently than did members of the control groups (Thomas and Ager, 1993).

Orford's Approach to UFT

The World Health Organization has used Orford's work to guide clinicians responding to the needs and pleas of family and friends of alcohol and drug users. This approach stresses that family and friends are at risk for stress-related physical and psychological disorders (Orford, 1994). To understand how to empower them to deal effectively with their situation, as well as to help them bring the substance user into treatment, Orford studied coping strategies commonly used by families, each of which has advantages and disadvantages. The eight common strategies he identified are as follows:

1. *Emotional reactions* express emotion about use.
2. *Tolerant strategies* support use.
3. *Inactive efforts* neither support nor discourage use.
4. *Avoidance techniques* put distance between oneself and the user.
5. *Controlling approaches* attempt to control use directly.
6. *Confronting tactics* communicate openly about one's own needs and the effects of use.
7. *Supporting strategies* help the person who drinks or takes drugs achieve alternative goals such as family involvement.

8. *Independent reactions* show a lack of dependence on the drinker or drug user.

Orford concluded that "some of the ways in which relatives cope are better than others for reducing the risks of ill health for themselves" and for "influencing drinking or drug use" by the loved one (Orford, 1994, p. 428). Which strategies work best depends on a relative's circumstances. Orford believes the clinician's most important role is to help relatives find effective ways of coping that reduce the risk to their own health and help reduce the substance-using person's excessive use. To do this, clinicians should

- Listen nonjudgmentally and provide reassurance.
- Provide useful information.
- Counsel nondirectively about ways of coping.
- Help strengthen social support and joint problem solving in the family.

Community Reinforcement Approach

The Community Reinforcement Approach (CRA) is a comprehensive therapeutic system originally developed in the 1960s to address a broad spectrum of areas affected by alcohol use, including unemployment, marital problems, social isolation, poorly developed social networks, and a lack of positive recreational activities (Hunt and Azrin, 1973). See also the forthcoming TIP, *Brief Interventions and Brief Therapies for Substance Abuse* (CSAT, in press [a]). The CRA seeks to reduce or stop drinking by working through legitimate employment, family support, and social activities. In this behavioral treatment program, the clinician teaches a nondrinking family member—usually the spouse—the following skills:

- *Reduce physical abuse* by recognizing signs of possible violence and taking self-protective action.

- *Encourage sobriety* by reinforcing periods of sobriety through rewarding behavior and by allowing the drinker to experience negative consequences of drinking—as long as they are not life-threatening. The clinician counsels the family member on how to behave when drinking is occurring and provides suggestions about appealing outside activities that do not involve alcohol.

- *Encourage the drinker to seek treatment* by identifying the best times to suggest seeking professional help (e.g., after occasions when the alcohol use was especially severe and the individual is keenly aware of the negative consequences of drinking). When the person who drinks agrees to come in, the clinician is available to meet with the marital couple immediately.

- *Assist in treatment* by participating with the drinker in couples counseling and helping him find work and discover alcohol-free activities. The drinker also receives a medical exam and disulfiram (Antabuse).

In a study of its effectiveness, this CRA required an average of 7.2 sessions compared with 3.5 for a more traditional program in which the clinician provided a spouse with supportive counseling and a referral to local Al-Anon self-help groups. Although requiring a greater time commitment, the CRA approach resulted in six of seven drinking persons entering treatment, whereas none entered treatment in the traditional approach (Sisson and Azrin, 1986). See Chapter 7 for discussion on the use of CRA during the maintenance stage.

Community Reinforcement Approach to Family Training

CRA has been modified by enhancing its proven features (Meyers and Smith, 1997). Referred to as the Community Reinforcement Approach to Family Training (CRAFT), this approach contends that a concerned SO can have an impact on a loved one's drinking or drug use

and can influence that person to enter treatment, if appropriate. See also the forthcoming TIP, *Brief Interventions and Brief Therapies for Substance Abuse* (CSAT, in press [a]). Using this approach, the clinician's tasks are to

- Encourage the SO to express frustration about the loved one's substance use and also assure the participant that the responsibility for the situation lies with the person who drinks or takes drugs.

- Work with the SO to identify the triggers for and consequences of the loved one's substance use and analyze these for ways in which the SO can modify coping responses.

- Identify positive reinforcers the SO can use when the user is sober or working toward change and negative consequences of substance use that the SO may have unknowingly supported.

- Teach the SO to recognize the potential for domestic violence in response to behavioral changes in the home and to take appropriate precautions that reduce the risk of harm.

- Train the SO in seven communication rules that have been found effective for interacting with persons who misuse alcohol and drugs:
  1. Be brief
  2. Be positive
  3. Be specific and clear
  4. Label your feelings
  5. Offer an understanding statement once an issue has been viewed from the drinker's perspective
  6. Accept partial responsibility, when appropriate
  7. Offer to help

- Encourage the SO to find meaningful and rewarding activities that reduce stress and build a better quality of life regardless of whether the substance-using person changes.

- Coach the SO on nonthreatening ways to approach the loved one and suggest treatment through role-playing, rehearsing the language and voice tone to provide the best chance of success, and developing a "road map" of the best times to talk with the substance-using person.

- Make certain that treatment is available when a decision is made to begin treatment and also help the SO to support the client in treatment.

A clinical trial of CRAFT found this approach to be substantially more effective than either Al-Anon or the Johnson Intervention for engaging unmotivated problem drinkers and drug users in treatment (Miller and Meyers, in press). The combination of behavioral skills enhancement, well-chosen moments for bringing up the topic of change, techniques that the SO can use for positively reinforcing appropriate behavior by the drinking or drug-using loved one, and rapid intake into counseling are promising ways of moving precontemplators toward serious contemplation of change (Meyers and Smith, 1997).

Albany-Rochester Interventional Sequence for Engagement

The Albany-Rochester Interventional Sequence for Engagement (ARISE) was developed at a large outpatient treatment facility in Albany, New York. Following this approach, the clinician intervenes through family members with persons who abuse either drugs or alcohol, using a slower, less distressing way of introducing change rather than confrontation. The developers of this strategy were responding to three limitations of similar, currently available techniques: the expenditure of considerable time and effort in preparing for and rehearsing encounters with the substance-using person; the ultimatums in full-blown, traditional interventions that frighten some family members away; and a recent study in which clients who participated in formal interventions were twice as likely as those who

did not to return to drinking or drug use while in treatment (Stanton, 1997).

The ARISE process unfolds through three stages:

- *Stage 1: Informal intervention without a therapist present.* When a concerned person calls the clinic, an intervention specialist talks to her by telephone to determine the family configuration and to identify who should be involved. The clinician sets up a time to meet with all concerned persons, making clear that the substance user should also be invited.
- *Stage 2: Informal intervention with a therapist present.* In one to three sessions, as needed, the clinician works with the family to determine how best to urge the substance user to engage in treatment. Usually, the clinician suggests they telephone this person from the meeting.
- *Stage 3: Formal intervention.* If neither Stage 1 nor Stage 2 results in the substance user entering treatment, the clinician uses an intervention derived from the Johnson Institute model but less negative and more gentle than the original model. This intervention also incorporates attention to intergenerational patterns of alcohol problems.

In a retrospective analysis, 55 percent of drug users who participated in some phase of ARISE entered treatment, as did 70 percent of those with drinking problems. The success rates for other small studies of ARISE ranged from 25 to 92 percent. Tentative conclusions are that the strategy works best when the clinician is readily available to catch the identified substance user at the right moment for enrolling in treatment and when a large number of persons are assembled for an intervention (Stanton, 1997).

Motivational Enhancement and Coerced Clients: Special Considerations

An increasing number of clients are mandated to begin treatment by an employer or employee assistance program. Others are influenced to enter treatment because of legal pressures. In such cases, failure to enter and remain in treatment may result in specified sanctions or negative consequences (e.g., job loss, probation or parole revocation, prosecution, prison), often for a specified time or until satisfactory completion. Although generalizations are difficult to make from a number of separate studies, legal status at treatment entry does not seem to be related to treatment success (Anglin et al., 1992; CSAT, 1995b; Leukefeld and Tims, 1988). Mandated clients generally respond as well as those who are self-referred.

Your challenge is to engage coerced clients in the treatment process. As noted by Leukefeld and Tims, external pressures (e.g., legal) serve to influence an individual into treatment, but motivation and commitment to change must come from within the client (internal pressure) in order to effect and maintain recovery (Leukefeld and Tims, 1988). Although many of these clients are at the precontemplation stage of change, the temptation is to use action-oriented interventions immediately that are not synchronized with the client's motivation level. As already noted, this can be counterproductive. Clients arrive with strong emotions as a result of the referral process and the consequences they will face if they do not succeed in changing a pattern of use they may not believe is problematic. As always, remember that their perceptions may be accurate. It may be true that they rarely drink excessively but did so on a particular occasion that led to the referral.

In spite of these obstacles, coerced clients are at least as amenable to a motivational counseling style as any other. If you provide interventions appropriate to their stage, they may become invested in the change process and benefit from the opportunity to consider the consequences of use and the possibility of change, although that opportunity was not voluntarily chosen.

You may have to spend your first session with a coerced client "decontaminating" the referral process. Some clinicians say explicitly, "I'm sorry you came through the door this way." Important principles to keep in mind are as follows:

- Honor the client's anger and sense of dehumanization.
- Avoid assumptions about the type of treatment needed.
- Make it clear that you will help the client derive what the client perceives is needed and useful out of your time together.

TIP 12, *Combining Substance Abuse Treatment With Intermediate Sanctions for Adults in the Criminal Justice System* (CSAT, 1994e), offers suggestions for engaging offender clients as full participants in their treatment and recovery.

A critical requirement in working with coerced clients is establishing what information will be shared with the referring agency. This must be formalized with both clients and the agency through a written consent for release of information that adheres to Federal confidentiality regulations. Clients must be informed about and agree to exactly what information (e.g., attendance, urine test results, treatment participation) will be released. Be sure they understand what choices they have about the information to be released and what choices are not yours or theirs to make (e.g., information related to child abuse or neglect).

An Opening Dialog With a Coerced Client

This dialog illustrates the first meeting between a counselor and a client who is required to attend group therapy as a condition of parole. The clinician is seeking ways to affirm the client, to find incentives that matter to the client, to support the client in achieving his most important personal goals, and to help the client regain control by choosing to engage in treatment with a more open mind.

The setting is an outpatient treatment program that accepts both private referrals and court-ordered referrals to an evening counseling group for substance users. The program uses a cognitive behavioral approach based on the work of Drs. Albert Ellis and Maxie Maultsby. The primary interventional tool is rational behavior training. This is the first session between the counselor and the court-ordered probation client.

Counselor: Good morning. My name is Jeff. You must be Paul.

Client: Yep.

Counselor: Come on in and sit wherever you're comfortable. I received some information from your probation officer, but what would really be helpful to me is to hear from you, Paul, a little bit more about what's going on in your life, and how we might help.

Client: The biggest thing going on in my life is this 4-year sentence hanging over my head and all this crap I have to do to stay out of prison.

Counselor: Well, again, Paul, it sounds like you're busy and you have a lot of pressures, but I wonder if there's something the program offers that you could use.

Client: What I need from you is to get that blasted probation officer off my back.

Counselor: I'm not exactly sure what you mean, Paul.

Client: What I mean is that, I'm already running all over the place to give urine samples and meet all the other conditions of probation, and now I learn that the court says that in order for me not to go to jail, I've got to participate in this drug treatment program.

Counselor: I'm still a little confused. What is it that I can do that might help?

Client: You can tell my probation officer that I don't need to be here in the first place and that she should stay out of my business.

Counselor: I may be wrong, Paul, but as I understand the situation, that's not an option for either one of us. I certainly want to support you so that you do not get in conflict with your probation officer. For you and her to be in an angry relationship seems to me a real recipe for disaster. Further, I get the sense from listening to you that you are really committed not only to yourself, but to your family, and the last thing that you really want to do is to wind up in prison facing that 4-year sentence.

Client: You got that straight.

Counselor: So it seems to me you've made some good choices so far.

Client: What do you mean?

Counselor: Well, you could have just blown this whole appointment off, but you didn't. You made a series of choices that make it clear to me that you're committed to your family, yourself, your business, and for that matter your freedom. I can respect that commitment and would like to support you in honoring the choices you've already made.

Client: Does that mean I'm not going to have to come to these classes?

An Opening Dialog With a Coerced Client (continued)

Counselor: No, I don't have the power to make that kind of decision. However, you and I can work together to figure out how you might use this course to benefit you.

Client: I can't imagine getting anything out of sitting around with a bunch of drunks, talking about our feelings and whining about all the bad things going on in our lives.

Counselor: You just don't seem like a whiner to me. And in any case, that's not what this group is about. What we really do is give people the opportunity to learn new skills and apply those skills in their daily lives to make their lives more enjoyable and meaningful. What you've already shown me today is that you can use some of those skills to support even further the good choices that you've already made.

Client: Man, that's just a bunch of shrink talk. I already told you, all I need is to get my probation officer off my back and live my life the way I want to live it.

Counselor: Completing this program is going to help you do that. I think from what you've already demonstrated that you'll do well in the group. I believe you can learn something that you can use in your daily life and perhaps teach some of the other people in the group as well. I am certainly willing to work with you to help you accomplish your goal in terms of meeting the requirements of probation. My suggestion is that you take it one group at a time and see how it goes. All I would ask of you is what, in a sense, you have already demonstrated, and that is the willingness to keep your mind open and keep your goals for life clearly in front of you. I see that you're committed to your family, you're committed to yourself, and you're committed to your freedom. I want to support all three of those goals.

Client: Well, I guess I can do this group thing at least for now. I'm still not sure what I'm going to get from sitting around with a bunch of other guys, telling stories, but I'm willing to give it a try.

Counselor: That sounds like a reasonable and, once again, another good choice to me, Paul. Let me give you a handbook that will tell you a little bit more about Rational Behavioral Training, and I'll see you tomorrow night at 6:30 p.m. at this office for our first group. It's been nice to meet you. I look forward to getting to know you better.

Client: I'll see you tomorrow night. You know, this wasn't as bad as I thought it would be.

Jeffrey M. Georgi, Consensus Panel Member

It is wise to take into account the role of the client's defense attorney (if any) in releasing information. Finally, clearly delineate different levels of permission.

Other publications in the TIP series provide more specific guidance regarding legal and ethical issues affecting coerced clients and how to handle confidentiality issues. See Chapter 8 of TIP 17, *Planning for Alcohol and Other Drug Abuse Treatment for Adults in the Criminal Justice System* (CSAT, 1995b); Chapter 5 of TIP 11, *Simple Screening Instruments for Outreach for Alcohol and Other Drug Abuse and Infectious Diseases* (CSAT, 1994d); TIP 12, *Combining Substance Abuse Treatment With Intermediate Sanctions for Adults in the Criminal Justice System* (CSAT, 1994e); and TIP 30, *Continuity of Offender Treatment for Substance Use Disorders From Institution to Community* (CSAT, 1998b).

5   From Contemplation to Preparation: Increasing Commitment

Contemplation is often a very paradoxical stage of change...[and] ambivalence can make contemplation a chronic [and extremely frustrating] condition.... Clearly, interest [in change] is not commitment.... Ambivalence is the archenemy of commitment and a prime reason for chronic contemplation. Helping the client to work through the ambivalence, to anticipate the barriers, to decrease the desirability of the problem behavior, and to gain some increased sense of self-efficacy to cope with this specific problem are all stage-appropriate strategies.

DiClemente, 1991

This chapter describes strategies to increase clients' commitment to change by enhancing their decisionmaking capabilities. Central to most of the strategies is the process of eliciting and exploring through open-ended questioning and reflective listening skills, as described in earlier chapters. The chapter begins with a discussion of extrinsic (external) and intrinsic (internal) motivation, describing ways to help clients connect with internal motivators to enhance decisionmaking and thereby commitment. The second section focuses on decisional balancing strategies—effective ways to explore the benefits and costs of change and clients' values about changes they might make. The third section highlights the importance of personal choice and responsibility as clients get closer to making a decision to change.

Exploring and setting goals can also be effective in strengthening commitment, primarily because the process of envisioning what one's life would be like after change has been accomplished may strongly tip the decisional balance toward positive change. Finally, the important role of self-efficacy in client goal-setting is reemphasized. Although these strategies are introduced here in linear fashion, with each process of exploration unfolding from the last, in discussions with clients these processes can occur simultaneously or in a different order from that used here. For example, clients may begin to set goals or formulate a specific change plan (see Chapter 6) while continuing to explore their ambivalence (see Figure 5-1).

Changing Extrinsic to Intrinsic Motivation

To help your clients prepare for change, seek to understand the range of both extrinsic and intrinsic motivators that have brought them to this point. Many clients move through the contemplation stage acknowledging only the extrinsic motivators that push them to change—and that brought them to treatment. As discussed in Chapter 4, many different external motivators may cajole or coerce clients into treatment, including a spouse, an employer, a physician, or family and criminal courts. Although extrinsic motivators can be useful in bringing a client into treatment and increasing retention, self- or intrinsic motivation is important for substantive and abiding change.

Intrinsic motivation often begins at the point when clients recognize the discrepancies between "where they are" and "where they want to be." An intensive exploration of life goals and deep-seated values can be a way to strengthen internal motivation. Some clients, as they mature, cast off the rebelliousness or apparent nonchalance of adolescence to explore more existential concerns such as, *Where am I going?* and *Who am I?* In searching for answers, clients often reevaluate past mistakes and activities that were self-destructive or harmful to others. You can encourage this soul-searching through reflective listening. Then, through motivational strategies, you can promote the client's recognition of discrepancies between the current situation and hopes for the future. As described in earlier chapters, this awareness of disparities often creates a strong desire to improve. This is an essential source of self-motivation for positive change.

Sometimes intrinsic motivation emerges from role conflicts and family or community expectations. For example, a mother who has lost custody of children because of substance use may have a strong motivation to fulfill her role as a good mother. Other clients' chronic substance use severs cultural or community ties; they stop going to church or neglect culturally affirmed roles such as helping others or serving as role models for young people. A yearning to reconnect with cultural traditions as a source of identity and strength can be a powerful

---

Figure 5-1

Tips for Moving Clients Through Contemplation to Preparation

- Do not rush your clients into decisionmaking.
- Emphasize client control: "You are the best judge of what will be best for you."
- Acknowledge and normalize ambivalence.
- Examine options rather than a single course of action.
- Describe what other clients have done in a similar situation.
- Present information in a neutral, nonpersonal manner.
- Remember that inability to reach a decision to change is not a failed consultation.
- Make sure that your clients understand that resolutions to change often break down; clients should not avoid future contact with you if things go wrong.
- Expect fluctuations in your client's commitment to change—check commitment regularly and express empathy concerning the client's predicaments.

Source: Rollnick et al., 1992a.

Linking Family, Community, and Cultural Values to a Desire for Change

Working with a group of Hispanic men in the Southwest who were mandated into treatment as a condition of parole and had spent most of their lives in prisons, we found that as these men aged, they seemed to tire of criminal life. In counseling, some expressed concerns about losing touch with their families and culture, and many articulated a desire to serve as male role models for their sons and nephews. They all wanted to restore their own sense of pride and self-worth in the small community where many of their families had lived for generations. Newly trained in motivational interviewing, we recognized a large, untapped reservoir of self-motivation in a population that we had long before concluded did not want help. We had to change our previous conceptions of this population as not wanting treatment to seeing these men as requesting help and support to maintain themselves outside of the prison system and in the community.

Carole Otero, Consensus Panel Member

motivator for some clients, as can the desire to regain others' respect. Positive change also leads to improved self-image and self-esteem.

Helping clients change extrinsic to intrinsic motivation is an important part of helping them move from contemplating change to deciding to act. Start with the client's current situation and find a natural link between existing external motivators and intrinsic ones the client may not be aware of or find easy to articulate. Through sensitive and respectful exploration, untapped intrinsic motivation may be discovered even in clients who seem unlikely to become self-motivating.

In addition to standard practices for motivational interviewing, several other strategies are useful for identifying and strengthening intrinsic motivation. First, show curiosity about your clients. Show interest and maintain this attention over time. Because clients' desire to change is rarely limited to substance use, they may find it easier to talk about changing other behaviors. Most clients have concerns about several functional areas of their lives and wish they could reconnect with the community, improve their finances, find work, or fall in love. Many are highly functional and productive in some aspects of their lives and take great pride in special skills, knowledge, or other competencies they do not want to

jeopardize. Do not wait for clients to talk spontaneously about their troubles or capabilities. Show interest and ask about how their substance use affects these aspects of their lives. Even with clients who do not acknowledge any problems, question them about their lives to show concern and thus strengthen the therapeutic alliance.

Another useful strategy is to reframe clients' negative statements about perceived coercion by re-expressing their resentment with a positive connotation. A classic example is to reinterpret a client's hostility toward a threatening wife as a manifestation of his continued caring and investment in the marriage, which is pushing him to resolve and change the problem behavior and save the relationship.

Clients who were openly coerced into entering treatment pose a special challenge. With these clients, identify and strengthen intrinsic motivation so that change can come from within, rather than from external threats. Not only can external threats provoke resistance, but any achieved change may collapse if the threatened contingencies do not happen—if, for example, the threat of divorce or separation is not carried out by the wife when her husband's drinking resumes, or a parole officer does not revoke a client's freedom when the released offender fails to continue treatment. These clients must choose positive change of their own free will because change makes good sense and is desired, not because a punishment might be exacted if a violation is detected.

Tipping the Decisional Balance

In moving toward any decision, most people weigh the costs and benefits of the action being contemplated. In behavioral change, these considerations are known as *decisional balancing*, a process of cognitively appraising or evaluating the "good" aspects of substance use—the reasons *not* to change, and the less good aspects—the reasons *to* change. Research on self-change has shown that many people who have successfully modified addictive behaviors view this appraisal process as important to the resolution of their substance use problems (Sobell et al., 1996b).

At some point in the decisionmaking process, the decisional balance is redistributed, and a decision is made. The objective in moving a client toward positive change, of course, is to help that person recognize and weigh negative aspects of substance use so that the scale tips toward beneficial behavior. In examining ways in which people make major life changes, Baumeister described the inner process that seems to occur when the decisional balance is weighted toward change as a "crystallization of discontent" (Baumeister, 1994). He notes that it involves a conscious linking, perhaps for the first time, of perceptions regarding costs, problems, and other undesirable features of a situation. This conscious linking of negative aspects changes the person's perception of a situation "so that a broad pattern of dissatisfaction and shortcoming is discerned." See Chapter 8 for tools to use in decisional balancing exercises.

How do you shift the balance to the side of positive change and away from the status quo or negative change? Sobell and colleagues identified four overall objectives in using exercises to shift decisional balance with clients (Sobell et al., 1996b). The intent of such exercises, which weigh substance use and change separately, is to

- Accentuate or in a subtle manner make salient from the client's perspective the costs of the client's substance use.
- Lessen, when possible, the perceived rewards of substance use.
- Make the benefits of change apparent.
- Identify and attenuate, if possible, potential obstacles to change.

Summarize Concerns

If you have successfully elicited a client's concerns while providing personalized feedback after an assessment (see Chapter 4) or while exploring intrinsic and extrinsic motivations, you have gathered important information for influencing your client's decisional balance. You have a working knowledge, and perhaps even a written list, of issues and areas about which the client has negative feelings and which are important intrinsic motivators. A first step in helping the client to weigh the pros and cons is to organize the list of concerns and present them to the client in a careful summary that expresses empathy, develops discrepancy, and weights the balance toward change. Because it is important to reach agreement on these issues, the summary should end by asking whether your client agrees that these are her concerns.

Explore Specific Pros and Cons

Weighing benefits and costs of substance use and of change is at the heart of decisional balance work. Some clinicians find it helpful to ask the client to write out a two-column list. This can be done as homework and discussed during the session, or the list can be generated during a session. Some programs use a worksheet for listing pros and cons preprinted on two-copy carbonless paper so that clients can take one copy home and leave the other with the clinician for later use or revision during future sessions. A written list helps some clients quantify the factors going into the decision. Seeing a long list of reasons to change and a short list of reasons not to may finally upset the balance. On the other hand, a long list of reasons not to change and a short list of reasons to change can indicate how much work still must be done and can avert premature decisionmaking. Quantity is not the only determinant. Many clients find that one or two reasons not to change counterbalance the weight of a dozen reasons to change, creating powerful ambivalence. Knowledge about the true strength of each opposing force is important. Remember, too, that the reasons for and against continuing substance use—or the positive and negative aspects of change—are highly individual and emotional rather than rational. Factors that shift the balance toward positive change for one person may scarcely matter to another. Moreover, the value or weight given to a particular item in this inventory of pros and cons is likely to change over time.

Whether or not you use a written worksheet, always listen carefully when clients express ambivalence and highlight their reasons for opposing change or thinking change is impossible. Encouraging clients to openly clarify and state their attraction to substances can be fruitful because they seldom have a chance in treatment programs to examine what they like or enjoy about substance use. In addition, asking clients to express what they like about substance use (e.g., that it is enjoyable, sociable, exciting) establishes rapport and reassures the client of your nonjudgmental perspective. Starting with positive aspects of substance use also seems to lead clients spontaneously to discussing what is *less good* about substance use (Saunders et al., 1991).

Information about why substance use is attractive is helpful for judging the client's degree of commitment and sense of self-efficacy. For example, some clients may enjoy little about substance use, and their ambivalence stems from a strong belief that they cannot change. Work with such a client will proceed along different lines than with a client who describes substance use in highly attractive terms and sees little reason to change.

Another reason some clients cling to excessive substance use is pharmacological dependence. Some substances, including high levels of alcohol and barbiturates, have rebound effects of withdrawal that can be not only unpleasant but also dangerous. Tolerance—needing more of the substance to achieve the same effect—also explains why some users of sleeping pills or tranquilizers, for example, increase doses beyond the prescribed level. Habits developed in relation to drug taking or drinking are another powerful source of attachment to a substance and are difficult to break. The feeling of a glass in the hand when socializing at a party comes to be associated with relaxation and conviviality. Smokers may not know what to do with their hands or want some object in their mouths when they are trying to quit cigarette smoking.

Although your client's initial reasons for wanting to change may be few, each reason is important and should be explored and supported. Because support for change is often linked to a client's intrinsic motivators, reviewing these may elicit more items for the positive side of the balance sheet. As noted earlier, concerns about identity, roles, self-esteem and self-image, and returning to traditional cultural or family values may be linked to specific reasons for change.

Doing a decisional balance exercise with clients has yet another constructive function. Clients are forced to take both sides of the argument about change and articulate the competing sides of their ambivalence. This can be a complex process, however, requiring persistence and reanalysis of each factor several times as clients vacillate between determination and ambivalence.

Normalize Ambivalence

Clients engaged in decisional balance exercises often feel themselves moving closer to a decision—closer to changing long-standing behaviors than they may ever have ventured and, therefore, closer to inner conflict and doubt about whether they can or want to change. An important strategy at this point is to reassure your client that conflicting feelings, uncertainties, and reservations are common. Essentially, you normalize your client's ambivalence by explaining that many former clients have experienced similar strong ambivalence at this stage, even when they believed they had resolved most of their mixed feelings and were nearing a decision. Clients need your reassurance that many other people who have reached this point and seemed suddenly to lose their nerve have been able to recover their direction by continuing the work of exploration and discussion.

Reintroduce Feedback

As discussed in Chapter 4, personalized feedback following assessment can be very helpful in motivating clients. You can continue to use assessment results to influence clients' decisional considerations. Objective medical, social, and neuropsychological feedback from the assessment prompts many clients to contemplate change. Reviewing the assessment information can keep clients focused on the need for change. It has been noted that clients may become uneasy when the clinician seems more invested in their changing than they are (DiClemente and Scott, 1997). By reintroducing objective assessment data, you remind clients of their earlier insights about the need for change.

For example, a client may be intrinsically motivated to stop excessive drinking because of health concerns, yet overwhelmed by fear that quitting will prove impossible. Reintroducing feedback from the medical assessment about the risk of serious liver damage or a family history of heart disease could add significant additional weight to the decisional balance.

Examine the Client's Understanding Of Change and Expectations of Treatment

In working toward a decision, it is important to understand what change means to clients and what their expectations of treatment are. Some clients believe that quitting or cutting down means changing their entire life—moving from their neighborhood or severing ties with all their friends, even their family. Some believe they have to change everything overnight—an overwhelming prospect. Based on friends' experiences with treatment, some may think treatment involves stays of several weeks in an inpatient program or even longer sojourns in a residential treatment facility or that the leader of a therapy group will use confrontational methods in an attempt to "break them down," as in boot camp. Other clients have been in numerous treatment programs and have made many unsuccessful attempts to change. To these clients, the very idea of treatment—of making another attempt to change—connotes failure.

In exploring these meanings and expectations with the client, you will sense what actions might be negotiable and what are not. For example, a client might state that she could never move from her neighborhood, a well-known drug market, because her family is there. Another says he will not consider anything but moderation of his drinking. A third client may just as strongly state that total abstinence and a stay in a therapeutic community are the only options possible because all others have failed.

Exploration of treatment expectations provides an opportunity to introduce information about treatment and to begin a preliminary discussion with clients about available options. When clients' expectations about treatment correspond to what actually happens in treatment, they have better outcomes (Brown and Miller, 1993). Thus, it is never too soon to elicit clients' expectations and begin to educate them about treatment.

Re-explore Values in Relation To Change

Decisional balance exercises offer another opportunity to help clients explore and articulate their values and to make a connection between these values and positive change. Your clients' values will be reflected both in their reasons to change and in the reasons given not to. For example, an adolescent involved in drug dealing with a gang in his neighborhood may let you know that the option of leaving the gang is nonnegotiable because of his loyalty to the other members. Loyalty and belonging are important values to him, and you can relate them to other groups that can inspire similar allegiance such as a sports team or the military—organizations that create a sense of belonging and reflect his core values. A young woman who comes from a family with a history of hard work and academic achievement may wish to return to those values by finishing high school and becoming financially independent.

Hearing themselves articulate their core values helps your clients increase their commitment to positive change. If they can frame the process of change within the larger context of values shared with their family, community, and culture, they may find it easier to contemplate change.

Other Issues in the Decisional Balance

Loss and grief

Because giving up a way of life can be as intense as the loss of a close friend, many clients need time for grieving. They have to acknowledge and mourn this loss before they are ready to move on and build a strong attachment to sobriety. Pushing them too fast toward change can ultimately weaken their determination. Patience and empathy are reassuring at this time. You can help clients believe that their losses will be replaced by gains.

Reservations or resistance

As discussed earlier, serious reservations about change, often called resistance (but more commonly misidentified as denial), can be a signal in motivational interviewing that you and your client have different perspectives. As clients move into the preparation stage, they may become defensive if pushed to commit to change before they are ready or if their goals conflict with yours. They may express this resistance in behaviors rather than words. For example, some will miss appointments, sending a message that they need more time and want to slow the process. Continue to explore ambivalence with these clients and reassess where they are in the change process.

Premature decisionmaking

Decisional balance exercises also give you a sense of whether your clients are ready for change. If clients' articulation of pros and cons is unclear, they may express goals for change at this stage that are unrealistic or reflect a poor understanding of their abilities and resources. You may sense that clients are saying what they think you want to hear. In one way or another, clients who are not ready to make a decision to change will let you know. Allowing clients to set themselves up for failure could result in their abandoning the change process altogether or losing trust in your judgment and care. Delay the commitment process and return with them to the contemplation stage.

Keeping pace

Some clients enter treatment after they have stopped using substances on their own. Others stop substance use the day they call the clinic for the first appointment. They have already made a commitment to stop. If you try to elicit these clients' concerns or conduct decisional balance exercises, you might fail to provide the encouragement, incentives, and skills needed to help the action-oriented and action-ready individual make progress. Such clients can become impatient or frustrated at having to articulate pros and cons and or describe the concerns that led to their decision. Move with these clients immediately to create a change plan and enter the action stage but be alert for ambivalence that may remain or emerge.

Free choice

Many people begin using drugs or alcohol out of rebelliousness toward their family or society, usually in adolescence. Continued substance use may be their expression of continued freedom—freedom from the demands of others to act or live in a certain way. (Tobacco advertisers often tap into this dimension of smoking as an expression of autonomy and independence.) Thus, you may hear clients say that they cannot change because they do not want to lose their freedom. Because this belief is tied to some clients' early-forged identities, it may be a strong factor in their list of reasons not to change. However, as clients age they may be more willing to explore whether the freedom to rebel is actually freedom, or its opposite. If you are attuned to this issue, you can explain that adolescent rebellion may really reflect a

limitation of choices—the person must do the opposite of what is expected. As clients age, they may be more open to making a choice that represents real freedom—the freedom not to rebel, but to do what they truly choose.

Emphasizing Personal Choice and Responsibility

In a motivational approach to counseling, it is not your task to *give* a client a choice—choice is not yours to give but the client's to make. You do not *allow* a client to choose because the choice already and always belongs with the client. The *client* chooses. Your task is to help clients make choices that are in their best interests. A consistent message throughout the motivational approach is the client's responsibility and freedom of choice. At this stage of the change process, the client should be accustomed to hearing from you such statements as the following:

- "It's up to you what to do about this."
- "No one can decide this for you."
- "No one can change your drug use for you. Only you can."
- "You can decide to go on drinking or to change."

Exploring and Setting Goals

Once the client has decided to make a positive change and the commitment is clear, goals should be set. Goal-setting is part of the exploring and envisioning activities characteristic of the early and middle preparation stage. Having summarized and reviewed the client's decisional considerations, you are now prepared to ask about ways in which your client might want to address some of the reasons to change listed on the positive side of the balance sheet (see Figures 5-2 and 5-3). Although goal-setting is an interactive

> ## Figure 5-2
> ## Recapitulation
>
> At the end of decisional balance exercises, you may sense that the client is ready to commit to change. At this point, it is important to summarize once more the client's current situation as reflected in your interactions thus far. The purpose of the summary is to draw together as many reasons for change as possible, while simultaneously acknowledging the client's reluctance or ambivalence. Your recapitulation should include as many of the following elements as possible:
>
> - A summary of the client's own perceptions of the problem, as reflected in self-motivational statements
> - A summary of the client's ambivalence, including what remains positive or attractive about the problem behavior
> - A review of whatever objective evidence you have regarding the presence of risks and problems
> - A restatement of any indication the client has offered of wanting, intending, or planning to change
> - Your own assessment of the client's situation, particularly at points where it converges with the client's own concerns

process, it is the client's responsibility. The process of talking about and setting goals strengthens commitment to change.

Clients may set goals in multiple areas of their life, not just for changing substance use patterns. Those who set several goals may need help with prioritization. Their goals should be as realistic and specific as possible and should address the concerns they articulated earlier about their substance use. Regaining custody of children, reentering the workforce, becoming financially independent, leaving an abusive relationship, and returning to school are all goals that clients may work toward. The more hopeful clients feel about future success in life, the more likely they are to follow through with treatment goals. Initial goals should be short-term, measurable, and realistic so that clients can begin measuring success and feeling good about themselves as well as hopeful about the change.

If your client sets goals that seem unreachable to you, discuss your concerns. This is an important part of the interactive process of goal-setting. Witnessing how your clients set goals and the types of goals they specify provides you with useful information about

their sense of self-efficacy, level of commitment, and readiness for change.

Your client might choose a course of action with which you do not agree or that is not in line with agency policy. A decision to reduce use, for example, may conflict with your strong belief in immediate abstinence or the agency's policy of zero tolerance for illicit substance use. Figure 5-4 addresses this in more detail.

Goal Sampling and Experimenting

Before committing to long-term change, some clients may benefit from experimenting with abstinence or cutting down their use for a short period. Success—or failure—can greatly enhance commitment to a goal of abstinence and long-term change. Presenting the trial period as a personal challenge can be particularly effective. A 3-month experimental period is recommended, based on findings that 3 months of abstinence predict long-term remission of alcohol dependence. Some clients may find this too long, and a shorter trial can be negotiated. The following list summarizes advantages of an abstinence trial (Miller and Page, 1991):

- The client receives an opportunity to learn how it feels to be clean and sober.

Figure 5-3
Key Questions

The recapitulation outlined in Figure 5-2 is a final step before the transition to commitment and leads directly to strategic, open-ended questions intended to prompt the client to consider and articulate the next step. The following is a list of possible key questions:

- What do you think you will do?
- What does this mean about your drinking?
- It must be uncomfortable for you now, seeing all this. What's the next step?
- What do you think has to change?
- What could you do? What are your options?
- It sounds like things can't stay the way they are now. What are you going to do?
- Of the things I have mentioned here, which are the most important reasons for a change?
- How are you going to do it?
- Where do we go from here?
- How would you like things to turn out now for you, ideally?
- What concerns you about changing your use of drugs?
- What would be some of the good things about making a change?

Source: Miller and Rollnick, 1991.

- Current, habitual consumption patterns are interrupted and tolerance reduced.
- You and the client are helped to discover the degree, if any, of physiological dependence.
- The client can demonstrate and experience a period of successful self-control.
- A period of recovery from acute cognitive impairment is provided.
- Others (e.g., a spouse, the court) are shown that the client is sincerely interested in changing and capable of taking a first step.
- Extra time is allowed for recovery and stabilization of health, mood, sleeping patterns, and so forth.
- You and the client are helped to ascertain situations in which the client needs additional coping skills to overcome psychological dependence on the substance.

The usefulness of a month-long abstinence trial for adult marijuana smokers has been examined (Stephens et al., 1994). The participants were assigned to a three-session intervention consisting of assessment, personalized feedback of the assessment results, and brief intervention counseling. At the end of the second session, the counselor announced that the third session would be a month later and also asked whether clients would like to try some changes during that time period so that they could discuss the results at the next meeting. A month of abstention was proposed as "do-able"—long enough to try out changes but not long enough to seem like too much commitment. In reference to marijuana use, the study found that the three-session clients had the same outcomes at periodic posttreatment followups as a group that received 18 sessions of treatment during the same period.

Besides trial abstention, two other "warm turkey" approaches have been described (Miller and Page, 1991).

Figure 5-4
When Goals Collide

What do you do when your client's goals differ from yours or those of your agency? This issue arises in all treatment but is particularly apparent in a motivational approach where you listen reflectively to your clients and actively involve them in decisionmaking. As you elicit goals for change and treatment, some clients may not reflect what you think is best for them. How you handle this sensitive clinical situation can determine whether the client continues to pursue change.

Before exploring different ways of handling this common situation, try to clarify the differences and boundaries between the client's goals and your own (or your agency's). For clients, goals are by definition the objectives they are motivated (ready, willing, and able) to work toward. If the client is not motivated to work toward it, it is not a goal. You or your agency, on the other hand, may have particular aspirations, plans, or hopes for the client. It is important to realize that *goal* can have different meanings to you and to your client. You cannot impose your hopes and plans on a client. If you want your client to adopt a goal, your task is to motivate.

What are your clinical options when goals collide? You can choose from the following tactics:

- **Give up on the client.** Although it sounds unappealing, this option is surprisingly common. If clients do not accept the goals prescribed by the clinician or agency, they are dismissed. This often amounts to discharging clients for the same reasons they were admitted. In the past, this option arose from (or at least was rationalized by) a mistaken view of motivation as a slowly progressing linear process. Clients were actually told, "Go away and come back when you're ready [i.e., to do what I tell you]."

- **Negotiate.** Find goals on which you and your client can agree and work together on those. Start with areas in which the client is motivated to change. Women with alcohol or drug problems, for example, often come to treatment with a wide range of other problems, many of which they see as more pressing than making a change in substance use. Clinicians have had good results by starting with the problems that are most urgent from the client's perspective and then addressing substance use when its relationship to other problems becomes apparent.

- **Approximate.** Even if a client is not willing to accept all your recommendations, it is often possible to agree on a goal that constitutes a step in the right direction. Your hope, for example, might be that the client would eventually become free from all psychoactive substance use. The client, however, is most concerned about cocaine and is not ready to talk about changing marijuana, tobacco, or alcohol use. Rather than dismiss the client for not accepting a goal of immediate abstinence from all substances, you can focus on stopping cocaine use and then consider a next step.

- **Refer.** If your client's goals are personally unacceptable to you even after trying to negotiate or approximate, you can refer. Sometimes a client might benefit from working toward a goal, but the clinician is personally uncomfortable (e.g., for ethical or professional competency reasons) in continuing treatment. For example, some clients are unwilling to consider immediate abstinence when they enter treatment. Even though alternatives exist (e.g., tapering down, trying problem-free moderate use, agreeing on a short trial period of abstinence [Miller and Page, 1991]), not all clinicians are comfortable working toward any goal other than immediate abstinence. In such cases, it often is preferable to refer these clients to another clinician who will work with them, rather than terminate treatment altogether.

Tapering down

This "warm turkey" approach has been widely used with cigarette smokers to reduce their dependence level before the quit date. This approach consists of setting progressively lower daily and weekly limits on use of the substance while working toward a long-range goal of abstinence. The client keeps careful daily records of consumption and schedules sessions with the clinician as needed.

Trial moderation

Trial moderation may be the only acceptable goal for some clients who are highly resistant to abstinence. It is important to avoid sending the message: "Go try it, and when you've failed, come back." A more friendly and motivational approach is: "If that's what you want, let's give it the best try we can and see how it works." However, seek agreement from the client that, if the moderation experiment fails after a reasonable effort, abstinence will be considered. A long-term followup of 99 problem drinkers who systematically tried to moderate drinking showed that more of them ultimately decided to abstain than maintain stable and problem-free moderation. At followup, more than half of those who ultimately abstained attributed their success to the insight gained from the moderation trial about their need to abstain (Miller et al., 1992).

Although immediate abstinence is the usual prescription, no studies have confirmed that cold turkey is the best or only way to initiate lasting sobriety. Additional studies are needed to determine who are optimal candidates for "warm turkey" approaches; clinical and research experience indicates that these methods are successful with some clients, particularly those with less severe problems (Miller et al., 1992).

Enhancing Commitment in the Late Preparation Stage

Commitment to change still must be reinforced even after your client has initially decided to change and has begun to set goals. Vacillation is to be expected at any point in the change process. Three additional strategies are available for enhancing commitment at this point: taking smaller steps, going public, and envisioning.

Taking small steps

You have asked your client key questions such as "What is next?" and have presented a variety of options (see Chapter 6) to convey the message that it is the client's choice to change and to select the areas on which to focus. Reminders that clients have choices to make and that they control the change process can reinforce commitment. If clients seem overwhelmed by the changes they are contemplating, reassure them that they can moderate the pace of change and can choose to begin with small steps. With some clients, it might be especially helpful to provide a case history of someone who made large and seemingly impossible life changes by taking one step at a time. The importance of such stories and models should not be underestimated in motivating people to change.

Going public

Disclosing the desire to change to at least one other person besides the clinician seems to be very important in helping clients become accountable as well as aware of any inner resistance. This other person can be a spouse, friend, family member, coworker, church friend, or Alcoholics Anonymous (AA) member. Telling significant others about one's desire to change usually enhances commitment to change. Going public can be a critical step for some clients in the late preparation stage who may not have been ready to tell others until this point. AA has applied the clinical wisdom of public commitment to change through use of the "white chip." An attendee at an AA meeting who is not yet ready to quit but has a strong desire to do so can pick up a white chip, as a public acknowledgment of the desire to quit drinking.

Envisioning

Specifically envisioning a different life after changes are made can be a powerful motivator and an effective means of strengthening your client's commitment. In addition, stories about how others have successfully achieved their goals can be excellent motivators. An exercise for envisioning change is to ask clients to picture themselves after a year has passed, during which time they have made the changes they desire in the areas of their lives most hurt by their substance use. Some clients may find it valuable to write a letter to themselves that is dated in the future and describes what life is like at that point. The letter can have the tone of a vacation postcard, wishing you were here. Others will be more comfortable describing these scenes to you.

The Importance of Self-Efficacy

Even clients who acknowledge a serious problem are not likely to move toward positive change unless they have some hope of success. Self-efficacy is a critical determinant of behavior change—it is the belief that they can act in a certain way or perform a particular task and thereby exercise control over events. Self-efficacy can be thought of as hope or optimism, but clients do not have to have an overall optimistic perspective to believe a particular behavior can be changed.

Clients are most likely to make statements about self-efficacy when they are negotiating

goals or developing a change plan (see Chapter 6). Statements about self-efficacy could include the following: "I can't do that," "That is beyond my powers," "That would be easy," or "I think I can manage that." From such statements, you can ascertain what the client feels able—and unable—to do.

Self-efficacy is not a global measure, like self-esteem. Rather, it is behavior-specific. Underlying any discussion of self-efficacy is the question, "efficacy to perform what specific behavior?" In relation to substance dependency, self-efficacy can be conceptualized into five categories (DiClemente et al., 1994):

1. *Coping self-efficacy* involves successful coping with specific situations that might tempt a person to use the substance, such as being assertive with friends or talking with someone when upset rather than using the substance.
2. *Treatment behavior self-efficacy* involves the client's ability to perform behaviors relevant to treatment, such as self-monitoring or stimulus control.
3. *Recovery self-efficacy* relates to the client's ability to recover from a recurrence of the addictive behavior.
4. *Control self-efficacy* focuses on the client's confidence in her ability to control the behavior in a variety of provocative situations.
5. *Abstinence self-efficacy* involves the client's confidence in her ability to abstain from substance use in the various situations that are cues or triggers.

Another way to conceptualize self-efficacy is as the client's perceived ability to engage in meaningful or pleasurable, nonsubstance-related activities. This should be assessed before you engage in change strategies related to your client's daily activities.

Self-efficacy is a dynamic rather than a static construct. Self-efficacy for coping with each particular situation increases with success and decreases with failure. Thus, it is important to give clients skills to be successful in situations that present a risk for recurrence of use in order to enhance their belief that they can maintain desired changes.

Clinicians and researchers have found it useful to measure self-efficacy by examining situations or states that present a risk for recurrence of substance use. Clients may have high self-efficacy in some situations and low self-efficacy in others. (See Chapter 8 for descriptions of instruments you can use to measure a client's self-efficacy in particular situations.) According to one study, most recurrence of substance use occurs in one or more of the following four situations (Cummings et al., 1980):

1. *Negative emotional states* such as anger, depression, or frustration
2. *Social pressures* such as seeing others drinking at a bar or being on vacation and wanting to relax
3. *Physical and other concerns* such as having a headache, feeling tired, or being worried about someone
4. *Withdrawal symptoms and urges* such as craving or feeling drawn to test one's willpower

Before you and the client discuss self-efficacy for changing substance use behavior, explore other areas and activities in the client's life for which the client has demonstrated high self-efficacy. Then you can discuss how your client's skills could apply to new efforts to change. For example, a client who is working on restoring an old car may spend dozens of hours figuring out why the engine will not run smoothly—systematically taking apart and reassembling various parts of the engine until the problem is found. This persistent and patient approach to problem solving and the curiosity behind it can be reframed as valuable strengths for identifying and solving problems with substance use. Other ways to support your client's self-efficacy include the following (Marlatt and Gordon, 1985):

- Stress that change is a gradual process.
- Focus on acquisition of new skills versus cessation of "immoral" activity.
- Provide timely and specific feedback regarding progress.

6 From Preparation to Action: Getting Started

Strong commitment alone does not guarantee change. Unfortunately, enthusiasm does not make up for ineptness.... Commitment without appropriate coping skills and activities can create a tenuous action plan.... Anticipation of problems and pitfalls appears to be a solid problem-solving skill.

DiClemente, 1991

At the end of the preparation stage, clients make a plan for change to guide them into the action stage. This chapter focuses on negotiating this specific change plan with clients. Changing any long-standing, habitual behavior requires preparation and planning. As your clients move from contemplating to actually implementing change in their lives, they are in an intermediate stage in which they increase their commitment to change by exploring, clarifying, and resolving their ambivalence and making a decision to act. In the transtheoretical model, this stage is known as preparation. Clients must see change as in their best interest before they can move into action. The negative consequences of ignoring the preparation stage can be a brief course of action followed by rapid return to substance use.

During the preparation stage, your tasks broaden. Where before you were using motivational strategies to increase readiness—the goals of the precontemplation and contemplation stages—now you will use these strategies to strengthen your client's commitment and help this person make a firm decision to change. Clients who are committed to change and who believe change is possible are prepared for action.

Clients and clinicians in the preparation stage are equipped with important knowledge from the personalized feedback of assessment information described in Chapter 4. The activities and strategies described in Chapter 5 were intended to solidify your client's commitment to change and set the stage for developing a plan for moving into action. Clients should now have a clearer picture of how their substance use affects many aspects of their lives, and they should have begun to recognize some of the consequences of continued use. In addition, many clients sense the hopeful possibilities inherent in the growing therapeutic alliance. If you have exercised the principles of motivational interviewing, your clients should recognize that they are in a safe environment for exploring their feelings and thoughts about change and that they are in control of the change process.

This chapter explains how and when to negotiate a change plan with the client and suggests ways to ensure a sound plan—by offering the client a menu of options, contracting for change, identifying and lowering barriers to action, enlisting social support, and helping the client anticipate what it will be like to participate in treatment.

Recognizing Readiness To Move Into Action

As clients proceed through the preparation stage, be alert for signs of their readiness to take action. Clients' recognition of important discrepancies in their lives is an uncomfortable state in which to remain for long; thus change should be initiated to decrease discomfort, or clients may retreat to using defenses such as minimizing or denying. Mere vocal fervor about change, however, is not necessarily a sign of determination to change. Clients who are vehement in declaring their readiness may be desperately trying to convince themselves, as well as you, of their commitment (DiClemente, 1991). The following are several confirming signs of readiness to act:

- *Decreased resistance*. The client stops arguing, interrupting, denying, or objecting.
- *Fewer questions about the problem*. The client seems to have enough information about his problem and stops asking questions.
- *Resolve*. The client appears to have reached a resolution and may be more peaceful, calm, relaxed, unburdened, or settled. Sometimes this happens after the client has passed through a period of anguish or tearfulness.
- *Self-motivational statements*. The client makes direct self-motivational statements reflecting openness to change ("I have to do something") and optimism ("I'm going to beat this").

- *More questions about change*. The client asks what she could do about the problem, how people change once they decide to, and so forth.
- *Envisioning*. The client begins to talk about how life might be after a change, to anticipate difficulties if a change were made, or to discuss the advantages of change.
- *Experimenting*. If the client has had time between sessions, he may have begun experimenting with possible change approaches (e.g., going to an Alcoholics Anonymous [AA] meeting, reading a self-help book, stopping substance use for a few days) (Miller and Rollnick, 1991).

When you conclude that a client is becoming committed to change, determine what is needed next by asking a key question (see Chapter 5). You might say, "I can see you are ready for a change. How would you like to proceed?" If the client indicates that she wishes to pursue treatment with your help, you can begin negotiating a plan for change.

Negotiating a Plan for Change

Creating a plan for change is a final step in readying your client to act. A solid plan for change enhances your client's self-efficacy and provides an opportunity to consider potential obstacles and the likely outcomes of each change strategy before embarking. Furthermore, nothing is more motivating than being well prepared—no matter what the situation, a well-prepared person is usually eager to get started. A sound change plan can be negotiated with your client by the following means:

- Offering a menu of change options
- Developing a behavior contract
- Lowering barriers to action
- Enlisting social support
- Educating your client about treatment

Chapter 5 describes the process of exploring clients' goals as a way of enhancing commitment and envisioning change. The change plan can be thought of as a roadmap to realizing those goals. Some clients begin spontaneously suggesting or asking about specific things they can do to change. You can prompt others to make suggestions by asking key questions such as, "What do you think you will do about your drinking/drug use?" or "Now that you've come this far, I wonder what you plan to do?" (see Chapter 5 for a list of key questions).

Clients will create plans that reflect their individual concerns and goals. Most plans are not limited to stopping or moderating substance use, and ensuring success is the central focus of the plan. The plan can be very general or very specific, and short term or long term. Indeed, some clients may be able to commit only to a very limited plan, such as going home, thinking about change, and returning on a specific date to talk further. Even such a restricted and short-term plan can include specific steps for helping the client avoid high-risk situations as well as specific coping strategies for the interim.

Some clients' plans are very simple, such as stating only that they will enter outpatient treatment and attend an AA meeting every day. Other plans include details such as handling transportation to the treatment facility or arranging alternative ways to spend Friday nights. As discussed below, specific steps to overcome anticipated barriers to success are important components of many change plans. Some plans lay out a sequence of steps. For example, working mothers with children who must enter inpatient treatment may develop a sequenced plan for arranging for child care and training temporary replacements for their jobs before entering treatment.

Although the change plan is the client's, creating it is an interactive process between you and the client. One of your most important

tasks is to ensure that the plan is feasible. When the client proposes a plan that seems unrealistic, too ambitious, or not ambitious enough, a process of negotiation should follow. The following areas are ordinarily part of interactive discussions and negotiations:

- *Intensity and amount of help needed*—for example, the use of only self-help groups, enrolling in intensive outpatient treatment, or entering a 2-year therapeutic community
- *Timeframe*—a short- rather than a long-term plan and a start date for the plan
- *Available social support*—including who will be involved in treatment (e.g., family, Women for Sobriety, community group), where it will take place (at home, in the community), and when it will occur (after work, weekends, two evenings a week)
- *Sequence of subgoals and strategies or steps in the plan*—for example, first to stop dealing marijuana, then stop smoking it; to call friends or family to tell them about the plan, then visit them; to learn relaxation techniques, then to use them when feeling stressed at work
- *How to address multiple problems*—for example, how to deal with legal, financial, and health problems

Clients may ask you for information and advice about specific steps to incorporate in the plan. Provide accurate and specific facts, and always ask whether they understand them. Eliciting responses to such information by asking, "Does that surprise you?" or, "What do *you* think about it?" can also be helpful in the negotiation process.

How prescriptive should you be when clients ask what *you* think they should do? Providing your best advice is an important part of your role. It is also appropriate to provide your own views and opinions, although it is helpful to insert qualifiers and give clients permission to disagree.

Other techniques of motivational interviewing, such as developing discrepancy, empathizing, and avoiding argument, remain as useful during these negotiations as they are at all other stages of the change process. Guard against becoming overly focused on the negotiations and on the plan such that you forget to use these strategies. Acknowledge and affirm the client's effort in making the plan.

Some clients have found the Change Plan Worksheet (see Figure 6-1) a useful tool in focusing their attention on the details of the plan. The following is a list of considerations for completing the worksheet (Miller et al., 1995c):

- *The changes I want to make are...* Be specific. Include goals that are positive (wanting to increase, improve, do more of something),

and not just negative goals (stop, avoid, or decrease a behavior).

- *My main goals for myself in making these changes are...* What are the likely consequences of action or inaction? Which motivations for change are most compelling?

- *The first steps I plan to take in changing are...* How can the desired change be accomplished? What are some specific, concrete first steps? When, where, and how will the steps be taken?

- *Some things that could interfere with my plan are...* What specific events or problems could undermine the plan? What could go wrong? How will the client stick with the plan despite these particular problems or setbacks?

Figure 6-1
Change Plan Worksheet

The changes I want to make are:
The most important reasons I want to make these changes are:
My main goals for myself in making these changes are: ·
I plan to do these things to reach my goals: *Plan of Action*   *When*
The first steps I plan to take in changing are:
Some things that could interfere with my plan are:
Other people could help me in changing in these ways: *Person*   *Possible ways to help*
I hope that my plan will have these positive results:
I will know that my plan is working if:
Sources: Miller and Rollnick, 1991; Miller et al., 1995c.

- *Other people could help me in changing in these ways…* What specific things can another person do to help the client take the steps to change? How will the client arrange for such support?
- *I will know that my plan is working if…* What will happen as a result of taking the different steps in the plan? What benefits can be expected?

It can be helpful to estimate your client's readiness and self-efficacy for the changes that your client lists in the plan. For example, on a scale from 1 to 10 (1 = no confidence, 10 = most confidence), the client may rate himself as a "9" in regard to readiness for a making a particular change in behavior, but only as a "4" on self-efficacy. This could help you guide your client about where to start on the change plan.

Offering a Menu of Change Options

Researchers and clinicians working in the motivational framework find that one way to enhance motivation is to offer clients a choice from a variety of treatment alternatives. For example, a client who will not go to AA may go to a meeting of Rational Recovery or Women for Sobriety, if such groups are available. A client who will not consider abstinence may be more amenable to a "warm turkey" approach (Miller and Page, 1991), as described in Chapter 5. Encouraging clients to learn about treatment alternatives and to make informed choices enhances commitment to the change plan. Choices can be about treatment options or about other types of services.

Treatment Options and Resources

In our alcohol treatment program, I found that having lists of both community resources and diverse treatment modules enables case managers to engage clients, offer individualized programming, and meet clients' multiple needs. The following are some options we offer our clients:

Treatment Module Options

- Values clarification/decisionmaking
- Social skills training (assertiveness, communication)
- Anxiety management/relaxation
- Anger management
- Marital and family therapy
- Adjunctive medication (disulfiram [Antabuse], naltrexone [ReVia])
- Problem-solving group
- Intensive group therapy

Community Treatment Resources

- Halfway houses
- Support groups (AA, Narcotics Anonymous [NA], Rational Recovery, Women for Sobriety)
- Social services (child care, vocational rehabilitation, food, shelter)
- Medical care
- Transportation
- Legal services
- Psychiatric services
- Academic and technical schools

Carlo C. DiClemente, Consensus Panel Member

No single approach to treating substance abuse works equally well for all clients. Determining what works best for whom and under what conditions can be a difficult undertaking. Evidence of treatment effectiveness is becoming increasingly specialized and, to some extent, more confusing, as more elements are added to evaluation formulas, including client characteristics, outcome measures, therapist qualities, treatment components, and quality of implementation.

Familiarity with the available treatment facilities in your community and with the relevant research literature pertaining to optimal choices for the types of clients you see is enormously helpful in providing your clients with appropriate options. It is also useful to know about the range of community resources in other service areas, such as food banks, job training programs, special programs for patients with coexisting disorders, and safe shelters for women in abusive relationships. A clinician who knows not only program names but also contact persons, program graduates, typical space availability, funding issues, eligibility criteria, and program rules and idiosyncrasies is an invaluable resource for clients. Additionally, knowledge about clients' resources, insurance coverage (or participation in some form of managed care), employment situation, parenting responsibilities, and other relevant factors is obviously crucial in considering alternatives. Information from an initial assessment is helpful, too, in establishing a list of possible treatment options and setting priorities.

Although you may have a wealth of knowledge about local resources, your program's administration has the final responsibility for developing liaisons with other agencies to ensure appropriate referrals for services and for keeping clinicians informed. In many places, a central agency compiles and regularly updates a comprehensive directory of community resources that contains information about services, costs, location, hours of operation, and eligibility criteria. Every program should have a manual of appropriate referral resources, with cross-references by program type, or should obtain current listings from local, State, or national sources (see Chapter 5 of TIP 24, *A Guide to Substance Abuse Services for Primary Care Clinicians* [CSAT, 1997]). The Internet offers new possibilities for accessing information about community resources and for linking clients with programs and services. For example, in Washington, DC, a computer system linking criminal justice agencies with substance abuse treatment programs gives up-to-the-minute information about space availability and program changes. Workers in the justice system can set up intake appointments for clients online. Those in rural areas where resources are scarce may find the Internet especially valuable.

As you discuss treatment choices with clients, you can acquaint them with the concepts of levels of care, intensities of care, and appropriate fit. Do not, however, overwhelm them with a complicated description of all possibilities. Avoid professional jargon and technical terms for treatment types or philosophies. Limit options to several that are appropriate, and describe these, one at a time, in language that is understandable and relevant to individual concerns of clients. Explain what a particular treatment is intended to do, how it works, what is involved, and what clients can expect. Ask clients to postpone a decision about treatment until they understand all the options.

As each option is discussed, ask clients if they have questions and ask for their opinions about how they would handle each alternative. Although the goal is to choose the right approach initially, some clients may choose an option that you believe is inappropriate. Offer advice based on your clinical experience and knowledge of the research. You are searching for change strategies with which to begin, and, ideally, the client will view some appropriate options positively.

While you are exploring treatment options with a client, also review the concept of change as a wheel or cyclical process (see Chapter 1). Each person moves through the stages of change—forward or backward—over a substantial period of time (Prochaska and DiClemente, 1984; Prochaska et al., 1992b). This cycling sometimes takes the form of an upward spiral, with gradual improvement in the spacing, length, and severity of periods of problematic behavior (Miller, 1996). Because most people typically move around the cycle several times before exiting into stable recovery, let clients know that they should not become discouraged if their first treatment option does not work. Point out that, with all the possibilities, they are certain to find some form of treatment that will work. Reassure them that you are willing to work with them until they find the right choice.

Clients sometimes resist the idea that change is a cyclical process and prefer to view change as "all or nothing." The resistance may stem from fear that acknowledging the possibility of a lapse represents giving oneself permission to actually have one. It is of the utmost importance to convey to your clients that they can return to see you no matter what, even after a slip.

You also should be sensitive to the client who resists an idea you have found motivational for others. In this case, you might say, "It sounds like this issue is really important to you. Tell me more about that," or "It sounds like you would not want to go through that again, and I can understand why, at this point, you would not want to talk about those things. So, to help you with this, let me know how I can help you avoid the things that led to recurrence in the past, while at the same time help you avoid discussing the things that you do not think are helpful." The hope is that in discussing previous returns to problem behavior (while conveying your agreement with the client's wish that it not happen) you can "ease" into the possibility of recurrence and how to handle it.

Clinicians are accustomed to the idea that treatment success means completing a formal program and, conversely, dropping out means treatment failure. However, research has shown that a significant number of clients stop treatment because they do not need further help and can implement change on their own (DiClemente and Scott, 1997). Often, they only need assistance in maximizing their readiness to change and enhancing their motivation. No further aid is wanted—no negotiating, no plan, no contract—just encouragement and reassurance that they can return if they need more help. The danger is that some clients, such as those with a long history of excessive and relatively uninterrupted substance use, may take this opportunity to run away from treatment. When these clients suggest trying to change on their own, discuss your concerns about their leaving prematurely.

Several programs offer time-limited check-in modules to prepare clients for change. For example, a treatment program in Austin, Texas, periodically offers a 2-hour group for people who smoke. The program contains educational and motivational components as well as some elements of self-help through group support. Although participants are told how to access treatment if necessary, the group is designed to help participants initiate self-change. Research suggests that some people can change substance-dependent behaviors on their own without treatment (DiClemente and Prochaska, 1985; Klingemann, 1991; Sobell et al., 1993b; Tuchfield, 1981).

Developing a Behavior Contract

A written or oral contract is a useful tool for helping clients start on their change plans. A contract is a formal agreement between two parties. Literate clients may choose to make a signed statement at the bottom of the Change Plan Worksheet or may prefer a separate document. Explain to literate clients that other people have found contracts useful at this stage and invite them to try writing one. The act of composing and signing a contract can be a small but important ceremony of commitment. Avoid writing the contract for clients and encourage them to use their own words. With some, a handshake is an adequate substitute for a written contract, particularly with the client who lacks literacy.

Establishing a contract raises issues for fruitful discussion about your client's reasons for desiring change. Whom is the contract with? What parties does it involve? Some contracts include the clinician as a party in the contract, specifying the clinician's functions and responsibilities. Other clients regard the contract as a promise to themselves, to a spouse, or to other family members.

Contracts are often used in treatment programs that employ behavioral techniques. For many clinicians, contracts mean contingencies—rewards and punishments—and programs often build contingencies into the structure of their programs. For example, in many methadone maintenance programs, take-home medications are contingent on substance-free urine screens. Rewards or incentives have been shown to be highly effective reinforcers of abstinence. In a treatment program study of 40 cocaine-dependent adults (Higgins et al., 1994b), one group received vouchers exchangeable for retail items contingent on submitting cocaine-free urine specimens during weeks 1 through 12 of treatment. The other group received no vouchers. Seventy-five percent of the voucher group completed 24 weeks of treatment, compared with 40 percent of the control group, and the duration of continuous cocaine abstinence in the voucher group was nearly twice as long as that of the control group (11.7

weeks versus 6 weeks). See Chapter 7 for more discussion of incentives.

In developing a contract, the client may decide to include contingencies, especially rewards or positive incentives. Rewards can be highly individual. Enjoyable activities, favorite foods, desired objects, or rituals and ceremonies can all be powerful objective markers of change and reinforcers of commitment. Rewards can be tied to duration of abstinence, to anniversaries of the quit date, or to achievement of subgoals. One client might plan to spend the afternoon at a baseball game with his son to celebrate a month of abstinence. Another might buy a pair of red shoes after attending her 50th AA meeting. Still another might light a candle at church, and another might hike to the top of a nearby mountain to mark an improvement in energy and health.

Lowering Barriers to Action

Identifying barriers to action is an important part of the change plan. As clients decide what options are best for them, ask whether they anticipate any problems with those options or any obstacles to following the plan and achieving their goals: What could go wrong? What has gone wrong in past attempts to change? As mentioned earlier, certain clients resist the idea that something could go wrong. Here, it is better to get the information by asking about what has gone wrong in the past. It is sometimes easier to discuss past difficulties than to acknowledge the possibility of difficulties in the future.

One common barrier to action involves referring your client to another treatment program or other services following initial consultation or evaluation. When you refer clients, make sure they have all the necessary information about how to get to the program, whom and when to telephone, and what to expect during the call (e.g., what type of personal information might be requested).

Giving your client "insider information" also reduces the client's anxiety and eases the way. For example, you may know that the receptionist at the program is a friendly person, or that many people get lost by entering the building on the wrong side, or that a nearby lunch counter serves good food. One inpatient program takes clients on field trips to the outpatient aftercare site before discharge to ensure a smooth transition.

Research has shown that giving the client a name and telephone number on a piece of paper is far less effective than more personalized referral methods (Miller, 1985b). Consider helping your client make the telephone call to set up the intake appointment at the chosen program. Some clients may want to make the phone call from your office, whereas others might wish to call the program from home and call you later to inform you that they made an appointment. Still others prefer to think things over first and make the call from your office at the next session. Let your clients know that you are interested in knowing how everything goes.

Anticipating problems

As suggested in the Change Plan Worksheet, one question to ask clients is, "If down the line the plan fails, what do you envision might be the cause?" Clients can predict some barriers better than you can, and it is important to allow them to identify and articulate these problems. Do not try to anticipate everything that could go wrong; focus on events or situations that are likely to be problematic and build alternatives and solutions into the plan.

Some problems may be clear from the outset. A highly motivated client sitting in your office may plan to attend an outpatient treatment program 50 miles away three times a week, even though such a plan involves both bus and train schedules and late-night travel. Referral to a less distant program may be the solution, although helping the client make some

telephone calls to the program could identify a participant willing to provide a ride.

Recognizing barriers to action

Barriers to action are frequently encountered and should be discussed, if only briefly, when the change plan is being negotiated. Consider specific strategies and coping behaviors, and help clients explore what works best for them. Potential barriers exist in several areas.

Family relations can be critical barriers to initiating and maintaining action. A client's changed behavior may throw family relationships off balance, and problems that were suppressed as long as family dynamics centered on the substance use behavior may begin to surface. For example, the client may want to take back control. A wife who has made all family decisions by herself for a long time may react negatively to sharing power. A teenager who is used to coming and going unnoticed may rebel over a new curfew. Some family members may have deep resentment and criticism about the client's past behavior that they cannot wait any longer to express.

Such family disruptions and crises can contribute to a return to substance use, and clients can anticipate and learn specific strategies and coping behaviors to avoid such an outcome. Some clients may decide to institute a family meeting at a certain time each week for discussing problems and averting crises; the first one can be scheduled in your office. Some families benefit from more formal family therapy, which can be incorporated into the change plan. Other clients may identify a respected older person, such as a grandfather or friend, who would be willing and capable of acting as an arbiter in family disagreements. Also, people in recovery attend frequent meetings, which decreases the time they have available for family. Clients may consider attending meetings during the lunch hour or at other times that do not reduce family time.

Sometimes, fellow attendees in AA and Narcotics Anonymous groups provide unsound advice that is not in the family's best interest. Another important issue is the rebonding of a relationship or a marriage. Usually the male client is eager to return to a sexual relationship, and the female is cautious because of the past pain and mistrust. The male then reacts to the tension that develops from not having a commitment for sexual activity from his partner. In some cases, sexual behavior is used as a device to control the recovering person, and when the expectations of the recovering person are not met, tension builds.

Health problems present obstacles to recovery for many clients with serious physical or mental health disorders. Some become sick after entering treatment; others have chronic conditions that require monitoring and treatment and can produce periodic health crises (e.g., HIV/AIDS, diabetes, hypertension). Clients may be in chronic pain from injuries or self-neglect (e.g., back pain, dental problems). Abstinence sometimes reveals underlying mental illnesses, such as depressive or psychotic disorders (see TIP 9, *Assessment and Treatment of Patients with Coexisting Mental Illness and Alcohol and Other Drug Abuse* [CSAT, 1994b]; and TIP 29, *Substance Abuse Treatment for People With Physical and Cognitive Disabilities* [CSAT, 1998a]). Medications taken for physical and mental health problems may cause distressing side effects.

All of these conditions and situations can increase the risk of returning to substance use. Although some of these problems cannot be anticipated, clients may have to build health supports and improvements into the plan. Some clients, especially those with strong concerns about their health, may wish to include a schedule for physical and dental checkups or arrangements with specific physicians and clinics for ongoing care of chronic problems. Subgoals for acquiring medical care may involve applying for entitlement programs or checking insurance coverage. A depressed client, for example, may plan to see a mental health worker for an evaluation if she is still feeling depressed after 30 days of abstinence, or she may decide to see one sooner if her symptoms increase the risk of returning to substance use. It should be reemphasized that some clients (e.g., those with coexisting disorders) need more intensive services.

System problems in the treatment program itself can be obstacles to immediate and sustained recovery. For example, many facilities have long waiting lists. Some programs require a great deal of paperwork to enter, which may put off clients with poor literacy skills. Clients with outstanding legal problems are not accepted in some programs. Financial support that clients counted on for treatment may disappear. For instance, a mother whose treatment is covered by Medicaid may lose her eligibility when she takes a higher paying job. Some highly motivated clients encounter significant language barriers at local programs if they do not speak English well. Clients with coexisting disorders who are on psychoactive medications may not be welcome at some AA groups.

Second thoughts and doubts occur to even the most highly motivated clients with carefully considered change plans. It is not uncommon to have an attack of regret or "cold feet." An expression used by AA members is "to come off the pink cloud." Second thoughts may emerge as soon as the client leaves your office—or several weeks into the change plan. Normalize this experience for clients and, at the same time, make specific plans for dealing with it. It is an important task to help clients overcome their doubts. You can insist that your client call you as soon as second thoughts arise or discuss other strategies such as attending extra AA meetings or calling a trusted support person (see below). Some clients keep a supply of disulfiram to use when they feel overwhelmed by urges and cravings.

Enlisting Social Support

Social support is an important influence on whether change happens and whether it is maintained (Sobell et al., 1993b). It is not sufficient to think of social support in terms of amount or even quality. When treating substance abuse, question whether the client's social support system is supporting continued substance use. For example, within Project MATCH, treatment outcomes were predictable from the extent to which the client's social network supported continued drinking or sobriety (Project MATCH Research Group, 1997a, 1997b). Those with good social support for sobriety fared better overall. Those whose social networks at intake supported continued drinking tended to have less abstinence at followup, with an important exception. These clients did much better if their treatment helped them get engaged in AA. In essence, AA provided them with a new social network supportive of sobriety (Project MATCH Research Group, 1997b). When your client has few or no significant others who are encouraging sobriety, it is important to help your client build a new social structure that will support the effort to change.

As a clinician, you are a central support for your clients, but you cannot provide all the support they need. In general, a supportive person is someone who will listen and not be overly judgmental (or who will at least withhold judgment). This supportive person should have a helpful and encouraging attitude toward the client, rather than being critical or nagging. Ideally, this person does not use or misuse substances and understands the processes of substance dependency and change. The Change Plan Worksheet (given in Figure 6-1) includes space for listing supportive persons and describing how they can help. As discussed in

Chapter 4, concerned significant others can learn the skills and techniques of motivational interviewing and become effective partners in change.

Because social support often entails taking part with the client in activities that are alternatives to substance use, close friends with whom the client has a history of shared interests other than substance use are good candidates for this helpful role. Of course, members of social groups organized around drinking and drug use are not likely to offer the kind of support your client needs during recovery.

In addition to repairing or resuming ties with helpful family members and significant others, clients can find supportive people in, for example, churches, recreational centers, and community volunteer organizations. To make these connections, encourage clients to explore and discuss a time in their lives before substance use became a central focus. Ask them what gave meaning to their lives at that time.

Clients may find supportive new friends in such prosocial organizations as mentoring groups modeled after Big Brothers and Big Sisters. Fellow members of AA and other self-help groups are important supports in the lives of many recovering clients. Oxford Houses and similar treatment-housing options have built-in social support systems. For some clients, especially those with chronic physical problems or severe mental illness, case management teams provide a sense of safety, structure, and support.

When helping clients to enlist social support, be particularly alert for those who have poor social skills or scant social networks. Some clients may have to learn social skills and ways to structure leisure time, and such small steps can be incorporated into the change plan. Some clients may not be connected to any social unit that is not organized around substance use. Furthermore, substance dependency may have so narrowed their focus that they have trouble recalling activities that once held their interest or appealed to them. However, most people harbor secret, unfulfilled wishes to pursue an activity at some time in their lives. Ask about these wishes. One client may want to learn ballroom dancing, another to learn a martial art or take a creative writing class. Planning for change can be a particularly fertile time for clients to reconnect with such lost hopes, and pursuing such activities provides opportunities for making new friends.

Finally, in helping clients enlist social support, avoid the stereotype of the self-sufficient loner. Although early views of people with substance dependency characterized them as cut off from primary relationships and living a kind of "alley cat" existence, accumulating evidence from several countries indicates that most are closely tied to their families (Stanton, 1997). In fact, their rates of contact with family members—especially mothers—are often much higher than rates for adults with no substance use problems. In addition to presenting evidence of these close ties and of the effectiveness of family support, Stanton provides a valuable overview of seven approaches to engaging clients in treatment by enlisting the support of family members and significant others. Describing these methods is beyond the scope of this TIP; however, this review is a valuable reminder that stereotypes such as the loner are significant barriers to effective treatment (Stanton, 1997).

Educating Your Client About Treatment

To ensure a smooth transition into treatment, elicit and explore your clients' expectations to search for any misunderstandings or misinformation they may have. This step is called role induction, which is the process of educating clients about treatment and preparing them to participate fully and obtain what they need. Ask them to anticipate what feelings they might have when they attend group therapy or a self-help meeting. Role induction brings the expectations of the client in line with the realities of treatment and reduces the probability of surprises. Research consistently demonstrates that retention in treatment has a strong positive relation with a client's expectancy and that role induction prevents early dropout (Zweben and Li, 1981).

If you refer clients to another program, review with them what you know of its philosophy, structure, and rules, as well as any idiosyncrasies with which you may be familiar. Available videotapes can give clients some sense of what individual and group therapy is like, or what to expect when attending an AA or other 12-Step meeting. Most programs also conduct their own role induction. For example, at intake clients are given a list of their rights and responsibilities, including rules about involuntary discharge, and have an opportunity to discuss the list.

When providing information about a program, be sure to check with your client that nothing you have described will disrupt the change plan. Some aspects of the program, such as cost, a requirement to bring a significant other to certain meetings, or location, could cause clients to believe that the program will not work for them. They may be reluctant to bring up the issue after progressing so far in the change plan. Such reactions should be explored, especially in terms of recurrent ambivalence. Often they involve a misunderstanding about the program.

Another important aspect of role induction is educating clients about what to expect in terms of physical withdrawal from substances. The symptoms—or rebound reaction—can range from minimal to extremely difficult and prolonged. Accurate information helps give clients a sense of control, although many reactions are subjective and difficult to anticipate. Nevertheless, it is important to tell your clients that certain physical and psychological reactions to stopping substance use are normal and relatively predictable. For example, many former heroin users report that the fourth day of abstinence is the most difficult. Clients may have a strong and visceral reaction to the sight of needles. A television commercial that shows a white powdered detergent may produce urgent cravings. Protracted and unexpected withdrawal syndromes can occur as long as 30 days after last use of some substances, such as benzodiazepines and cocaine. Some clients have such vivid dreams of using substances that they awaken believing they have actually returned to substance use, with all the accompanying fears and confusion. During the first weeks of abstinence, some clients report feeling as if they are going crazy. Knowing what to expect, then, will provide them needed reassurance.

Initiating the Plan

Many change plans have a specific start date. Some clients like to mark this new beginning with a ritual that not only looks forward but also symbolically leaves old behaviors behind. For example, some may burn or ritually dispose of substance paraphernalia, cigarettes, beer mugs, or liquor. Depending on whether clients plan to continue regular treatment sessions with you, follow up on a referral, or initiate self-change, decide with them whether and how often they will check in with you. Alternatively, if they do not expect to continue in counseling with you, you may arrange to call them periodically to show your support and continuing interest.

Whatever the arrangements, all clients should leave your office with the understanding that they can return or call for additional encouragement and support, or renegotiate the change plan. Many programs have agreements about communicating with other facilities or services to which they refer clients in order to ascertain whether the transition is completed satisfactorily. If not, you should have a protocol for contacting clients who do not follow through on the referral and inviting them back for further help.

Clients with a carefully drafted change plan, a knowledge of both risky situations and potential barriers to getting started, and a group of supportive friends or concerned relatives should be fully prepared and ready to move into action.

7 From Action to Maintenance: Stabilizing Change

> *The real test of change for...addictive behavior...is long-term sustained change over several years.... In this [maintenance] stage, the new behavior is becoming firmly established, and the threat of...a return to the old patterns becomes less frequent and less intense.... Helping clients increase their sense of self-efficacy is an important task at [these] stages.... Individuals in the action and maintenance stages may need skills training in addition to motivational strategies.*
>
> DiClemente, 1991

> *Maintenance is not an absence of change, but the continuance of change.*
>
> Prochaska and DiClemente, 1984

A motivational counseling style has been used mostly with clients in the precontemplation through preparation stages as they move toward initiating behavioral change. Many clients and clinicians believe that formal treatment is a different domain— conducted according to various philosophies and procedures that guide separate modalities— where motivational strategies are no longer required. This is not true for two reasons. First, clients still need a surprising amount of support and encouragement to stay with a chosen program or course of treatment. Even after a successful discharge, they need support and encouragement to maintain the gains they have achieved and to handle crises that may return them to problem behaviors. Second, many clients arrive at treatment in a stage of change that actually precedes action or they vacillate between some level of contemplation—with associated ambivalence—and continuing action. Moreover, clients who do take action are suddenly faced with the reality of stopping or reducing substance use. This is more difficult than just contemplating action. The early stages of recovery require only thinking about change, which is not as threatening as actually implementing it.

This chapter addresses ways in which motivational strategies can be used effectively at different points in the formal treatment process. The first section discusses the importance of understanding and offsetting clients' natural doubts and reservations about treatment immediately after admission so that they stay long enough to benefit from the process rather than dropping out prematurely. The next part outlines ways to help your clients plan for stabilizing change, develop coping strategies to avoid or defuse high-risk situations, and enlist family and social support. The third section describes types of alternative reinforcers that can be used, including a broad-spectrum approach that attempts to make a nonusing lifestyle more attractive and rewarding than previous self-destructive behavior.

Engaging and Retaining Clients in Treatment

Premature termination of treatment—early dropout—is a major concern of clinicians and researchers (Kolden et al., 1997; Zweben et al., 1988). The literature on treatment for users of illicit substances finds that the amount of time spent in treatment is a consistent indicator of more favorable outcomes (e.g., Simpson et al., 1997). Poorer outcomes in terms of continuing substance use and criminal behavior as well as a rapid return to daily substance use are associated with shorter treatment episodes (Pickens and Fletcher, 1991). This robust finding from outcome literature contrasts with other research findings that brief interventions can be as effective as more intensive care (Bien et al., 1993b) and that outcomes seldom differ when clients are randomly assigned to more versus less intensive treatment.

Causes of premature termination of treatment are varied. For some clients, dropping out, missing appointments, or failing to comply with other aspects of the treatment program are clear messages of discouragement, disillusionment, or change of heart. For others, dropping out of treatment without discussing this option with you may not indicate dissatisfaction or resistance, but rather a decision that things are going well and desired change can be achieved and maintained without your continuing help or monitoring (DiClemente, 1991).

Perhaps the strongest predictor of success versus failure or dropout in outpatient treatment is severity of substance dependence at treatment entry (McLellan et al., 1994) and, more specifically, submission of a drug-negative versus drug-positive urine specimen at treatment entry (Alterman et al., 1996, 1997). For example, one study found that cocaine-using patients with a positive urine screen at intake were less than half as likely to complete treatment or achieve initial abstinence as those submitting negative urine samples (Alterman et al., 1997). With alcohol problems, the relationship between severity and outcome is less obvious (Project MATCH Research Group, 1997a).

Although much research focuses on predictors of treatment retention, including client and therapist characteristics, treatment environment, therapeutic elements, and interactions among these variables, Kolden and colleagues conclude that there are too many factors for practical analysis and thus predictors of treatment compliance remain elusive (Kolden et al., 1997).

Nevertheless, these investigators and others report on variables that show some correlation with treatment retention or that seem, intuitively, to affect early termination. For example, the degree of congruence between clients' and clinicians' expectations about treatment elements and duration plays some role in retention, as does clinician interest expressed through such small actions as telephone calls between sessions or interactive exploration and agreement on the goals of treatment. "Failure" may be tied to a poor therapeutic alliance, which may reflect on clinical skillfulness. Social stability, previous treatment, expectations for reducing future substance use, higher methadone doses, and higher motivation—defined here as a desire or perceived need for help—seemed to predict that opiate-using clients would stay in methadone treatment for more than 60 days (Simpson and Joe, 1993). Furthermore, studies of therapeutic communities demonstrate that less severe psychopathology and higher motivation and readiness—defined as the wish to change and the use of treatment to change—are positive predictors of retention (e.g., DeLeon et al., 1994). By contrast, a combination of distrust of treatment programs and a sense of self-efficacy that says "*something* will work for me" are predictors of success in achieving sobriety through AA (Longshore et al., 1998). Studies also show large differences among clinical staff in the percentage of clients who drop out of treatment (Miller, 1985b).

At least three studies suggest that motivational interviewing can be a useful adjunct for increasing client retention and participation in treatment. In the first study, one group of residents admitted to a 13-day alcoholism treatment program received two sessions of assessment and prompt feedback provided in a motivational style stressing empathy and support (see Chapter 4) as part of the intake process (Brown and Miller, 1993). Although the motivational intervention added only 2 hours to the routine protocol, the therapists reported that residents who participated were more fully involved in later treatment than were counterparts not assigned to the motivational intervention. Moreover, the extra attention and support offered by the motivational intervention resulted in 64 percent of the group having favorable outcomes (i.e., abstinent or asymptomatic) at 3-month followup, compared with only 29 percent of the control group.

Similarly, Aubrey found significantly better treatment retention, lower alcohol use, and lower illicit drug use among adolescents given one session of motivational interviewing and personal feedback on entry to substance abuse treatment (Aubrey, 1998). Adolescents who received the motivational interviewing session completed nearly three times as many sessions (average of 17) compared with those receiving the same outpatient program without motivational interviewing (average of six sessions). Abstinence at followup was also twice as high when the single initial session was added.

In the third study, of opiate users in an outpatient methadone maintenance treatment program in Australia, an hour-long intervention that used motivational interviewing techniques at treatment initiation resulted in increased and more immediate commitment to treatment and abstention among participants (Saunders et al., 1995). Rather surprisingly for such a brief adjunct to treatment, these outpatients appeared to have fewer problems, more treatment compliance, better retention, and less rapid return to opiate use following treatment than a control group that received an educational intervention. Although 40 percent of the clients studied dropped out of treatment by the end of 6 months, only 30 percent of the clients who participated in the adjunct motivational intervention left treatment by this time, compared with nearly half (49 percent) of the control group.

Another interesting finding was that clients entering methadone treatment were not necessarily in an action stage of change as expected. Rather, they seemed to represent all stages and to cycle rapidly back and forth from precontemplation through maintenance. A large percentage (38 percent) of the group participating in the motivational intervention were contemplating change at admission, and 37 percent of this group were in an action stage 3 months later. By contrast, 35 percent of the control group were not yet considering change (precontemplation) at admission and an increased percentage (47 percent) were still in this stage of the change process at 3 months. This accentuates the need for assessing how *ready* clients are for change, no matter what the external circumstances. The boundaries between stages of change seem to be fluid, even for clients whose motivation for change is enhanced by the clinician's counseling style and therapeutic strategies.

Specific Strategies To Increase Engagement and Retention in Treatment

The strategies discussed in this section have been found by some clinicians to be useful in increasing clients' involvement or participation in treatment and decreasing early dropout. All entail some application of motivational approaches already outlined in earlier chapters.

Develop rapport

As noted in Chapters 3 and 4, clinician style is an important element for establishing rapport and building a trusting relationship with clients. The principles of motivational interviewing exemplify proven methods to get in touch with and understand your clients' unique perspectives and personal values, as opposed to yours or your program's. Accurate empathy and reflective listening (client-centered skills for eliciting clients' concerns through an interactive process that facilitates rapport) have been well described and tested in clinical research.

Clients will confide in you if they feel comfortable and safe within the treatment setting. Their natural reactions may depend on such factors as their gender, age, ethnicity, and previous experience. For example, ethnic minorities may bring a reticence to the clinic situation that is based on negative life experiences or problems encountered with earlier episodes of treatment. Initially, for these clients and others who have been oppressed or abused, safety in the treatment setting is a particularly important issue.

Programs can devise innovative ways to make their clients feel welcomed into a familiar milieu or a shared effort. For example, African-Americans call each other brother and sister, and Native Americans consider each other relatives. Some treatment programs refer to clients as members, a term that denotes participation and inclusion. Programs sometimes provide a meal to help clients feel part of a family. In one program that serves Native Americans, a client's trauma and pain are addressed with "honoring." For example, if a person is experiencing a problem, a sweat lodge can be requested as an appropriate and safe setting in which to disclose feelings and obtain feedback. It is important to honor the request, and it is an honor to be invited. Participating in a sweat lodge allows Native Americans to embrace their ethnic identity, gain ethnic pride, and honor Native American spirituality, thus encouraging a sense of belonging. In another Native American program, a young woman who was struggling to stop using substances had returned to using them. Rather than punish and isolate her, the group selected her to be fire keeper at the sweat lodge, a position of honor. The group's respect for the individual transcended her current behavior. The rationale is that without this continued bond, the woman would not have had an opportunity to choose to change her future behavior.

Indirect expression is another way of helping clients from some cultures feel comfortable. Metaphors, stories, legends, or proverbs can explain, through example, a situation that clients can then interpret. For instance, for those clients who appear to have trouble asking others for help, you might tell a story or use an expression to illustrate that point. Most clients will "get it" and have a clear understanding of what is being communicated without feeling any disrespect. You simply bring a concept to the table; clients then interpret it and draw their own conclusions.

Induct clients into their role

As discussed in Chapter 6, your clients must become acquainted with you and the agency.

Tell your clients explicitly what treatment involves, what is expected, and what rules there are. If the client has not been prepared by a referring source, review exactly what will happen in treatment so that any confusion is eliminated. Use language the client understands. Also be sure to encourage questions and provide clarification of anything that seems perplexing or not justified. Some will want to know why the clinic does not have more desirable hours, why loitering is discouraged, why they must come to group sessions on a particular schedule, or what it means to participate in treatment. This is the time to explain what information must be reported to a referring agency that has mandated the treatment, including what it means to consent to release information. Role induction by itself is not likely to prevent premature termination, but it does clarify to the client what is expected from the program's perspective (Zweben et al., 1988).

Explore client expectancies and determine discrepancies

One of the first things to discuss with new clients is their expectations about the treatment process, including past experiences, and whether there are serious discrepancies with the reality of the upcoming treatment. To decrease intrusiveness, ask permission before delving into these private and sometimes painful areas. Then ask clients to elaborate on what they expect and what their initial impressions, hopes, and fears about treatment are. Showing clients a list of concerns other people in treatment have had can help them feel more comfortable expressing their own, which will likely be similar. Some of these fears include the following:

- The clinician will be confrontational and impose treatment goals.
- Treatment will take too long and require the client to give up too much.

- The rules are too strict, and the client will be discharged for the slightest infringement.
- Medication will not be prescribed for painful withdrawal symptoms.
- The program does not understand women, members of different ethnic groups, or persons who take a particular substance or combination of substances.
- A spouse or other family member will be required to participate.

Many clients will have negative expectations based on previous and usually unsuccessful treatment episodes. A motivational approach can elicit a client's concerns without being judgmental. Each client needs an opportunity to vent anxieties or negative reactions to the treatment process and have these validated as normal—not punishable, but therapeutic. This is particularly important for clients who feel coerced into treatment to appease someone else (e.g., employer, court, wife) and fear revealing any worries or negative reactions lest these be used against them.

Unrealistic hopes about what treatment can accomplish—particularly without much work by the client—are equally dangerous and seductive but have to be brought out. The client may believe, for instance, that treatment will restore a marriage or erase guilt about the fatal auto accident that preceded admission. Perhaps the client hopes the program will include acupuncture as part of the treatment, and this is not an option. Be honest about what the program can do and what it cannot do (e.g., pay rent, remove effects of childhood sexual abuse, counteract a poor education).

It is important that you reach understanding with the client about positive and negative expectancies before you enter into the real work of change. Perceptions, hopes, and concerns will change: As old ones are resolved, new ones will likely emerge.

"Immunize" the client against common difficulties

During treatment, clients may have negative reactions or embarrassing moments when they reveal more than they planned, react too emotionally, realize discrepancies in the information they have supplied, or pull back from painful insights about how they have hurt others or jeopardized their own futures. One way to forestall impulsive early termination in response to these situations is to "immunize" or "inoculate" your client: Anticipate and discuss such problems before they occur, indicate they are a normal part of the recovery process, and develop a plan to handle them. Warn the client, for example, that he may not want to return to treatment immediately after such a situation and that this is a common reaction. Clients may want to keep a diary of any strong or adverse reactions so that these can be discussed or revealed to you in subsequent sessions or even by telephone between sessions (Zweben et al., 1988). Be culturally aware as you attempt to immunize clients against expected difficulties. The Native American culture, for example, is more comfortable with visual and oral exchange of information than with the written word. The use of art (e.g., drawing, collage) or the talking feather (in group) may be helpful in identifying common and expected difficulties to these clients.

Investigate and resolve barriers to treatment

As treatment progresses, clients may experience or reveal other barriers that impede progress and could result in early termination unless resolved. These barriers can include not understanding written materials easily, having difficulty making transportation or child care arrangements, or having insufficient funds or insurance coverage to continue treatment as initially planned. Sometimes clients do not feel ready to participate, or suddenly reconsider. This is usually because a planned change is too threatening in reality or in anticipation.

If barriers cannot be overcome by some mutually satisfactory arrangement, it may be necessary to interrupt treatment or make another referral. Discuss early disengagement from therapy at the onset and consider what options might be acceptable to you and your client. Stress that it is all right to take a break from treatment, if necessary, to allow time to consider alternatives and prepare to act on them, but set up the expectation for or schedule a return to treatment. This type of "therapeutic break" is an option when other motivational techniques have failed (Zweben et al., 1988).

Increase congruence between intrinsic and extrinsic motivation

Ryan and colleagues found that internal motivation is associated with increased client involvement and retention in treatment, but a combination of internal and external motivation seems to promote an even more positive treatment response. They concluded that coercion or external motivation can actually fit into the clients' perceptions of problems and the need for treatment and change (Ryan et al., 1995). Thus, explore the significance of external motivators to your clients. Perceiving coercive forces as positive—and compatible with the clients' concerns—may be more helpful than trying to convert all external motivation to intrinsic motivation. These investigators also hypothesized that some amount of emotional distress about problems, rather than a rational catalog of the negative impact of substance use, may be helpful to enhance client motivation for change. Anxiety or depression about life problems may be more significant indicators of readiness to change than the intensity of substance use itself.

Examine and interpret noncompliant behavior

Noncompliant behavior often is a thinly veiled expression of dissatisfaction with treatment or the therapeutic process. For example, clients miss appointments, arrive late, fail to complete required forms, or remain mute when asked to participate. Any occurrence of such behavior provides an opportunity to discuss the reasons for the behavior and learn from it. Often, the client is expressing continuing ambivalence and is not ready to make a change. You can explore the incident in a nonjudgmental, problem-solving manner that probes whether it was intentional and whether a reasonable explanation can be found for the reaction. For example, a client might be late as a gesture of defiance, to shorten what is anticipated as a distressing session, or because her car broke down. The significance of the event must be established and then understood in terms of precipitating emotions or anxieties and ensuing consequences.

As with all motivational strategies, drawing out your client's perceptions and interpretation of the event is important. Generally, if you can get clients to voice their frustrations, they will come up with the answers themselves. Asking a question such as, "What do you think is getting in the way of being here on time?" is likely to elicit an interpretation from clients and open a dialog. You can respond with reflective listening and add your own interpretation or affirmation. For example, you can observe that clients who come late to appointments often do not complete treatment and describe how other clients solved the problem in the past. However, do not forget to commend the client for simply getting there.

Finally, alternative responses to similar situations have to be explored so that the client finds a more acceptable coping mechanism that is consistent with the expectations of treatment. Often, this exploration of noncompliant behavior reveals ways in which the goals or activities of treatment should be slowed or changed. Use noncompliance as a signal that you have to get more information or shift your strategy. This is much more useful than the client's simply retreating and dropping out (Zweben et al., 1988). Means of responding to missed appointments are listed in Figure 7-1.

Research-based clues or indicators of continuing ambivalence or lack of readiness that could result in premature and unanticipated dropout unless explored and resolved include the following (Zweben et al., 1988):

- The client has a history of appointment cancellations or early dropout from treatment.
- The client feels coerced into treatment and fears offending that coercive source.
- The client has little social stability.
- The client is hesitant about scheduling appointments or does not think that he can follow a routine schedule.
- The client does not appear to feel confident about capabilities for positive change and seems to resent the loss of status involved in getting help.

Figure 7-1

Options for Responding to a Missed Appointment

- Telephone call
- Personal letter
- Contact with preapproved relatives or significant or concerned others
- Personal visit
- Contact with referral source

- The client resents completing intake forms or assessments.
- The treatment offered is significantly different from any the client has been exposed to previously.
- The client has difficulty expressing feelings and revealing personal information.

Reach out

Certain life events, such as a client's wedding, the birth of a child, a client's traumatic injury or illness, or several missed appointments, might require you to reach out to the client to demonstrate personal concern and continuing interest in the interest of preserving the therapeutic relationship and enhancing the recovery process. However, you must be careful not to cross professional boundaries or put the therapeutic relationship at risk by violating a client's privacy or confidentiality rights. An example of a violation might be attending the funeral for a member of a client's family, without the client's consent, when the family and friends do not know the client is receiving substance abuse treatment.

Any contemplated change in the boundaries of the clinician–client therapeutic relationship must be supported theoretically, well thought out, discussed with your clinical supervisor, consistent with program policies, and reviewed for any legal or ethical issues that could arise. For example, it may be your program's policy that clients are treated only in the program's offices. If a client is hospitalized, however, it may be necessary for you to go to the hospital to continue the client's treatment. Such a move should be discussed with your supervisor. Privacy and confidentiality issues that should be addressed include obtaining the client's written authorization for release of information to the hospital, the client's physician, and ancillary personnel; and what to do if the client has a roommate, receives a phone call during the treatment session, and if a session is interrupted by hospital staff.

Early in treatment, you should identify the client's social support network. Tactfully discuss with the client her preferred avenues for keeping in touch with her, such as written consent to contact certain relatives or friends. She will perhaps want to provide letters to referral sources authorizing them to respond if you contact them. In addition, you should be aware of and abide by your clients' cultural mores regarding contact outside the substance abuse treatment setting.

Brief adjunctive motivational intervention

The brief adjunctive motivational intervention in one study (Saunders et al., 1991) used the following strategies:

- Elicit the client's perceptions of the so-called "good" things about substance use.
- Help the client inventory less good things about substance use.
- Invite the client to reflect on the lifestyle once envisaged, current life satisfactions, and what lifestyle is anticipated for the future.
- Have the client determine which, if any, of the elicited problems are of real concern.
- Assist the client in comparing and contrasting the costs and benefits of continuing current behavior.
- Highlight areas of greatest concern, emphasizing discrepancies that generate discomfort and genuine emotional reactions to the current behavior and consequences.
- Elicit and agree on future intentions regarding the target behavior.

Planning for Stabilization

In addition to handling problems that can interrupt treatment prematurely, work to stabilize actual change in the problem behavior. This requires considerable interactive planning, including conducting a functional analysis, developing a coping plan, and ensuring family and social support.

Conducting a Functional Analysis

Although a functional analysis can be used at various points in treatment, it can be particularly informative in preparing for maintenance. A functional analysis is an assessment of the common antecedents and consequences of substance use. Through functional analysis, you help clients understand what has "triggered" them to drink or use drugs in the past and the effects they experienced from using alcohol or drugs. With this information, you and your clients can then work on developing coping strategies to maintain abstinence. The following approach is adapted from Miller and Pechacek, 1987.

To begin a functional analysis, first label two columns on a sheet of paper or blackboard as "Triggers" and "Effects." Then begin with a statement such as, "I'd like to understand how substance use has fit into the rest of your life."

Next, find out about your client's antecedents: "Tell me about situations in which you have been most likely to drink or use drugs in the past, or times when you have tended to drink or use more. These might be when you were with specific people, in specific places, or at certain times of day, or perhaps when you were feeling a particular way." Make sure to use the past tense because the present or future tense may unsettle currently abstinent clients.

As your client responds, listen reflectively to make sure that you understand. Under the Triggers column, write down each antecedent. Then ask, "When else in the past have you felt like drinking or using drugs?" and record each response.

If your client completed a pretreatment questionnaire about substance use, you may be able to use this information to elicit any triggers the client did not mention. For example, "I notice on this questionnaire you marked that

you might be 'very tempted' to drink when you…. Tell me about this." Then write down any additional antecedents in the Triggers column.

After the client seems to have exhausted the antecedents of substance use, ask about what the client liked about drinking or using drugs. Here you are trying to elicit the client's own perceptions or expectations from substance use, not necessarily the actual effects.

As the client volunteers this information, respond with reflective listening to ensure that you understand, and make sure not to communicate disapproval or disagreement. Write down each desired consequence in the Effects column. Then ask, "What else have you liked about drinking or using drugs in the past?" and record each response.

Again, if the client completed a pretreatment questionnaire about the desired consequences of substance use, you can use this information to elicit more consequences the client may not have brought up. For example, "I notice on this questionnaire you marked that you often used drugs to…. Tell me about this." Write down any new consequences in the Effects column.

Once the client has finished giving antecedents and consequences, you can point out how a certain trigger can lead to a certain effect. First, pick out one item from the Triggers column and one from the Effects column that clearly seem to go together. Then ask the client to identify pairs, letting the client draw connecting lines on the paper or blackboard.

For trigger items that have not been paired, ask the client to tell you what alcohol or drug use might have done for her in that situation, and draw a line to the appropriate item in the Effects column. Sometimes there is no corresponding item in the Effects column, which suggests that something has to be added. Then do the same thing for the Effects column. It is not necessary, however, to pair all entries.

With this information, you can develop maintenance strategies. Point out that some of the pairs your client identified are common among most users. Next, you can say that if the only way a client can go from the Triggers column to the Effects column is through substance use, then the client is psychologically dependent on it. Then make clear that freedom of choice is about having options—different ways—of moving from the Triggers to the Effects column. You can then review the pairs, beginning with those the client finds most important, and develop a coping plan that will enable the client to achieve the desired effects without using substances (Miller and Pechacek, 1987).

Developing a Coping Plan

You can conduct functional analyses and develop coping strategies for every treatment goal. This approach addresses many factors that influence the well-being of the client trying to cope with recovery. Developing a coping plan is a way of anticipating problems before they arise and of recognizing the need for a repertoire of alternative strategies (see Figure 7-2). A list of coping strategies that others have found successful can be particularly useful in developing a plan and in brainstorming ways to deal with anticipated barriers to change.

One way to help your client learn how to develop coping strategies is to conduct a functional analysis on a pleasurable activity. The process of developing a coping plan

---

Figure 7-2

Coping Strategies

Coping strategies are not mutually exclusive (i.e., different ones can be used at different times) and not all are equally good (i.e., some more than others involve getting close to trigger situations). The point is to brainstorm, involve the client, reinforce successful application of coping strategies, and consider it as a learning experience if a particular strategy fails.

Example #1: Client X typically uses cocaine whenever his cousin, who is a regular user, drops by the house. Coping strategies to consider would include (1) call the cousin and ask him not to come by anymore, (2) call the cousin and ask him not to bring cocaine anymore when he visits, (3) if there is a pattern to when the cousin comes, plan to be out of the house at that time, or (4) if someone else lives in the house, ask them to be present during the cousin's visit.

Example #2: Client Y typically uses cocaine when she goes out for the evening with a particular group of friends, one of whom often brings drugs along. She is particularly vulnerable when they all drink alcohol. Coping strategies to consider might include (1) go out with a different set of friends, (2) go along with this group only for activities that do not involve drinking, (3) leave the group as soon as drinking seems imminent, (4) tell the supplier that she is trying to stay off cocaine and would appreciate not being offered any, (5) ask all her friends, or one especially close friend, to help her out by not using when she is around or by telling the supplier to stop offering it to her, or (6) take disulfiram [Antabuse] to prevent drinking.

Example #3: Client Z typically uses cocaine when feeling tired or stressed. Coping strategies might include (1) scheduling activities so as to get more sleep at night, (2) scheduling activities so as to have 1 hour per day of relaxation time, (3) learning and practicing specific stress relaxation techniques, or (4) learning problem-solving techniques that can reduce stressful circumstances.

provides an opportunity for positive reinforcement. You can use the activity to boost a client's self-esteem by saying, "What can we learn about where you are in recovery from your actions? For example, when you went to the trigger location and didn't use alcohol, how did you do it?" You can point out that something must have changed if the client can now go into a bar or restaurant and not drink. However, explore the motivation for going to the bar and ascertain whether there is a good reason or whether the behavior is reckless. A client who has developed sound coping strategies should be conscious of the danger, but not reckless.

Occasionally, you may find that your clients have not pursued the new activities you have suggested. In these situations, strategies similar to those suggested earlier for a missed appointment may help strengthen coping strategies. Reevaluate the plan and modify it as necessary. Ask your client to rehearse coping strategies while in a counseling session and then try to implement the strategy in the real environment.

Ensuring Family and Social Support

Clients are embedded in a social network that can be either constructive or destructive. One task for you and your client is to determine which social relationships are supportive and which are risky.

Substance-free family and friends can be especially helpful in stabilizing change because they can monitor the client and model and reinforce new behavior. They can keep track of the client's whereabouts and activities, involve the client in new social and recreational activities, and be a source of emotional and financial support. Other types of support are instrumental (e.g., babysitting, carpooling), romantic, spiritual, and communal (i.e., belonging to a particular group or community).

Sources of support, however, also can be stressors—for example, if a female client has family members who both depend on her and support her. Support can have costs that sometimes leave your client feeling, "Now I owe you." Help the client pinpoint the reasons for using or not using different sources of support. Ask clients the following questions:

- What kinds of support do you want?
- What sources of support do you have?
- What holes are there in your network of support?

By identifying the array of support sources your client has available, you can help determine any gaps in the support system. At the same time, caution the client not to rely too heavily on any one source of support. Next, you can help the client develop an early warning system with a partner or significant other; this person can learn to recognize the triggers and signs that your client is returning to substance use and can intervene effectively (Meyers and Smith, 1997). In a 12-Step program, the sponsor fills this role.

Try to ascertain what clients are willing to change in their lives. How your clients want to make changes and what timing is appropriate are of particular concern. In many communities, although it can be dangerous to interact with active users in terms of triggers and ready access, for some clients it is just as dangerous to cut ties with their substance-using social network.

Sometimes, heroin users will welcome a member of the group who has stopped using back into the network. Clients who use substances have to be innovative in coming up with solutions to unique problems. Clients surrounded by substance-using friends may have to have acceptable reasons to offer as to why they are not currently using substances— for example, the client's wife is pregnant and can't use, or the client must submit drug-free urine regularly to keep a job.

Your clients also need help in figuring out how to handle drug suppliers. Assist them in describing the nature of these relationships and the level of emotional support provided. Some clients do not really know the meaning of friendship—what they can expect or count on for support as well as their reciprocal responsibilities. Use motivational interviewing techniques to develop discrepancies, find out what clients intend and are willing to do to decrease perceived discrepancies, and introduce the concept of setting boundaries. The case studies in Figures 7-3, 7-4, and 7-5 depict different support scenarios you and your clients may encounter.

Involving a spouse or significant other in the treatment process also provides an opportunity for a firsthand understanding of the client's problems. The significant other can offer valuable input and feedback in the development and implementation of treatment goals. Additionally, the client and the significant other can work collaboratively on issues that might stand in the way of attainment of treatment goals. Project MATCH, a multisite clinical trial of patient–treatment matching sponsored by the National Institute on Alcohol Abuse and Alcoholism, included motivation enhancement therapy (Miller et al., 1992). In this trial, the greatest number of subjects chose spousal support as the maintenance factor most helpful in maintaining their resolution to change. This finding is consistent with those of treatment

Figure 7-3

Case Study 1: Client With Drug-Using Social Support

Client context: Mary is a pregnant 30-year-old woman who lives with her young son. Her boyfriend, the father of both children, visits frequently and provides total financial support for Mary. He is a crack dealer and user. Mary's urine test, administered in routine prenatal care, was positive for cocaine. Her health care provider referred Mary to a treatment clinic.

Therapeutic realities: In Mary's situation, the goal of ending her relationship with the boyfriend is not realistic, although, in the long term, she may be able to break away from this man. A direct confrontation on this issue would be counterproductive.

Therapeutic strategies: It is possible to use motivational counseling to encourage Mary's progress. Functional analysis can be used to develop some discrepancy and tension between her goal to cease cocaine use during pregnancy and the realities of her living situation. The pros of maintaining the relationship include continued financial and emotional support. The cons include exposing her son and unborn child to cocaine. Given the situation, what is Mary willing to do?

Developing options: Mary never uses cocaine in front of her son, but she doesn't feel she can ask her boyfriend not to. Through therapy, Mary does some problem solving and develops coping strategies to allow her to continue seeing the father of her children without having drugs in her house. The therapeutic relationship is used to enhance her motivation to take some kind of positive action, to revisit her motivation and commitment (which currently is to the boyfriend), and to explore potential responses that will begin to put limits on this situation.

Note that you might be legally required to report to the child welfare agency any concern about drug use occurring in front of the woman's son. (For more information on this issue see the forthcoming TIP, *Substance Abuse Treatment for Persons With Child Abuse and Neglect Issues* [CSAT, in press (b)]).

> ### Figure 7-4
> ### Case Study 2: Client Lacking Social Support
>
> **Client context**: Susan is a 41-year-old woman in an abusive marital relationship. She has suffered from alcohol dependence most of her adult life but has initiated recovery efforts through five counseling sessions. Her mother has paranoid schizophrenia, and therapy reveals that her father, also suffering from alcohol dependence, molested Susan for years when she was a child.
>
> **Therapeutic realities**: Susan is estranged from her mother and abusive husband. Therapy now reveals that Susan's sole source of support is the father who molested her. She telephones him and cuts off contact. As she progresses in recovery, however, she is no longer numbed and made compliant by alcohol and begins to have serious problems with her own children. They do not support her recovery efforts—they want her to return to being an easygoing drinking mom. The therapeutic reality is that now, because of the recovery process, Susan has less emotional and social support.
>
> **Therapeutic strategies**: As a starting point, Susan can be brought into a 12-Step program or similar mutual-help group to replace the support for recovery she has lost. Additionally, your support as a clinician is integral to her recovery. Provide support, referral, and followup, and make special efforts to be available to her.

studies and natural recovery studies that family environment is one of the most notable factors associated with positive outcomes (Azrin et al., 1982; Sobell et al., 1993b).

Finally, some therapists model social behaviors in public for their clients as part of therapy. Examples would include modeling the behavior and skills required for everyday activities, such as opening a bank account or going grocery shopping. Some theoreticians argue that providing realistic *in vivo* guidance is preferable to rehearsed and stilted play-acting in the office.

Whether or not you choose to provide this type of "help" depends, of course, on your therapeutic orientation, guidelines, program policies, and awareness of the client's cultural mores. Before undertaking such a strategy you should carefully think through it, weighing the benefits versus the potential harm and discussing the plan with your supervisor. For example, going out with a client can be easily misinterpreted by the client as an act of friendship or even intimacy rather than therapy. This can lead to boundary and therapeutic

relationship problems that can put both you and your client in awkward situations that complicate treatment.

Developing and Using Reinforcers

After clients have planned for stabilization by identifying risky situations, practicing new coping strategies, and finding sources of support, they still have to build a new lifestyle that will provide sufficient satisfaction and compete successfully against the lure of drug use. Ultimately, a broad spectrum of life changes must be made if the client is to maintain lasting abstinence. These changes must be adequately extensive and pervasive so that they supplant the client's former substance-using lifestyle. This represents a formidable task for the client whose life has become narrowly focused on acquiring and using substances. You can support this change process by using competing reinforcers and external contingent reinforcers in the early phases of treatment to encourage positive behavioral change.

Figure 7-5

Case Study 3: Payday as a Trigger

Client context: Joseph is a member of the Mohawk, living on tribal lands in New York State. Along with the other members of the band, Joseph receives regular payments from the Federal government for land use and treaties, as well as checks for his share of the proceeds from the group's casino. Receipt of these checks is often a trigger for substance use. The checks have replaced Joseph's motivation for gainful employment; they also have removed the need for criminal behavior to procure drugs. Because casino checks are becoming larger, the issue is becoming increasingly severe for Joseph.

Therapeutic reality: Joseph uses his casino checks as sole support, yet receiving them may serve as a trigger to his drinking.

Therapeutic strategies: The paychecks in this case are an example of ongoing support that occurs regardless of substance abuse. Elicit from the client other ways in which the money could be used that would be rewarding, consistent with the client's life goals, constructive to family or community, health-promoting, and so forth. Elicit from the client practical ideas about how to prevent the receipt of checks from triggering substance use. Consider how supportive others might help the client redirect income from substance use to other reinforcing options.

Natural Competing Reinforcers

Competing reinforcers are effective in reducing substance use. A competing reinforcer is any source of satisfaction for the client that can become an alternative to drugs or alcohol. Research has demonstrated, for example, that laboratory animals are less likely to begin and continue taking cocaine when an alternative reinforcer (in this case, a sweet drinking solution) is available in their cages (Carroll, 1993). This principle applies to humans as well; other studies in laboratory settings have shown that if given a choice between substances and money, people will choose to forgo substances when the alternative is sufficiently attractive (Hatsukami et al., 1994; Higgins et al., 1994a, 1994b; Zacny et al., 1992). Clearly, people do make choices about their substance use, and it helps when the alternative choices are explicit, immediately available, and sufficiently attractive to compete with substance use. This is the ideal you are trying to work toward, and external reward systems can be especially helpful. (See the section on the voucher incentive system later in this chapter.)

The essential principle in establishing new sources of positive reinforcement is to get clients to generate their own ideas. You can guide them toward social reinforcers, recreational activities, 12-Step programs, and other positive behavioral reinforcements by developing a list of common pleasurable activities (Meyers and Smith, 1995). Couples therapy is useful to help clients reconnect to things they used to do before they became heavily involved in substance use, or to activities that never occurred during a couple's relationship because they came together as a substance-using couple.

It is important to examine all areas of a client's life for new reinforcers, which should come from multiple sources and be of various types. Thus, a setback in one area can be counterbalanced by a positive reinforcer from another area. Additionally, because clients have competing motivations, help them select reinforcers that will prevail over substances over time. Especially when substances permeate their lives, stopping can be a fundamental life change. As the motivation for positive change becomes harder to sustain, clients need strong reasons for overcoming the challenges they will face.

Small steps are helpful, but they cannot fill a whole life. Abstaining from substances is an abrupt change and often leaves a large blank space to fill. You can help your client fill this void by suggesting potential activities, such as the following:

- Do volunteer work. This alternative is a link to the community. The client can fill time, reconnect with prosocial people, and improve self-efficacy. Volunteering is a direct contribution that can help resolve guilt the client may feel about previous criminal or antisocial behavior. For example, a California program for Hispanics and African-Americans in recovery involved clients in a door-to-door survey, collecting data for the community and identifying people in crisis following the Los Angeles earthquake. Although the clients themselves did not get a monetary reward, the community benefited, and the daily debriefing solidified clients' commitment to their recovery by affirming their ability to help someone else.
- Become involved in 12-Step activities. Similar to volunteering, this fills a need to be involved with a group and contribute to a worthwhile organization.
- Set goals to improve work, education, health, and nutrition.
- Spend more time with family, significant others, and friends.
- Participate in spiritual or cultural activities.
- Learn new skills or improve in such areas as sports, art, music, and hobbies. In the Native American community, for example, counselors take clients to the country and teach them about the gifts of nature (e.g., herbs, trees, animals) and how these gifts contribute to healing and continued recovery.

Clients do not have to make a big commitment or investment; they can just sample available opportunities (Meyers and Smith, 1997). Peer acceptance and meeting peer expectations within the context of a residential treatment or high-functioning therapeutic group serve as reinforcement. People in 12-Step programs, for example, try to excel in a newfound social network with the goal of reaching an altruistic state in the 12th step.

External Contingent Reinforcers

The principles of contingent reinforcement can be applied to sustain abstinence while clients work on building a substance-free lifestyle. The specific awards chosen can be tailored to the values of the clients and resources of the program. Besides natural reinforcers, some programs have used temporary contingencies to change substance use. Voucher incentive programs have several benefits that recommend their use. First, they introduce a clear and systematic point system that provides structure and clarifies expectations for both clients and staff. Second, they allow clients to select for themselves the rewards that they find desirable, which should maximize the effectiveness of the procedure. Finally, voucher systems have been tested in research and shown to be effective (Budney and Higgins, 1998). Because it may take some time to establish the other new behaviors, these programs probably should be in place a minimum of 3 to 6 months.

Voucher incentives

Voucher programs are a type of contingency reinforcement system, and research has shown that they can be effective for sustaining abstinence in substance users. The rationale is that an appealing external motivator can be an immediate and powerful reinforcer to compete with drug reinforcers. Because a common correlate of substance addiction is the need for immediate gratification, vouchers and other incentives can be used to satisfy this need appropriately.

The reinforcers used in voucher incentive programs should be attractive and engaging to the individual client. Research has demonstrated that money or an equivalent alternative is nearly always appealing. Vouchers are slips of paper showing points the client has earned for abstinence. Each point has a cash value (e.g., $1). Additional points are accumulated each time the client submits drug-free urine, for example. The voucher acts as an IOU from the program. In a typical voucher system, clients trade in their points for goods and services. Clients often want to pay bills with their voucher or spend their money on retail purchases (e.g., groceries, clothing, shoes). Staff members arrange to pay the bills and purchase these items. An alternative to this system is to give the clients cash and let them make the purchases themselves. This is a risky option, however, because clients could use the money to buy substances. Therefore, the extra work for staff can be worth the effort.

Research has shown that voucher reinforcers work well to promote treatment retention and sustained abstinence among cocaine abusers enrolled in outpatient treatment. For example, Higgins and colleagues, who developed and tested voucher incentives, showed that this procedure combined with an intensive behavioral counseling program could retain between 60 and 75 percent of cocaine abusers in an outpatient treatment program for 6 months (Higgins et al., 1993, 1994b). In contrast, control patients in the investigators' clinic who received intensive counseling therapy but no vouchers had a 40 percent retention rate, and control patients who received 12-Step counseling had an 11 percent retention rate. In voucher programs, patients not only stay in treatment but also remain substance free. In two published studies, 68 percent and 55 percent of patients in the voucher program were cocaine free for 8 consecutive weeks, whereas only 11 and 25 percent of the control patients who did not receive vouchers stayed cocaine free. In these studies, voucher incentives were given only for the first 3 months of treatment, with lottery tickets offered during the second 3 months as an incentive for drug-free urine (Higgins et al., 1993, 1994b, 1995).

Voucher incentives can be effective for controlling cocaine use among methadone maintenance patients who chronically abuse cocaine (Silverman et al., 1996). In this study, patients receiving vouchers for cocaine-free urine samples achieved significantly more weeks of cocaine abstinence and significantly longer durations of sustained abstinence than controls. Forty-seven percent of patients who were offered vouchers sustained 7 or more weeks of continuous cocaine abstinence whereas only one control patient achieved more than 2 weeks of sustained abstinence. These results are impressive because it is typically difficult to get methadone maintenance patients to stop using supplemental drugs during treatment. Voucher-like interventions have been used effectively to motivate reductions in substance use and other behavior change among schizophrenics, people with tuberculosis, homeless, and other special populations of illicit substance abusers (Higgins and Silverman, 1999).

Other innovative programs have been tried. For example, one program used vouchers to encourage pregnant women to quit smoking. Staff solicited retail items from the community that could be earned by clients following each appointment if they passed a carbon monoxide breath test indicating they had not smoked. Although a range of products and services were available for purchase by the vouchers, mothers most often chose baby items, affirming their motivation to quit smoking for their children's health.

A reinforcement system that is monetary but relies on the individual rather than a voucher is to help clients identify specific items they would like to have or enjoy—for example, a new bedroom set or computer. Clients then set aside money on a daily or weekly basis that would have been spent on substances and eventually purchase the item. Obviously, there would be concern that any accumulated money could be used as part of a recurrence. As a solution to this problem, the saved money could be kept with a nonusing family member or friend.

In the Community Reinforcement Approach (CRA), monetary incentives (external motivators) are meant to be spent on activities or retail items that will directly increase the client's chance of achieving stated goals (intrinsic motivators). Under this model, external and intrinsic factors must be congruent or the voucher system will have little influence (see the section later in this chapter).

When families are included in treatment, a voucher incentive can be developed with the client and key family members. For example, when the client is abstinent for 90 days, he can visit his parents for Sunday dinner, or when another client has made 90 meetings she can have her children over for a visit. Parents might want to work out vouchers with recovering children; for example, after six therapy sessions the child can go out on the weekend or use the car, and after 90 days of sobriety the allowance or other "goodies" can be reinstated.

What types and amounts of incentives should be used? The voucher programs tested so far have offered more than $1,000 that could be earned during a 3-month period. Research with cocaine abusers has demonstrated that the greater the value of the monetary incentive, the more powerful a reinforcer it is—that is, more people become abstinent (Silverman et al., 1997).

Aside from theoretical issues about the optimal size of rewards, there are practical considerations having to do with financial, staffing, and administrative resources of the clinic. Voucher systems offering smaller incentive values have not been systematically tested yet, but they are likely to work for some clients. Treatment programs can consider soliciting prizes from local businesses as a source of program incentives.

Clinicians and programs may also find creative ways to make naturally occurring sources of financial support contingent on abstinence. Family members have often spent large amounts of money treating, supporting, and handling the adverse consequences experienced by a substance-dependent loved one. It is possible to negotiate with the family to stop all such noncontingent support, and instead, offer financial support in a manner that helps the person establish sobriety. By special arrangement (e.g., with the client's consent), noncontingent support checks could be channeled through a contingency plan.

Not all contingent incentives must have a monetary value. In many cultures, money is not the most powerful reinforcer. For example, offering money would be disrespectful among cultures that value benefits to the community over individual gain. In more communal cultures (e.g., Native American, African-American), spirituality may be interwoven in the ethnic value system. Contingency incentives can reflect those ceremonies and activities that support the sacred. In the Native American community, these can include gifting, earning a feather, honoring spiritual kinship, using a talking feather, and smoking a prayer pipe. The case study in Figure 7-6 highlights the importance of cultural values as motivators for change. Contingency incentives should be culturally appropriate and linked to the clients' values.

Community Reinforcement Approach

CRA emphasizes the development of new natural reinforcers that are available in the everyday life of the substance user and that can

---

Figure 7-6
Using Cultural Values as Motivators

John and Mary Red Fox, surviving through part-time jobs and seasonal work, lived in fairly impoverished circumstances on a reservation with their three children. Both were high school dropouts. John, age 27, and Mary, age 22, abused alcohol, although John completed an inpatient treatment program for alcoholism just prior to his recent return to use. The children were described by their parents as unmanageable, easily distracted, difficult to communicate with, and hyperactive. There were indications that Mary had been physically and sexually abused as a child and that Mary's stepbrother had sexually abused her two older children.

The Tribal Law Enforcement Center made the referral to a rural social work agency after John was arrested for suspicion of spouse abuse. As he began an assessment, the social worker learned that members of the family had periodically received counseling from various agencies and that John and Mary had sporadically attended AA meetings. Apart from medical and dental services, however, the services they had received were deemed ineffective.

On the face of it, the problems seemed overwhelming: (1) family instability and crisis were heightened by the couple's use of alcohol and John's threatening behavior to Mary; (2) the couple's lack of job skills and education elevated their risk of poverty; (3) frequent marital discord was partly a result of alcohol abuse and inconsistent parenting; (4) the children were struggling with significant impairments, perhaps contributed to by fetal alcohol syndrome; and (5) alcohol abuse was ubiquitous in the community in which they were living.

However, there were also several strengths. The family had remained intact, with both parents eager to salvage their relationship. John and Mary had developed their talents, and their neat and orderly home was colorfully decorated with Native American arts and crafts. Finally, the recent establishment of a program in their community, designed to revitalize traditional Indian beliefs and culture, offered an alternative to traditional agency-oriented interventions. This program included a summer camp for children in beautiful surroundings with canoes, wigwams, tepees, and an earth lodge.

The social worker encouraged the school system to refer John and Mary's children to this camp, and then encouraged the camp director to reach out to John and Mary and invite them to become teachers. Mary responded positively and helped teach skills in making Indian dance regalia. While initially hesitant, John eventually agreed to help with the planning of a children's powwow, including building a sweat lodge. Both parents became invested not only in their children's experiences in the camp but also in earning respect for themselves. John participated in many sweats and aspired to live his recovery and life to earn the honor to become a pipe carrier and to take part in the Sun Dance Ceremony.

As the family became more involved in the program, there were no further instances of alcohol abuse or domestic violence. Both parents rejoined AA, completed their general equivalency diplomas, and began college, and their children had fewer problems in school.

Source: Wahlberg, 1996.

---

compete with powerful psychoactive substances. (See Chapter 4 for a discussion of CRA in the contemplation stage.) Essentially, this holistic approach uses behavioral strategies in an attempt to make a person's abstinent lifestyle more rewarding than the destructive patterns associated with drinking or drug use. This entails bolstering alternative sources of positive reinforcement derived from legitimate employment, family support, and social activities. Furthermore, the clinician tries, insofar as possible, to make these alternative sources of reinforcement immediately contingent on sobriety in order to boost motivation for remaining substance free. CRA also builds new competencies through skills training, with information about the need for particular coping skills derived from a functional analysis that identifies high-risk situations. Some of the strategies used in CRA include

- Using motivational counseling to move participants toward their goals
- Building competency
- Applying competing reinforcers
- Tying reinforcers to abstinence
- Emphasizing the multifaceted nature of recovery

Tying natural reinforcers to abstinence is a central feature of CRA. Unlike vouchers, natural reinforcers such as praise for a job well done, occur in a client's normal, daily environment. A natural, uncontrived reinforcer can also be internal, such as perceiving oneself as a good worker. While straightforward in concept, the attempt to link reinforcers to abstinence can be difficult to implement in practice. For example, an ideal situation would be one in which an employer would agree to allow people to work and earn money only on days when they test drug and alcohol free. In this way, the benefits of work, including the money that can be earned, are tied to abstinence and denied temporarily in the event of substance use. The treatment program would either have to make special arrangements with employers or operate its own worksite, and easy access to a drug-testing laboratory would be needed to provide immediate feedback. The

workplace described in Figure 7-7 is an example of this type of program.

Another source of immediate reinforcement is the romantic or marital partner or other substance-free supporter. Much research indicates the efficacy of behavioral marital therapy (O'Farrell, 1993). In CRA, a contract can be negotiated between clients and their partners that outlines abstinence contingent interactions. For example, partners may agree to prepare special meals or take part in activities that clients enjoy so long as they remain abstinent. Alternatively, if there is evidence of a recurrence of substance use, the partner agrees to forego favored activities and withhold social reinforcers, possibly even leaving the home temporarily until there is evidence of return to abstinence. To make this work, the treatment program should provide regular information to partners about drug-test results (after obtaining consent from clients) so they can take appropriate action in accordance with the contract. Partners also most likely need support, encouragement, and problem-solving help from the clinician.

New social and recreational activities can be important sources of alternative reinforcement. This is often a difficult area in which to make changes, however, and clients may need support to get started on new activities. CRA involves the clinician as an active change agent, helping the client directly achieve the goal and modeling new behaviors. This can be especially valuable in encouraging new social or recreational activities.

In addition to arranging for appropriate delivery of reinforcers in the natural environment, setting goals, and modeling new behaviors, the CRA clinician teaches skills that the client may need for acquiring and sustaining alternative reinforcers. This may include social skills, problemsolving skills, and various self-management skills such as assertiveness. Particularly for clients from disadvantaged

---

Figure 7-7

Therapeutic Workplaces for Individuals With Substance Abuse Disorders

The opportunity to learn and work can be reinforcing for persons with substance abuse disorders, particularly if they are paid for participating. Remedial academic programs, vocational training, and actual worksites all can be places where skills are enhanced while abstinence is sustained. This is done by allowing these individuals to participate and be paid only when their urine tests are drug free.

A therapeutic workplace developed by Dr. Kenneth Silverman in Baltimore, Maryland, illustrates this principle. This workplace offers intensive remedial academic training and job skills to drug users who grew up in an impoverished inner city environment and may never have learned basic reading or mathematics. So far, the program has been tested only with women who are concurrently enrolled in a comprehensive program for pregnant drug users. Participants report every weekday for 3 hours of training and can earn voucher points at a rate that corresponds to their duration of abstinence and participation (average compensation is roughly $10 per hour). A skilled remedial education teacher conducts an intensive class, where participants can rapidly improve their academic skills and learn job-related skills.

Research has shown that the women who participate in this program have long periods of abstinence from heroin and cocaine and that they have much better drug use outcomes than a similar sample of control women who were not invited to participate in the therapeutic workplace. The women who join this program are happy with their chance to improve their academic and job skills and believe that this training will better prepare them to compete in the job market.

Source: Silverman et al., 1997.

---

groups, it may be especially important to teach the skills needed to get a job.

A special component of CRA called the Job Club offers clients skills training, critique of job applications, tips on making telephone calls to potential employers and dressing for interviews, and practice in being assertive and positive with potential employers (Azrin and Besalel, 1980; Meyers and Smith, 1995). The four key areas of emphasis are

- Telephone contact skills
- Telephone contact goals
- Job application skills
- Job interview skills

Job Club is a highly structured program that guides participants toward higher levels of concrete action—for example, by making 10 phone calls per day to relatives or friends who have jobs and making "cold calls." Research supports its efficacy in helping clients find employment (see, for example, Azrin and Besalel, 1982).

The program also coaches individuals with substance abuse disorders on the sensitive issues they face. A man, for example, who spent several years in jail can benefit by learning how to handle gaps in his employment history that may be questioned during a job interview. The program also emphasizes identifying competencies from the client's history and putting them in the résumé. For example, a woman with young children may not have held a paying job for years, but she may have performed volunteer work. This experience should be included in her résumé.

Job Club counselors make clear that finding a job is sometimes difficult. Because disappointments inherent in any job search can present the first setback for clients after they enter treatment, Job Club coaches them on how to handle rejection and gives them a safe setting in which to work through any sense of failure. It also gives participants a forum where they can talk and reduce their feelings of isolation and loneliness.

When clients get jobs, their participation in Job Club ends. At that point, it is usually up to the counselor or clinician to continue any work needed for sustaining employment (i.e., check client expectations versus perceived realities, identify and solve job-related problems).

Job Club is particularly valuable because employment and financial support are crucial elements of identity and lifestyle. Both stopping substance use and getting a job reflect large, abrupt changes in lifestyle; however, the skills needed to achieve one goal can complement attainment of the other. Job Club fills a need because it helps clients take action. In terms of the model of change, research shows that clients need to feel successful in changing behavior to stay in the action and maintenance phases. Although Job Club may seem directive, it assists with behavioral change that can promote treatment success.

Motivational techniques can be used when talking to clients about their vocational goals and even when implementing skills training aimed at finding a job. The clients' commitment to becoming employed may have to be revisited using decisional balance techniques. Expectancies can be discussed about both the skills-training and job-finding processes. The value of program-based skills training, however, is that fears can be allayed by repeated role-playing performed in a protected environment with a clinician who will provide objective, nonjudgmental feedback.

Finally, job-skills training may have to be broadened to include a component on job maintenance—or how to keep a job. Keeping a job requires skills that are often eroded by substance abuse disorders, including being punctual and organized, being able to solve problems that arise on the job, and being able to trust others and work effectively in a team.

Employment serves as an immediate reinforcer by meeting the practical need for money, but other aspects of employment take time to become reinforcing. For example, employment builds self-efficacy. It also gives clients an opportunity to learn new work skills and meet new drug-free people. Other areas of a client's life—socializing, romance, family, recreation, education, and spirituality—also may take time to realize full potential as alternative reinforcers. For this reason, voucher incentive programs can be useful at the start of therapy to bridge the gap. The delay in gratification inherent in starting new activities also suggests that the CRA counselor should encourage and assist clients in developing new behaviors and contacts in as many areas as possible because clients may not follow through in all areas and some areas may become reinforcing sooner than others.

As your clients focus on changing each area of their lives, there will be new opportunities both to teach skills and to enhance the network of nondrug social reinforcers. For example, studies have shown that women who attend parenting classes to learn about normal stages of child development generally develop social ties with other mothers and reap social benefits in addition to improving parenting skills. Peterson's research in this area suggests that it would be beneficial to build parenting classes into treatment programs because of these multiple benefits (Peterson et al., 1996; Van Bremen and Chasnoff, 1994). Another novel concept is a parenting class for parents of teenagers, which would serve a similar need while enhancing social ties. Although such programming is not provided in most community treatment programs, it could be valuable.

CRA is a comprehensive approach to delivering therapy to clients. CRA counseling on its own has proven effective when tested with alcoholics, and CRA plus vouchers has proven highly effective as a treatment with cocaine abusers. CRA recognizes the importance of motivation and incorporates motivational techniques including abstinence contingencies to build alternative substance-free lifestyles. Establishing a satisfying substance-free life takes time and perseverance, with many hurdles along the way. Commitment and motivation are recurrent issues. CRA and other motivational techniques can be valuable tools for the clinician as clients seek to change their lifestyles.

Motivational Counseling During Maintenance

To this point, this chapter has focused on helping clients prepare for and stabilize their recovery. As a final note, a motivational approach can also be quite useful in counseling clients during the maintenance stage. The most likely reason for your seeing a client after action-oriented treatment has concluded, of course, is a recurrence of substance use and related problems.

As described in the opening chapters, this TIP has been developed with a keen awareness of the language that is used in treatment and the underlying assumptions implied by common terms. The term "relapse" has been intentionally omitted because of the baggage it carries. The Consensus Panel sought not to find a euphemism for relapse but to write in a manner that fundamentally reconceptualizes the recurrence of substance use after treatment. This reconceptualization recognizes several well-documented observations:

- Recurrence of use is the norm rather than the exception after treatment. It is so common as to be thought of now as a normal part of the change and recovery process.
- The term "relapse" itself implies only two possible outcomes—success or failure—that

do not describe well what actually occurs. Client outcomes are much more complex than this. Often in the course of recovery, clients manage to have longer and longer periods between episodes of use, and the episodes themselves grow shorter and less severe.

- The binary assumptions inherent in the "relapse" concept can also be a self-fulfilling prophecy, implying that once use has resumed there is nothing to lose, or little that can be done. Instead, the point is to get back on track as soon as possible.
- The relapse concept, when applied to substance abuse, also lends itself to moralistic blaming or self-blaming. In fact, recurrence of symptoms is common to addictive behaviors, and indeed to chronic health problems in general.

Part of a motivational approach in maintenance, then, has to do with a mental set about the meaning of recurrent use and how to respond. When one thinks in terms of "relapse," there is a temptation to lapse into lecturing, educating, even blaming and moralizing ("I told you so"). The very same principles described for helping precontemplators and contemplators can be used here. In fact, recurrence of use in a way constitutes a return to one of these stages. The reason for not considering change may be different, of course, the second or fifth time around. It may have more to do with discouragement, low confidence in the ability to change, or a defensive rationalization of resumed use. Your job is to help your client not get stuck at this point but move back into preparation and action.

There are no special tricks here. The approach is the same. Ask for your client's own perceptions and reactions to resumed use. Elicit from your client the self-motivational reasons for change, the reasons to get back on track. Explore what can be learned from the experience; a functional analysis of the process of resumed use may be helpful. Normalize the experience as a common and temporary part of the spiral of recovery. Have your client talk about the advantages of abstinence. Use plenty of reflective listening, not just a string of questions. Explore the client's values, hopes, purpose and goals in life. Ask a key question—what does the person want to do now—and move on toward a plan for renewed change.

8 Measuring Components of Client Motivation

Motivation is multidimensional, not a single domain that can be easily measured with one instrument or scale. This chapter describes a variety of tools for measuring the building blocks of motivation discussed throughout this TIP. This chapter should be regarded as a progress report because concepts of motivation for change are evolving, and new approaches for assessment are being tested. Measures often have to be adapted, and their psychometric characteristics change when they are applied to new problems and populations. There are also specificity challenges in assessing motivation. For example, clients are often at very different points of readiness with regard to different substances. A person may be in the action stage for cocaine, the contemplation stage for alcohol, and the precontemplation stage for marijuana and tobacco. No doubt, motivation measures will become more precise in the years ahead.

In this chapter is a set of measures endorsed by the Consensus Panel. For most measures, there is good psychometric documentation, but some are at earlier stages of validation. Most have not been normed for different racial or ethnic groups. Many clinicians have found these formal tools to be valuable and appreciate the structure and focus these instruments can provide—the sense that their work with the client is task-centered and grounded in reality. The results also provide one more type of

feedback to use with clients throughout the change process to enhance motivation. For some clients, test scores add a dimension of objectivity to the counseling situation, which may otherwise seem highly subjective. One risk to be aware of in using these tools, however, is that some clients might focus too heavily on scores indicating their vulnerabilities rather than on those indicating their strengths.

This chapter offers ways of measuring the following dimensions of motivation:

- Self-efficacy
- Readiness to change
- Decisional balancing
- Motivations for using substances
- Goals and values

The purpose of this chapter is to aid you in assessing where clients are in terms of motivation levels and also to help you apply the motivational principles and appropriate strategies for different stages of change that are discussed in Chapters 4 through 7. A variety of valuable and psychometrically sound instruments and scales that are easy to administer are now available (Allen and Columbus, 1995). You may wish to try several different instruments to find those that work best with your clients, that measure the dimensions of most interest to you, and that match your clinical style. Many of the instruments discussed in this chapter appear in Appendix B.

Self-Efficacy

Individuals in recovery have very different levels of confidence regarding their ability (self-efficacy) to change and abstain from substances. Some are overly confident, while others feel hopeless about achieving sobriety or even reducing use. Self-efficacy, particularly with respect to capabilities for overcoming alcohol dependence or abuse, is an important predictor of treatment outcome (DiClemente et al., 1994). Because certain situations are more likely to lead to setbacks for those in recovery (Marlatt and George, 1984), identifying these high-risk situations is an important step in treatment.

Self-efficacy questionnaires ask clients to rate how risky certain situations are and to estimate their confidence in how well they would do in avoiding the temptation to use substances in these situations. The numerical scores provide an objective measure of a client's self-efficacy for a specific behavior over a range of provocative situations. Some computerized versions of these instruments generate small bar graphs that add a visual dimension to the numbers. By using these tools, clients gain an understanding of where their individual risks lie—high-risk situations in which they have low self-efficacy. This information can be extremely useful in setting realistic goals and developing an individualized change plan and can provide a sound basis for self-monitoring. Clients who rank many situations as high risk (i.e., low self-efficacy) may need to learn new coping strategies.

Situational Confidence Questionnaire

The Situational Confidence Questionnaire (SCQ) has been used specifically with those who drink heavily. The instrument consists of 100 items that ask clients to identify their level of confidence in resisting drinking as a response to the following eight types of situations (Marlatt and Gordon, 1985):

1. Unpleasant emotions
2. Physical discomfort
3. Testing personal control over substance use
4. Urges and temptations to drink
5. Pleasant times with others
6. Conflicts with others
7. Pleasant emotions
8. Social pressure to drink

Clients are asked to imagine themselves in each situation and rate their confidence on a 6-point scale, ranging from not at all confident (a rating of 0) to totally confident (a rating of 6) that they can resist the urge to drink heavily in that situation. The SCQ generally takes about 20 minutes to complete, using either pencil and paper or computer software that automatically scores answers and generates a profile of the client's alcohol use. The SCQ is accompanied by an Inventory of Drinking Situations that assesses the frequency of heavy drinking in different situations. The results of this questionnaire can be used to provide personalized feedback to the client as well as for treatment planning (Annis and Davis, 1991). High confidence scores have been shown to predict positive treatment outcomes (Annis and Davis, 1988), whereas low confidence scores have identified clients who are likely to have poor treatment outcomes (Sobell et al., 1997). An amended version of the SCQ, the SCQ-39, is the version recommended by the questionnaire's developer (see Appendix B).

Brief Situational Confidence Questionnaire

The Brief Situational Confidence Questionnaire (BSCQ) was developed as an alternative to the SCQ because some treatment programs found the length and scoring and graphing systems of the original instrument to be too time-consuming in clinical practice (Sobell, 1996).

The eight items of the BSCQ, reproduced in Appendix B, correspond to the eight subscales in the original SCQ. Respondents in a community study (Sobell et al., 1996b) were asked to rank their confidence at the time of taking the questionnaire in resisting using alcohol or a primary drug in each situation on a scale from 0 (not at all confident) to 100 (totally confident). A comparison of the brief and long versions of the SCQ (Breslin et al., 1997) found that the shorter version is also effective and corresponds well with the longer version on most subscales. The BSCQ, although not as comprehensive and not yet as extensively tested, has several clinical advantages over the longer version. It can be administered in a few minutes, is easily interpreted by clinicians, provides immediate feedback for the client, and can be used easily in primary care and other nonaddiction-specific settings (Breslin et al., 1997). The BSCQ is also available in Spanish.

Alcohol Abstinence Self-Efficacy Scale

The Alcohol Abstinence Self-Efficacy Scale (AASE) measures an individual's self-efficacy in abstaining from alcohol (DiClemente et al., 1994). Although similar to the SCQ, the AASE focuses on clients' confidence in their ability to abstain from drinking across a range of 20 different situations derived from the eight high-risk categories listed above. The AASE consists of 20 items and can be used to assess both the temptation to drink and the confidence to abstain (see Figure 8-1). Clients rate their temptation to drink and their confidence that they would not drink in each situation on separate 5-point Likert scales that range from 1 (not at all likely) to 5 (extremely likely). Scores are calculated separately for temptation and self-efficacy (DiClemente et al., 1994). The items in this version are divided into several subcategories that measure four types of recurrence precipitants: negative affect, social

situations, physical or other concerns, and craving and urges. A study conducted on 266 adults in treatment at an outpatient treatment program for alcohol use disorders over a 24-month period found strong indices of reliability and validity for this scale (DiClemente et al., 1994). This brief version also appears to be equally effective with men and women. It is easy to use, comprehensive, and a psychometrically sound measure of self-efficacy to abstain from drinking.

Readiness To Change

An instrument for assessing the importance of change has been developed (Sobell et al., 1996b), based on a four-question scale originally used with smokers (Richmond et al., 1993). The questions were modified to inquire about drinking, with responses in a specific range for each question. A composite motivation score is calculated with a possible range from 0 to 10, based on the sum of the responses. The four questions are

1. Would you like to reduce or quit drinking if you could do so easily? (No = 0, Yes = 1)
2. How seriously would you like to reduce or quit drinking altogether? (Not at all seriously = 0, Not very seriously = 1, Fairly seriously = 2, Very seriously = 3)
3. Do you intend to reduce or quit drinking in the next 2 weeks? (Definitely no = 0, Probably no = 1, Probably yes = 2, Definitely yes = 3)
4. What is the possibility that 12 months from now you will not have a problem with alcohol? (Definitely not = 0, Probably not = 1, Probably will = 2, Definitely will = 3)

As discussed throughout this TIP, readiness to change can be considered a prerequisite for responding to treatment. However, motivational states are not binary—with clients either motivated or not motivated. Rather, readiness exists along a continuum of steps or

Figure 8-1
20-Item Alcohol Abstinence Self-Efficacy Scale

Negative Effect

- When I am feeling angry inside
- When I sense everything is going wrong for me
- When I am feeling depressed
- When I feel like becoming angry because of frustration
- When I am very worried

Social/Positive

- When I see others drinking at a bar or at a party
- When I am excited or celebrating with others
- When I am on vacation and want to relax
- When people I used to drink with encourage me to drink
- When I am being offered a drink in a social situation

Physical and Other Concerns

- When I have a headache
- When I am tired
- When I am concerned about someone
- When I am experiencing some physical pain or injury
- When I dream about taking a drink

Craving and Urges

- When I am in agony because of stopping or withdrawing from alcohol use
- When I have the urge to try just one drink to see what happens
- When I am feeling a physical need or craving for alcohol
- When I want to test my will power over drinking
- When I experience an urge or impulse to take a drink that catches me unprepared

Source: DiClemente et al., 1994.

stages and can vary rapidly, sometimes from day to day. The stages-of-change model has inspired instruments for assessing readiness to change or a client's motivational change state. Depending on the level of readiness—or change stage—different motivational intervention strategies will be more or less effective (see Chapters 2 through 7).

Readiness Ruler

The Readiness Ruler, developed by Rollnick and used extensively in general medical settings, is a simple method for determining clients'

readiness to change by asking where they are on a scale of 1 to 10 (see Figure 8-2). The lower numbers indicate less readiness, and the higher numbers indicate greater readiness for change. Depending on how ready to change clients think they are, the conversation can take different directions. For those who rate themselves as "not ready" (0 to 3), some clinicians suggest expressing concern, offering information, and providing support and followup. For those who are unsure (4 to 7), explore the positive and negative aspects of treatment. For clients who

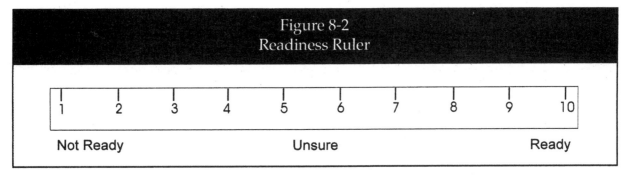

Figure 8-2
Readiness Ruler

1 2 3 4 5 6 7 8 9 10

Not Ready   Unsure   Ready

are ready for change (8 to 10), help plan action, identify resources, and convey hope (Bernstein et al., 1997a). As clients continue in treatment, you can use the ruler periodically to monitor how motivation changes as treatment progresses. Remember that clients can move both forward and backward. Also, helping clients move forward, even if they never reach a decisionmaking or action stage, is an acceptable outcome. Most clients cycle through the change stages several times, sometimes spiraling up and sometimes down, before they settle into treatment or stable recovery. One significant feature of the readiness to change scale is that clients assess their own readiness by marking the ruler or voicing a number. Another feature is that the clinician can pose the question, "What would it take to move from a 3 to a 5?" or can recognize movement along the continuum by asking, "Where have you come from last year to now?" Chapter 4 provides more information about fostering readiness.

In other similar studies (Sobell et al., 1993b; Sobell and Sobell, 1993, 1995b), clients responded on a scale of 0 to 100 to the following two questions:

1. At this moment, how important is it that you change your current drinking? (Not important at all = 0, About as important as most of the other things I would like to achieve now = 50, Most important thing in my life now = 100)

2. At this moment, how confident are you that you will change your current drinking? (I do not think I will achieve my goal = 0, I have a 50 percent chance of meeting my

goal = 50, I think I will definitely achieve my goal = 100)

Both goal importance and confidence ratings have been associated with better treatment outcomes (Sobell et al., 1996b).

University of Rhode Island Change Assessment Scale

The University of Rhode Island Change Assessment Scale (URICA) was originally developed to measure a client's change stage in psychotherapy (McConnaughy et al., 1983) in terms of four stages of change: precontemplation, contemplation, action, and maintenance. The scale has 32 items, with eight items for each of the four stage-specific subscales (see Appendix B). Respondents rate items on a five-point Likert scale from 1 (strong disagreement) to 5 (strong agreement). Scores for each of the four stages are obtained. The instrument is designed for a broad range of concerns and asks clients general questions about their "problem."

A 28-item version of the URICA, with seven items corresponding to each stage, has also been used with clients in alcoholism treatment (DiClemente et al., 1994). Subscale scores from this instrument can then be used to create profiles related to the stages of change or to create a single readiness score by adding together the contemplation, action, and maintenance mean scores and subtracting the precontemplation score. In various research studies, these scores have been related to treatment outcome. In Project MATCH, a multisite clinical trial of psychosocial treatments for alcohol problems that involved 1,726 clients, the readiness score predicted abstinence from drinking outcomes at a 3-year followup (Project MATCH Research Group, 1997a).

Stages of Change Readiness and Treatment Eagerness Scale

The Stages of Change Readiness and Treatment Eagerness Scale (SOCRATES) measures readiness to change, with items specifically focused on problem drinkers. Developed in 1987 by William R. Miller, the initial set of items was circulated for comment among colleagues in substance abuse treatment research. A 32-item version was then produced, using five-point scales ranging from five (strongly agree) to one (strongly disagree). The current 19-item version of SOCRATES, reproduced in Appendix B, was initially developed in 1991 and was used as a self-administered paper-and-pencil questionnaire in Project MATCH (Miller and Tonigan, 1996). The items on this short version do not measure the five stages of change constructs, but relate to three factors that have little overlap with each other: taking steps, recognition, and ambivalence.

Clinicians can use SOCRATES to provide clients with feedback about their scores as a starting point for discussion. Changes in scores when the scale is readministered could assess the impact of an intervention on problem recognition, ambivalence, and progress on making changes. Parallel forms have been developed to assess motivation to change substance use as well as the motivation of a significant other to help change a partner's substance-using patterns. The SOCRATES variables can also be helpful, in combination with other measures, for understanding the structure of motivation and readiness for change. Spanish translations are available.

Readiness To Change Questionnaire

The Readiness To Change Questionnaire (RCQ) was developed to help professionals who are not substance abuse treatment specialists assess the change stage of clients who drink excessively (Rollnick et al., 1992b). The 12 items, which were adapted from the URICA items, correlate closely with three change stages—precontemplation, contemplation, and action—and reflect typical attitudes of persons in each of those readiness levels. For example, a person not yet contemplating change would likely give a positive response to the statement, "Drinking less alcohol would be pointless for me," whereas a person already taking action would agree with the statement, "I have just recently changed my drinking habits." Another individual already contemplating change would be expected to agree with the item, "Sometimes I think I should cut down on my drinking." A five-point scale is used for rating responses, from strongly agree (5) to strongly disagree (1).

The RCQ, which can be self-administered, has been shown to have good psychometric properties with heavy drinkers in nontreatment settings. When the instrument was used as a screening tool with heavy drinkers in general hospitals, it accurately reflected patients' readiness to change and also predicted changes in respondents' alcohol consumption patterns at 8 weeks and 6 months following hospital discharge. That is, those who were least ready to change showed the least improvement in drinking patterns at followup, whereas those who were most ready to act did so (Heather et al., 1993). An additional test of the instrument found that men identified as heavy drinkers in general hospital wards and as being in early stages of change responded more favorably to brief motivational interviewing than to skills-based counseling with respect to reduced alcohol consumption. The inverse, however, was not found to be true. Men rated as ready to change did not respond any more favorably to skills-based counseling than to brief motivational interviewing. The study authors concluded that more research is necessary to ascertain what type of counseling is most suitable for persons identified as excessive drinkers in opportunistic settings who are also in a state of readiness to change (Heather et al., 1996a).

In repeated uses of the RCQ, Heather and colleagues have refined the scoring method for this instrument. The initial "quick method" simply sums the raw scores for each separate change-stage scale and uses the score that is farthest along the continuum of change stages as the most accurate reflection of the client's readiness to change. This method is appropriate if you need a quick way of determining readiness. A more accurate and refined method and a better predictor of change for research and clinical purposes is to omit any illogical and unreliable responses and add a preparation stage to the calculations. A revised version of the *Readiness To Change Questionnaire User's Manual* provides more specific information about calculating scores using this method.

The RCQ (Treatment Version) (RCQ [TV]) is a recent revision of the original RCQ (Heather et al., 1996b) that is a more appropriate alternative for determining the stage of change for persons who are seeking or already undergoing treatment for alcohol problems. This version, reproduced in Appendix B, responds to criticisms that the original RCQ was intended only for use with heavy or hazardous drinkers identified in opportunistic settings (Gavin et al., 1998), although it was being administered, inappropriately, to some alcohol-dependent persons already applying for treatment of a substance use disorder. The major problem was that drinkers identified in health care settings often chose to reduce consumption to safe limits instead of abstinence, which is the more typical decision of severely impaired persons in need of traditional treatment.

Although the developers of the revised instrument initially hoped to add questions that would identify persons in the five stages of change and to modify the questions to reflect goals of either reduced drinking or abstinence, only the latter aim was achieved with the revised instrument (Heather et al., 1996b). The RCQ (TV) has 30 items, with six questions corresponding to each change stage, which are rated on a five-point scale ranging from strongly agree to strongly disagree. Many of the questions and statements are adaptations of those in the original RCQ that now include abstinence as a goal. For example, "I have started to carry out a plan to cut down or quit drinking." Other new questions reflect the two additional change stages, "I've succeeded in stopping or cutting down drinking and I want to stay that way" (maintenance) or, "I have made a plan to stop or cut down drinking and I intend to put this plan into practice" (preparation).

The developers of this psychometrically sound instrument claim it is clinically useful for deciding what types of services are most appropriate for persons entering treatment. Those who are identified as ready to change can immediately be offered skills-based, action-oriented services, while those who are not yet in an action stage should be given further motivational interventions until they progress further along the readiness continuum. More research is necessary to strengthen one of the scales and to determine the instrument's ability to predict drinking outcomes accurately (Heather et al., 1996b).

Decisional Balancing

As discussed in Chapter 5, exercises and instruments that examine decisional balancing investigate the positive and negative aspects of a particular behavior. The general benefits of the behavior—and also of changing it—are weighed against the costs, allowing clients to appraise the impact of their behavior and make more informed choices regarding changing it. The scale reproduced in this section can be used to accentuate the costs of the client's substance use, lessen its perceived rewards, make the benefits of recovery more apparent, and identify possible obstacles to change.

The decisional balancing exercise was developed by Sobell and colleagues to help individuals identify benefits and costs of substance use as part of a cognitive appraisal process often associated with self-directed change (Sobell et al., 1996b). Such a purposeful comparison of the costs and benefits appears to facilitate the recognition and resolution of associated problems. Ask individuals who are interested in making a behavioral change to list benefits and costs of changing and not changing in parallel columns. Then ask them to carefully consider, "Are the costs worth it?" Figure 8-3 is an example of an exercise on the decision to change.

In another decisional balancing exercise, the Alcohol (and Illegal Drugs) Decisional Balance Scale, developed by DiClemente and reproduced in Appendix B, respondents are asked to indicate on a five-point scale how important each statement is in making a decision to change drinking or drug-using behavior.

Alcohol and Drug Consequences Questionnaire

The Alcohol and Drug Consequences Questionnaire (ADCQ) is a relatively new instrument for assessing the costs and benefits of changing a substance problem (Cunningham et al., 1997). It is reproduced in Appendix B. The 29 items included on the questionnaire were derived from information reported by clients participating in a brief cognitive–behavioral intervention for guided self-change at an outpatient substance abuse treatment facility. The items are divided into two categories: costs of change and benefits of change. Respondents are asked the importance of each item if they were to stop or cut down their use of substances

---

Figure 8-3
Deciding To Change

Changing	Not Changing
Benefits	**Benefits**
■ Increased control over my life ■ Support from family and friends ■ Decreased job problems ■ Financial gain ■ Improved health	■ More relaxed ■ More fun at parties ■ Don't have to think about my problems
Costs	**Costs**
■ Increased stress/anxiety ■ Feel more depressed ■ Increased boredom ■ Sleeping problems	■ Disapproval from friends and family ■ Money problems ■ Could lose my job ■ Damage to close relationships ■ Increased health risks

Source: Sobell et al., 1996b.

(0 = not applicable, 1 = not important, 3 = moderately important, 4 = very important, 5 = extremely important). The score is determined by adding the cost items and the benefits items to obtain two separate scores that can be compared.

In initial tests of the instrument, respondents' anticipated costs and benefits of change were significantly related to the importance they attached to achieving treatment goals, and, for problem drinkers, to their drinking outcomes. Respondents whose scores were higher on the costs of change measures were more likely to have consumed more drinks in the year following treatment, whereas those who believed the benefits of change were more important than costs were likely to reduce drinking levels posttreatment (Cunningham et al., 1997).

Motivation for Using Substances

An underlying purpose of the instruments described in this section is to encourage clients to express their expectations about substance use by completing such statements as, "If I were to stop using substances, I would expect to feel…." Research suggests that expectancies play an important role in the progression from use to abuse (Brown, 1993; Connors and Maisto, 1988; Leigh, 1989a). Knowledge of clients' expectations regarding the effects of substances may help you understand the rationale for their substance-using behavior—clients who expect good things from substance use in most situations are likely to continue using at the same level until there is a change in perspective. Based on clients' expectations, find discrepancies between clients' behaviors and hopes and select strategies to help them address reasons for their substance use.

As with other measurement areas, less is known about motivations for using drugs than

for using alcohol. The scales discussed in this section vary in length and have not all been tested on clinical samples. Leigh has reviewed and presented sample items and instructions for several questionnaires that purport to measure motivation (Leigh, 1989a).

Alcohol Expectancy Questionnaire

The Alcohol Expectancy Questionnaire is the most widely used of these instruments (Brown et al., 1987). It is reproduced in Appendix B. It contains 90 items and uses a dichotomous agree/disagree response format. The items are grouped into six categories of perceived benefits from alcohol:

1. Global positive changes
2. Social and physical pleasure
3. Sexual enhancement
4. Increased social assertion
5. Tension reduction/relaxation
6. Increased arousal and aggression

This scale measures only positive expectancies, not negative ones, and has been useful in showing that clients with continued positive expectancies at the end of treatment have poorer outcomes. It has been used with adults in both clinical and nonclinical populations (Sobell et al., 1994). A 120-item version that used the same format was developed for adolescents (Christiansen et al., 1982).

Alcohol Effects Questionnaire

The Alcohol Effects Questionnaire, reproduced in Appendix B, was constructed after researchers questioned whether the original Alcohol Expectancy Questionnaire measured the strength or intensity of alcohol-related expectancies (Collins et al., 1990). Subjects in a study were asked to rate the strength of their beliefs in addition to the agree/disagree responses in the standard Alcohol Expectancy Questionnaire. It was hoped that this study would clarify the distinction between two types of alcohol expectancies—the nature of an attitude toward a behavior and the strength of that attitude or confidence about behavior change. Subjects were asked to report how strongly they agreed or disagreed with a particular belief on a 10-point Likert scale where 1 = mildly believe and 10 = strongly believe. The results supported the idea that the strength of an individual's belief or disbelief in alcohol-related expectancies assessed by the Alcohol Expectancy Questionnaire is different from merely agreeing or disagreeing with these same expectancies.

Other Scales

The Effects of Drinking Alcohol scale has 20 items, each rated on a five-point scale that ranges from unlikely to very likely. The items, which reflect expected reactions to alcohol use, are grouped into five factors: nastiness, cognitive/physical impairment, disinhibition, gregariousness, and depressant effects (Leigh, 1989a).

The Alcohol Effects Scale is a 37-item, forced-choice adjective checklist that measures three factors: stimulation/perceived dominance, pleasurable disinhibition, and behavioral impairment (Southwick et al., 1981). This scale measures client expectations of how a moderate amount or excessive amount of alcohol would affect them.

The Alcohol Belief Scale was developed to assess clients' expectations regarding the usefulness of drinking different amounts of alcohol in different contexts (Connors and Maisto, 1988; Connors et al., 1987). The scale measures clients' beliefs regarding whether, for example, alcohol reduces discomfort in proportion to the amount consumed ("The more I drink, the better I feel") (Connors et al., 1987). The greatest positive expectations are reported by those with the most severe drinking problems.

The Marijuana Effect Expectancy Questionnaire (MEEQ) and the Cocaine Effect Expectancy Questionnaire (CEEQ) are two related scales that assess motivation to use substances (Schafer and Brown, 1991). The MEEQ (70 items) and CEEQ (64 items) use a yes/no format with agree/disagree instructions similar to those of the AEQ. Subjects are asked to respond to the items according to their own beliefs and whether they have actually used the substance. Further research is needed; it appears, however, that expectancies differ across substance types in relation to the properties of the substance (e.g., expectation of arousal from alcohol and cocaine use but not from marijuana use).

Goals and Values

Your clients must value a treatment goal to progress toward it. In fact, unless clients value them, they are not goals from the clients' perspectives. From a motivational standpoint, you should understand what your clients' goals are and what they value in life. It is usually best to start where your clients are—with what is important from their own perspective.

Clinicians can assess goals and values through an open-ended interview, asking questions like, "What things are most important to you?" or, "How would you like your life to be different 5 years from now?" or "What would you like to have happen in treatment?" As an aid to this process, some clinicians use a sheet showing a number of bubbles that contain the names of issues that a client might wish to discuss and ask, "Which of these would you like to work on while you are here?" or "What might you like to work on first?" Some bubbles should be left empty, too, because clients may have goals other than those listed on the sheet. In developing a treatment plan, one can begin with all blank bubbles and fill in possible goals of treatment, then prioritize them. Miles Cox has developed and tested a clinical Motivational Structure Questionnaire for identifying goals and their associated degrees of commitment, outcome expectancy, and self-efficacy (Cox et al., 1993).

There are also more structured ways to assess what clients want and value. Clinicians can use the What I Want From Treatment Questionnaire, which lists a number of possible goals and aspects of treatment and asks new clients to rate the importance of incorporating each item into their own treatment (see Appendix B for a copy of this questionnaire). Clients can also be asked at the end of treatment the extent to which they received these same treatment elements. One study using this instrument found a positive relationship between favorable outcomes and clients reporting at discharge that they had received those treatment elements they said they wanted at intake (Brown and Miller, 1993). Receiving other treatment elements they did not want was unrelated to outcomes. In other words, clients improve to the extent they receive what they want from treatment.

Extensive literature exists on measuring values in general. For example, the Study of Values Questionnaire developed in 1960 has been widely used (Allport et al., 1960). In a classic volume on the subject, Rokeach introduced a method for ranking instrumental (means) and terminal (ends) values (Rokeach, 1973). His well-researched instrument, which is available in a published form, allows clients to prioritize their values by arranging small labels in hierarchical fashion (Rokeach, 1983). Another instrument has clients sort and prioritize cards dealing with a wide variety of values expressed in contemporary language (Miller and C'de Baca, 1994).

9 Integrating Motivational Approaches Into Treatment Programs

How do the motivational approaches discussed in this TIP fit into the real world of health care delivery? Although the demand for treatment of substance abuse continues to far exceed its availability, changes in health care economics are placing greater pressure on providers and their clients. Payors increasingly demand evidence that the services being provided are not only effective, but cost-effective. Clinicians and programs are increasingly challenged if they do not use research-supported, current methods. Public funding is scarce, and third-party payors exert great pressure to provide treatment that is shorter, less costly, and more effective. In sum, clinicians are asked to do more with less.

The incorporation of motivational approaches and interventions into treatment programs may be a practical and efficacious response to many of these challenges. Recent research (Brown and Miller, 1993; Kolden et al., 1997; McCaul and Svikis, 1991) supports the integration of motivational interviewing modules into programs to reduce attrition, to enhance client participation in treatment, and to increase the achievement and maintenance of positive behavioral outcomes. Other studies have shown brief interventions using motivational strategies and motivational interviewing to be more effective than no treatment or being placed on a waiting list, and not inferior to some types of more extensive care (Bien et al., 1993a, 1993b; Noonan and Moyers, 1997). A review of the cost-effectiveness of treatments for alcohol use disorders concluded that brief motivational counseling ranked among the most effective treatment modalities, based on weighted evidence from rigorous clinical trials (Holder et al., 1991). Brief motivational counseling was also the least costly—making it the most cost-effective treatment modality of the 33 evaluated. Although cautioning that it was an approximation that requires refinement, the same study found a negative correlation between effectiveness and costs for the most traditional forms of treatment for alcohol use disorders and highlighted a growing trend to favor effective outpatient care over less effective or less studied—but far more expensive—inpatient, hospital-based, or residential care (Holder et al., 1991).

This chapter begins with a discussion of the treatment continuum into which motivational interventions must be incorporated and ends with descriptions of motivational approaches that have been used in specific treatment settings. Also discussed is the importance of involving a significant other to enhance a client's motivation for change.

The Treatment Continuum and Stepped Care

In 1990, the Institute of Medicine (IOM), in a special report to Congress, called for broadening the base of treatment for alcohol use disorders (IOM, 1990a). Both before and after that summons, modalities and special interventions to treat problems related to substance use have proliferated. In the year following the IOM report, Holder and associates reviewed the effectiveness and costs of 33 separate types of treatment for alcohol problems that had been subjected to controlled clinical trials (Holder et al., 1991). The costs are much larger if specialized treatment services for substance-related problems are added to the base. However, these multiple modalities are not always used appropriately. Moreover, services are not always available to all who need or want them because of costs, lack of physical accessibility, and too few staff members.

The IOM report called attention to several important suppositions that underlie its efforts:

- Substance use problems are not homogeneous—they differ in intensity, duration, effects, and other important dimensions.
- Individuals who have problems with substance use are also diverse and have preferences about the treatments they will accept.
- The magnitude of substance-related problems is too large to be handled by specialized treatment programs that are isolated from mainstream health care and other social services.

In an era of managed care and decreasing public funds for services that are demonstrated as not cost-effective, the provision of health care must necessarily be limited. However, funds can still be allocated in a rational, fair, and effective way if the most expensive treatments are reserved for the most serious cases and the least intensive interventions that have a reasonable chance of success are applied as a first response. This *stepped care* approach to delivering treatment services operates according to the following principles (Sobell and Sobell, 1999):

- Both assessment and treatment should be individualized, with different types and intensities tailored to the presenting problem (or problems) and client characteristics.
- The treatment initially recommended should be the least intensive and least costly treatment that is most likely—based on research, assessment findings, and clinical judgment—to resolve the identified problem.
- More intensive and expensive treatments should be reserved for more serious problems and for clients who do not respond to less intensive interventions.
- Where two interventions are equally effective for clients with certain characteristics, the less costly treatment should be tried first. This principle applies to the use of group treatment instead of individual care and to counseling by telephone, Internet, or mail instead of a personal meeting when these approaches are demonstrated to be equally effective.
- All recommended treatments should be based on solid research or, in the absence of adequate data, peer-established best practice guidelines.
- When making recommendations, clinicians should consider the client's preferences regarding treatment. "It makes little sense to refer clients to treatments that they believe are inappropriate and where the referrals are likely to result in those individuals dropping out of treatment" (Sobell and Sobell, 1999).

- Both assessments and treatments should be ongoing, increasingly comprehensive processes, not one-time activities. That is, simple screening and brief interventions may be sufficient for excessive drinkers identified in opportunistic settings, but more comprehensive assessments and more intensive treatments should follow if clients do not respond satisfactorily to initial care based on empirically established outcome measures. The need for additional treatment is based on both performance in the initial setting and another, more thorough assessment. Additional treatment may consist of more sessions in the original setting or referral to an alternative intervention, depending on clinical judgment, assessment findings, and client preferences.

The implications for motivational interventions of a stepped care approach to planning and service delivery are many. First, this model reflects many of the same principles underlying motivational approaches, including the importance of offering treatment options to clients and respecting their informed choice in treatment decisions. Second, the stepped care model supports an increase in brief outpatient interventions that could effectively address mildly impaired persons without providing unnecessary services for them, while meeting public health objectives for reducing the high social costs of hazardous drinking and drug use. Motivational approaches entailing an assessment and only a few clinical sessions have proven effective and could be offered in a wide range of health care settings, provided staff members are properly trained and agree with the method. Finally, since a stepped care approach to planning and allocating treatment services is performance-based and does not specify a hierarchy of interventions, motivational approaches can be applied in different formats. For example, clinicians can experiment with the number, duration, or frequency of sessions to find the format that best meets individual needs.

Applications of Motivational Approaches In Specific Treatment Settings

No single method to incorporate motivational approaches into service delivery systems is superior to others. A few obvious opportunities present themselves, but applications have been and continue to be a matter of clinical creativity. Some of the ways in which motivational interventions have been used are as

- A means of rapid engagement in the general medical setting to facilitate referral to treatment
- A first session to increase the likelihood that a client will return and to deliver a useful service if the client does not return
- An empowering brief consultation when a client is placed on a waiting list, rather than telling a client just to wait for treatment
- A preparation for treatment to increase retention and participation
- A help to clients coerced into treatment to move beyond initial feelings of anger and resentment
- A means to overcome client defensiveness and resistance
- A stand-alone intervention in settings where there is only brief contact
- A counseling style used throughout the process of change

Often, there is a relatively short period of time in which you, the clinician, can make a beneficial impact. This may be because length of service is restricted by reimbursement policies or by the nature of a program (e.g., an employee assistance program) or the setting may allow for only a single encounter, such as an emergency department. Moreover, the average length of stay in substance abuse treatment is very short. If you do not make an impact in the first session or two, you may make no impact at all. Thus, it is wise to make the best use of the first contact with a client.

However, this may conflict with the practical demands of a clinical setting in which paperwork must be done for admission, a waiting room is full of clients, or a treatment plan must be completed by the fourth session. Nevertheless, it is usually a mistake to *start* a session with filling out forms. Take some time at the very beginning just to listen to your client, to understand him, and enhance motivation for change. If one contact is all you get with this client, filling out a questionnaire alone is unlikely to help. Research shows that even a single session of motivational interviewing does make a difference.

The rest of this chapter describes creative ways in which the motivational approaches described in this TIP have been implemented.

In the Emergency Department

One of the first demonstrations of the power of brief interventions was implemented in the emergency department at Massachusetts General Hospital in the late 1950s. Morris Chafetz was concerned that many of the patients treated in the emergency department were there because of health problems and injuries related to their drinking. Yet nothing was being done about it. A resident might shake a finger at the patient and say, "You really have to quit drinking," but never follow up. In fact, less than 5 percent of these patients sought treatment for their alcohol problems.

Chafetz wondered what would happen if an empathic counselor were present to listen to these patients after they had been treated medically, encouraging them to come back for treatment. Thus, he conducted two studies in which patients coming into the emergency

department with alcohol-related medical problems were assigned, at random, to meet with a counselor for a short conversation (15 to 20 minutes) following their medical treatment. In both studies (Chafetz et al., 1962, 1964), patients were 12 times more likely to return for treatment of their alcohol problems if they had talked with an empathic counselor (65 and 78 percent), compared with patients receiving only emergency department care (5 and 6 percent).

At Boston Medical Center's Emergency Department, doctors developed Project ASSERT (an acronym for Alcohol and Substance abuse Services and Educating providers to Refer patients to Treatment), originally funded by the Center for Substance Abuse Treatment. Project ASSERT employs health promotion advocates who screen emergency department patients for substance use, establish rapport, explore change issues, assess readiness to change using the readiness ruler, negotiate a plan, and facilitate access to the substance abuse treatment system. The program also trains and involves the residents in emergency medicine. Published followup data show a 45-percent reduction in severity of drug problems, a 56-percent reduction in alcohol use, and a 64-percent reduction in frequency of binge drinking. Additionally, 50 percent of the patients reported keeping an appointment for treatment (Bernstein et al., 1997a).

In Obstetric Clinics

Another example of an effective motivational intervention is the pilot study conducted by Nancy Handmaker with pregnant women who attended obstetric clinics. Women who reported some drinking in the past month underwent a structured assessment and were assigned to receive either a motivational intervention or written materials informing them of the risks of drinking during pregnancy. In the nonjudgmental personal interviews the women reported considerably more drinking than they did on screening questionnaires. Among women with higher estimated peak blood alcohol concentrations, motivational intervention was more effective in reducing consumption during the next 2 months of pregnancy (Handmaker et al., 1999).

In Medical Settings

Several studies have used motivational interventions in medical settings. Hospitalized teen smokers benefited from brief motivational interviews in their smoking dependence and number of days they smoked (Colby et al., 1998). Researchers determined the stage of change of patients in a primary care clinic who gave at least one positive response to the CAGE. Although the researchers had expected most of these individuals to be in the contemplation stage, the patients were found to be primarily in the action stage, and most were no longer using alcohol (Samet and O'Connor, 1998). This implies that primary care physicians can perhaps contribute best to their patients' sobriety by providing positive feedback about remaining abstinent and using relapse prevention techniques. Primary care providers who received a brief training program on patient-centered alcohol counseling improved their counseling skills and were much better prepared to intervene with problem drinkers (Ockene et al., 1997).

Motivational Interviewing and the Marijuana Checkup

A study conducted at the University of Washington offered a two-session Marijuana Checkup, publicized through the local media with a telephone number for inquiries. In the initial weeks of the program, the staff noticed that 60 percent of eligible callers who scheduled an assessment session failed to keep their appointments. This rate was reduced by half when the initial telephone intake protocol was modified. The new approach involved a 3- to 5-minute dialog during which the staff person asked a series of open-ended questions and, using reflective listening, discussed the caller's reasons for being interested in the program.

The Matrix Model for Drug Users

In 1994, the National Institute on Drug Abuse funded the development of a model intensive outpatient treatment program that was to be constructed from research-supported elements (Rawson et al., 1995). The first version of this model, intended for persons with stimulant use disorders, contained specific instructions for therapists and an articulated philosophy of treatment that emphasized a motivational approach:

> The therapist fosters a positive, healthy relationship with the patient and uses that relationship to reinforce positive behavior change. The interaction is realistic and direct but not confrontational or parental. Therapists are trained to view the treatment process as an exercise that will promote self-esteem, dignity, and self-worth. A positive relationship between patient and therapist is a critical element for patient retention. (p. 120)

The basic motivation-enhancing philosophy that characterized the original Matrix model of outpatient treatment for stimulant users has since been broadened to include protocols for substances. The model continues to be evaluated and refined according to the results of ongoing outcome studies.

Motivational Enhancement Therapy

The Commonwealth of Virginia has developed and is using a multicomponent model that incorporates Motivational Enhancement Therapy (MET). The program is called SATOE for its origins in the Substance Abuse Treatment Outcome Evaluation work group—a statewide gathering of clients and representatives from Virginia's local public substance abuse treatment agencies, universities, and the Department of Mental Health, Mental Retardation and Substance Abuse Services.

The evolving elements of the SATOE model include

- Assessments of clients
- Placements of clients in appropriate levels and types of services
- Utilization review and improvements of service delivery
- Treatment outcome evaluations

The SATOE model currently consists of five primary components:

- Diagnoses of substance abuse disorders according to criteria in the *Diagnostic and Statistical Manual of Mental Disorders*, 4th Edition (DSM-IV)
- MET assessments and interventions
- Addiction Severity Index (ASI) evaluation
- Standardized client placement criteria, such as the Patient Placement Criteria of the American Society of Addiction Medicine
- Utilization review using treatment services review

In the SATOE model, clients are typically given the University of Rhode Island Change Assessment (URICA)—a 32-item, self-report questionnaire that assesses the client's readiness to change problematic behaviors (see Chapter 8). URICA scores guide clinicians' judgment regarding clients' readiness for treatment. This instrument was selected because many public sector clients have diagnoses of a substance abuse disorder coexisting with mental health disorders, and this instrument allows respondents to specify the target problem, in contrast to other readiness instruments that are specific to substance use.

In one implementation version of the model, clients identified as precontemplators (and sometimes contemplators) by URICA-supported clinical assessments are placed in a separate, time-limited (4 to 8 weeks) motivationally oriented treatment track that uses MET principles and interventions. Although some clients find this course of MET-based treatment

sufficient for them to make desired behavioral changes, the MET-based treatment is more typically expected to increase clients' readiness for more traditional substance abuse treatment that also incorporates MET principles. Other approaches to implementing MET under the SATOE involve integrating MET principles throughout traditional outpatient and intensive outpatient models of treatment.

After the client completes the brief course of MET-based treatment, the program calls for a reevaluation of the client using such behavioral indicators as treatment compliance or urinalysis results in addition to another URICA assessment or an informal clinical assessment of readiness for change. Based on the findings, the client can be discharged or a new treatment plan can be developed that involves additional motivationally oriented treatment, traditional substance abuse treatment, other services such as case management or individual therapy and, in the case of clients referred by the criminal justice system, referral to criminal justice agencies for graduated sanctions. Although the State expects to support all of SATOE's components, initial emphasis has been placed on the readiness to change assessments and the ASI. A list of providers has been established to facilitate communication among users of the model or its components. In addition, a comprehensive evaluation of the implementation parameters and a cost-benefit analysis of the model are planned.

To facilitate implementation of SATOE, the State undertook several important activities. The first was to develop a manual of MET principles and techniques. Because the best-known protocol of MET for substance abuse treatment is the Project MATCH effort for brief *individual* treatment of clients, and *group* treatment is the prevalent modality in Virginia's public programs, the Virginia Addiction Technology Transfer Center developed a *group-based* model of MET treatment and produced a manual for this protocol (Ingersoll and Wagner, 1997). This model has been demonstrated to be effective in increasing readiness to change (Wagner et al., 1998). The second activity is a large-scale training initiative in which administrative staff is introduced to basic MET principles and implications for program changes, while clinical staff is trained in MET principles and related clinical interventions.

Virginia expects the SATOE model to evolve over time in response to feedback from the field. Serious attention is now being given to alternatives within the model that will allow local agencies to adjust it to their priorities and limitations. For example, some treatment agencies in the State have chosen to integrate MET principles throughout their substance abuse disorder services continuum or in specific services such as intensive outpatient therapy, rather than to have a separate MET-based treatment track. Whereas the standard MET protocol involves four sessions, the SATOE model will explore longer term and even open-ended versions to accommodate the expectations of local criminal justice agencies.

Implementation of the SATOE model represents a potential paradigmatic change for Virginia's delivery system for substance abuse treatment. The bottom line in all SATOE-related efforts has been the development of methodologies that permit public-sector agencies to provide the most appropriate and cost-effective services.

An African-Centered Application of Motivational Intervention

In working with African-American clients, the application of motivational intervention with a culturally congruent manner can be very effective in eliciting increased self-disclosure, engagement in the treatment process, and positive treatment outcomes. For example, in the development of discrepancy, amplifying discrepancies between substance use behavior

and the client's perceived purpose, reason for being, or destiny in life creates significant dissonance and reflective pause. Other culturally significant discrepancies include the discrepancy between substance use and commitment to the well-being of the community; substance use and relationships with others; substance use and fulfillment of destiny; substance use and one's spiritual development and hardiness; substance use and acting "out of character." These discrepancies relate to culturally meaningful principles among African-Americans—cultural principles that reflect their African cultural heritage (Grills and Rowe, 1998; Longshore et al., 1998). These include principles of interconnectedness, responsibility to the community, the belief that the essential core that is the self is divine essence, the belief that each person has a God-given purpose in life, and the importance of developing good character. Additionally, a reframing of healing (recovery) from a process of just healing the personal self to a process that stimulates healing of the community engages the client more substantively in a consideration of his substance use. One's own healing represents a healing of the community because of the essential interdependent nature of the African-American communities (Rowe and Grills, 1993).

Finally, the application of motivational intervention with African-American clients has been enhanced through the contextualization of personal substance use within a historical and societal reality. Substance use is understood not solely as a function of attributes of the individual but also within the context of very real historical and systemic forces of oppression and racism in the United States that aggressively impinge upon the well-being and life-affirming practices of the individual, the family, and the community. The adverse effects of substance use are considered to erode life chances, family life, cultural traditions, and sense of community life for African-Americans (Goddard, 1992).

This culturally congruent application of motivational intervention has been found effective in the movement of African-American clients from precontemplation to contemplation, contemplation to action, and from action to maintenance (Longshore et al., 1998).

Adolescents with Multiple Drug Problems

The adolescent treatment program at the University of New Mexico Center on Alcoholism, Substance Abuse, and Addictions works mostly with adolescents who have overwhelming problems. They use multiple drugs, are in trouble with the law, are failing in or have dropped out of school, have tumultuous and sometimes abusive family relationships, sometimes belong to gangs, and are engaged in many kinds of risky behavior. Almost none of them come for treatment of their own accord. They are sent by the courts, brought by a parent, or transported from a custodial setting. They are often angry, silent, brooding, confrontational, or defiant. They resent being told by adults that they should say no to drugs.

Even with all the external pressure from courts and family, retention is a significant problem. The average adolescent client admitted to the program stays for five outpatient sessions. To address this problem, motivational interviewing was used at intake (Aubrey, 1998). Adolescents entering the program were randomly assigned to receive the usual intake interview or one motivational interview that included personal feedback from assessment. Aubrey found that her adolescent clients responded very well to motivational interviewing, a counseling style quite different from what they had expected. They also stayed in treatment longer. Those who had a motivational interview at intake stayed for an average of 17 sessions compared to 6 sessions

for those receiving the regular intake procedure. Most important was the impact on adolescents' substance use. At the 3-month followup, adolescents who received the motivational interview had a significantly higher rate of abstinence than the control group (70 percent versus 43 percent), paralleling previous findings with adult inpatient (Brown and Miller, 1993) and outpatient populations (Bien et al., 1993b).

Women With Multiple Vulnerabilities

Individuals with substance abuse problems are more likely to have an accompanying health, mental health, or social problem than the general population. Women are especially vulnerable; studies indicate higher rates of coexisting disorders for women than men (Helzer and Pryzbeck, 1988; Regier et al., 1990). Recognizing that women may have multiple problems and that they may be prepared to change one aspect of their lives but not another, researchers in California developed the Steps of Change model, based on the stages of change (Brown et al., in press; Melchior et al., in press).

The Steps of Change assesses a woman's readiness to enter treatment by examining four categories: (1) readiness to change substance use behavior, (2) readiness to change high-risk sex practices, (3) readiness to change a domestic violence situation, and (4) readiness to deal with emotional problems. This allows a woman to consider her multiple needs and enter into appropriate types of treatment or integrated treatment. Initial results from the study showed that the four levels of stage of change do not indicate a single underlying desire to change, thus supporting the use of the Steps of Change to evaluate readiness in various domains, and that those problems presenting the greatest potential for immediate harm to women typically induce the greatest willingness to change. These are important considerations when predicting treatment entry and outcome

A Short-Term Residential Treatment Program

In a Southwestern treatment program that serves a population that is 95 percent Native American, a number of motivational strategies are being used to enhance treatment outcome in the various program components of the 150-bed facility. For example, the facility's clinical staff members wear name badges that identify more than the name and title of the clinician. Each clinician's name badge includes reference to the ethnic group or family of origin—tribal members are identified by one of two dozen clans that comprise the tribal identity in the native language and non-Native Americans are identified by their ancestry (e.g., European, African). Clients entering the 16½-day residential program are provided material to design their own individualized name badges that contain information regarding their families of origin. Clinicians are encouraged to integrate use of clan relationships in their individual and family interventions, so it is common to hear references to a client as younger brother, grandmother, or uncle. These references enhance the motivation of clients to participate in the treatment process and become engaged in the therapeutic dynamics of the Native American program.

In a 6-month followup of three dozen former clients, this program found that 70 percent of those completing the residential program were still doing better than prior to admission; they had lower rates of alcohol consumption and improved quality of life and family interactions. Although opportunity for continued improvement in those areas of functioning remained, cases of significant client change occurred. There were followup reports of individuals establishing places of residence after a number of months or years of alcohol abuse during which these clients had become homeless. Some clients began to build on the basic cultural teachings to which they had been exposed. Clients also attempted to find mentors outside the treatment program from whom they could learn more about traditions, such as how to run a sweat lodge and how to facilitate these ceremonies for family or friends. The importance of including familial relationships as part of the therapeutic process was key in motivating clients to begin changing drinking behaviors that standard treatment programs had deemed very difficult, if not impossible, to change.

One former client, a graduate of that followup cohort, left the region to enter a standard 30-day residential treatment program. After completing that 30-day program, the client was encouraged to volunteer and remain as a cultural advisor, as other members of the client's tribe were being admitted. Two years later, that client and volunteer returned home and obtained employment as a Traditional Counselor in the 16½-day program where he originally began recovery.

Group Settings

The current context of service delivery places heavy emphasis on group treatment. Many motivation-enhancing activities can take place in group therapy that cannot be done in individual treatment (e.g., clients can receive feedback from peers); however, several significant clinical issues arise in terms of conducting groups: attrition, structure of groups, group cohesion, and handling difficult clients (Dies, 1994). Conducting group therapy is considerably more complicated than conducting individual treatment, as it involves handling multiple clients simultaneously. Also, the use of behavioral materials and motivational strategies and techniques in groups must be done in such a way as to accomplish the same objectives as in

Motivational Enhancement in Group Therapy

Conducting motivational interventions in a group versus individual format is more difficult, more complex, and more challenging. Personally, however, I find it much more rewarding. In group therapy, particularly using motivational techniques and strategies, clients learn through the group. It is like a hall of mirrors; clients get the feel of how they come across. For me, when a client uses reflective listening with another client or points out another client's ambivalence, the group is like a living, learning laboratory of experiences practiced first in a safe environment before being tried in the real world. In the end, what the members have is a common goal to reduce or stop substance abuse, and it is here that their mutual support and peer pressure is effective.

Linda C. Sobell, Consensus Panel Member

individual therapy. Therefore, being a good clinician in an individual setting does not qualify a therapist to conduct group sessions; rather, the clinician must possess an understanding of group dynamics and have the necessary skills to conduct group therapy.

Efforts to date have yielded mixed results for motivational enhancement therapy in group settings. Some studies find that motivational interviewing in a group setting is less effective than in individual counseling; in one case, college students treated in a group actually fared slightly worse than those in a control group given no treatment (Walters et al., in press).

However, one team at the University of Washington found that heavy-drinking college students markedly reduced their drinking in response to a 6-week group program (Baer et al., 1992). Favorable results were also obtained in a recent, randomized clinical trial evaluating a motivationally based cognitive–behavioral intervention, Guided Self-Change (GSC) treatment. This trial demonstrated that motivationally based techniques and strategies were as successful in group format as in individual treatment for both alcohol and substance abuse (Sobell et al., 1995; Sobell and Sobell, 1998). Specifically, the results from this trial were (1) no evidence of differential attrition over the course of treatment as a result of random assignment to group or individual treatment, (2) very high group cohesion,

considered essential to successful group outcomes (Cota et al., 1995; MacKenzie, 1983; Satterfield, 1994), based on client reports that they were able to respond with relative openness, (3) similar outcomes for motivationally based GSC group and levels of client satisfaction as for individually treated clients, (4) a significant decrease in drinking and drug use from pretreatment to treatment in both the group and individual formats, and changes maintained 1 year following treatment, and (5) a considerable cost reduction when providing motivationally based treatment in a group rather than an individual format—41.5 percent cost savings for the actual service provision, and an eightfold reduction in missed appointments in the group format compared to individual sessions. Additionally, 80 percent of all individual and group clients said they would recommend the GSC program to a friend.

Because social support is intrinsic to group treatment, clients in a group can reinforce and help maintain each others' changes. People start to open up over the course of treatment as they receive feedback and are reinforced for self-disclosure—two important elements of group treatment and motivational interviewing. When using advice feedback materials in group, a "round robin" procedure can be used whereby clients engage in reflective listening and comment in a way that promotes discrepancy as well as points out observed ambivalence in their peers. In group therapy, all clients act as agents of change by helping each other, through a peer-based process, to strengthen their motivation and commitment to change. The group rather than the individual clinician is the agent of change (Dies, 1994).

Although this study offers much promise, it is the first study to use a motivationally based intervention in a group format. It seems reasonable that motivational approaches could be adapted for use in groups to increase cost effectiveness, yet it is clear that some efforts at group motivational intervention have failed or even been detrimental. Until effective group treatment methods are clarified, it would be wise to evaluate new programs to make sure they are accomplishing what is intended.

10 Directions for Future Research

Motivational intervention is a relatively new, but favorably received, approach to encouraging positive behavioral change. The approach is derived from a variety of sources, including client-centered counseling, cognitive therapy, systems theory, and a transtheoretical model of change (Miller and Rollnick, 1991). To date, motivational interventions have been successfully used with a variety of problems, client populations, and settings (see Chapter 2), and the methodology appears to be generally applicable, although it was primarily developed for heavy alcohol drinkers and cigarette smokers. A number of controlled clinical trials of motivational interviewing and brief interventions that use a motivational approach have been conducted with promising results (Bien et al., 1993; Noonan and Moyers, 1997).

As with many innovative treatment approaches, however, there are still many unanswered questions about motivational interventions—especially as the concept has evolved over its comparatively short lifespan. Many of these questions are issues for an ongoing and broad research agenda; others are more practical problems pertaining to clinical applications. Many of the questions are also complex and interrelated so that untangling answers presents a challenge.

Some of the questions or issues that call for additional research include the following:

- **What are the active ingredients of motivational interventions?** Although there has been some attempt to identify the common elements of brief interventions and to add more fundamental elements to motivational approaches, no structured research has yet parceled out the separate elements and determined which are most critical or which combinations are most useful. Reflective listening, structured feedback, discrepancy development, and decisional balances, for example, have each assumed some prominence in discussions of the approach. This question probably does not have a simple answer because some types of clients are likely to respond better to one aspect of the model than another and at different points in the change process.

- **Can motivational interventions be standardized?** A corollary of the first question regarding active ingredients is whether motivational approaches can be successfully integrated into training manuals so that clinicians can be taught the basic elements and monitored to determine their adherence to the model. One example of such a program is already available, the Project MATCH manual published by the National Institute on Alcohol Abuse and Alcoholism (Miller et al., 1995c).

- **What types of clients benefit most—and least—from motivational interventions?** There is a danger here that in the interest of health care cost containment, someone might conclude, "Why not give *only* motivational interventions?" Far too little is known at this time about who does and who does not respond to brief motivational counseling—and why. About half the studies of brief motivational interventions have been of heavy drinkers in medical settings who were *not* seeking treatment for alcohol problems. Other studies have shown that motivational intervention increases the effectiveness of subsequent treatment (Bien et al., 1993; Noonan and Moyers, 1997). Project MATCH tested a four-session motivational enhancement therapy against two 12-session outpatient treatment methods and found similar overall long-term outcomes, with some evidence that more severely dependent clients fared better in longer treatment (Project MATCH Research Group, 1997a). It is far too early to predict who needs only brief motivational counseling and who needs more intensive treatment.

- **What standard outcomes for motivational interventions can be defined and measured?** Motivational approaches have been used to influence a variety of factors, including substance consumption patterns, successful referrals, compliance with treatment, and successful completion of the prescribed regimen. Research evaluations must specify what outcomes are expected and how these will be measured. One issue with motivational interventions is the variable effect sizes in the studies to date (Noonan and Moyers, 1997). Similarly, where the intervention is targeted at compliance with medical or treatment advice (e.g., taking medications as prescribed, participating regularly in exercise or rehabilitation programs), how large an effect is expected and how long will it last? Another related question is what, if any, proximal outcomes predict longer term outcomes.

- **What characteristics of clinicians influence the effectiveness of motivational interventions?** Clinicians, as well as clients, have characteristics that negatively or positively influence how closely they can adhere to the model and what their expectancies are with regard to the potential effectiveness of motivational interventions. Clinicians who delivered brief advice with a medically authoritative voice or were not carefully trained may have compromised the *spirit* of motivational interviewing and negatively tainted research findings (Noonan and Moyers, 1997). Motivational interviewing is not an approach that is compatible with all clinicians.

- **Are stage-matched interventions appropriate?** Some evidence indicates that when clients are at early stages of readiness, they are most likely to respond favorably to a motivationally focused intervention rather than one that focuses on behavioral change (Heather et al., 1996b). This suggests that different treatment strategies may be optimal at different stages of change. A different question is whether certain motivational strategies are appropriate *only* at certain stages of change (Perz et al., 1996), or with certain populations (Obert et al., 1997). Do action-oriented treatments work better for clients in the action stage? Two studies found that outcomes were similar for action-stage clients given motivational interviewing versus behavioral change treatment (Heather et al., 1996; Project MATCH Research Group, 1997a;). Which interventions are better at which stages or with which populations? There is still much to learn.

- **How effective and cost-efficient are motivational interventions in relation to other established and more extensive substance abuse treatments?** At least one clinical trial has indicated that motivational interviewing was not inferior to a more

Motivational Interviewing With Dually Diagnosed Inpatients

I became interested in motivational interviewing (MI) when my team and I were trying to improve the rate of attendance at aftercare appointments for dually diagnosed patients discharged from our psychiatric units. I was surprised to see that little had been written about the efficacy of motivational interventions with this population. So, my team and I decided to conduct a study of MI's effectiveness with dually diagnosed patients. We randomly assigned half of our patients to standard treatment (ST), in which they received standard inpatient psychiatric care, including standard discharge planning where the team would encourage and explain the importance of aftercare. The other half were assigned to ST but also received a motivational assessment, feedback on the results at admission, and a 1-hour motivational interview just before discharge.

We found that dually diagnosed patients in the MI group attended their first outpatient appointment at a rate that was two and a half times greater than the ST group (Swanson et al., in press), suggesting that MI, with virtually no modification, was effective. The intervention appeared to be particularly effective for patients with very low motivation. This could have been because these patients were more verbal about their ambivalence than others and because we viewed MI as a perfect way to resolve ambivalence. Another thing we learned was that asking patients about why they would *not* attend aftercare had surprise value and greatly enhanced the rapport between therapist and patient. It appeared to let patients know that we were not only going to tell them about the importance of aftercare, but that we were actually willing to discuss their ambivalence about it.

Patients were also surprised when we did not directly counter their reasons for not going to aftercare. For example, if a patient said, "I'm better now, I don't need aftercare," we would not say, "But in order to stay well, you need to continue your treatment." Instead, we used *open-ended questions* (e.g., "What do you think helped you get better?" or simply, "Tell me more about that") or *amplified reflection* (e.g., "So, you're saying you probably won't need any other treatment ever again" or, for more fragile patients, "It's hard for you to imagine a reason why you might continue to need treatment"). When patients offered specific disadvantages of pursuing aftercare, such as loss of time from work or negative reactions from family, we similarly responded with open-ended questions and reflective listening (e.g., "It sounds like your job is very important to you and that you wouldn't want anything to get in the way of that"). Frequently such questions and reflections would lead a patient to counter his own initially resistant statements. It turned out that even difficult patients could sell themselves on the idea of aftercare better than we ever could, and MI gave us the perfect method for facilitating this process. What was most important, however, was what we did *not* do, namely, argue with the patient or even attempt to therapeutically dispute his (sometimes) illogical ideas about aftercare. Instead, we waited for kernels of motivation and simply shaped them along until the patient finally heard himself arguing in favor of seeking further services.

Michael V. Pantalon, Field Reviewer

extended support group in helping adult marijuana users reduce use or achieve and maintain abstinence (Noonan and Moyers, 1997). Similarly, in Project MATCH, a motivational enhancement approach yielded comparable overall outcomes at lower cost, compared with two longer treatment methods. Replications and refinements of this type of study must be conducted to ascertain whether motivational approaches are realistic and less costly alternative interventions for some clients.

- **How do culture and context influence the effectiveness of motivational interventions?** Project MATCH found no differences in the treatment response of African-American, Hispanic, and non-Hispanic white outpatients to motivational enhancement therapy and two other treatment approaches (Project MATCH Research Group, 1997a). Yet ethnicity was defined simplistically here, as in most studies, as a self-identified label. More sophisticated analyses of ethnic influences are needed, because within-group heterogeneity is missed by such crude categorization, also called "ethnic gloss" (Longshore and Grills, 1998). Levels of acculturation, language, and counselor–client match can influence the process and outcome of motivational interventions.

- **What kinds of training and support are necessary to teach motivational interventions?** The clinical approaches described in this TIP are more a motivational *style* of counseling, than a set of tricks or techniques. Clinicians differ in their effectiveness with motivational counseling (Project MATCH Research Group, 1998b). As the need to teach motivational interventions increases, questions to be considered will include the following: What are the "technology transfer" aspects of

teaching this motivational approach? What training formats are most effective in changing counselor practice behavior to influence clients' responses during and after treatment? What aspects of motivational intervention are the most important to teach, and how is such teaching best done? It seems likely, though, that more than a single workshop presentation would be necessary to change established clinical practices. Perhaps most promising is the incorporation of this approach into the training of *new* addiction professionals.

Conclusion

Many different motivational approaches have been discussed in this TIP. Certainly, the evidence to date is very encouraging that even brief interventions can influence client motivation and trigger significant improvement. However, we are just beginning to understand how and why these approaches work, and how best to incorporate them into health care services with various populations. The use of these promising methods in the future will depend on the creativity of clinicians and researchers to adopt, adapt, and evaluate them to make them effective for clients.

Appendix A
Bibliography

Agency for Health Care Policy and Research. *Smoking Cessation: Clinical Practice Guideline, Number 18.* Washington, DC: U.S. Government Printing Office, 1996.

Alcoholics Anonymous. *Alcoholics Anonymous: The Story of How Many Thousands of Men and Women Have Recovered From Alcoholism,* 3rd ed. New York: Alcoholics Anonymous World Services, 1976.

Allen, J.P., and Columbus, M., eds. *Assessing Alcohol Problems: A Guide for Clinicians and Researchers.* Bethesda, MD: National Institute on Alcohol Abuse and Alcoholism, 1995.

Allport, G.W.; Vernon, P.E.; and Lindzey, G. *Study of Values: A Scale for Measuring the Dominant Interests in Personality,* 3rd ed. Boston: Houghton-Mifflin, 1960.

Allsop, S.; Saunders, B.; Phillips, M.; and Carr, A. A trial of relapse prevention with severely dependent male problem drinkers. *Addiction* 92:61–73, 1997.

Alterman, A.I.; Kampman, K.; Boardman, C.R.; Cacciola, J.S.; Rutherford, M.J.; McKay, J.R.; and Maany, I. A cocaine-positive baseline urine predicts outpatient treatment attrition and failure to attain initial abstinence. *Drug and Alcohol Dependence* 46:79–85, 1997.

Alterman, A.I.; McKay, J.R.; Mulvaney, F.D.; and McLellan, A.T. Prediction of attrition from day hospital treatment in lower socioeconomic cocaine-dependent men. *Drug and Alcohol Dependence* 40:227–233, 1996.

American Psychiatric Association. *Diagnostic and Statistical Manual of Mental Disorders,* 4th ed. Washington, DC: American Psychiatric Association, 1994.

American Psychiatric Association. Practice guidelines for the treatment of substance use disorders: Alcohol, cocaine, opioids. *American Journal of Psychiatry* 152(11 Suppl.):1–59, 1995.

American Society of Addiction Medicine. *Patient Placement Criteria for the Treatment of Psychoactive Substance Use Disorders,* 2nd ed. Washington, DC: American Society of Addiction Medicine, 1996.

Anderson, P., and Scott, E. The effect of general practitioners' advice to heavy drinking men. *British Journal of Addiction* 87:891–900, 1992.

Anglin, M.D.; Hser, Y.; Crits-Cristoph, P.; Cummings, L.; Hall, S.; Kosten, T.R.; and Martin, W.R. Treatment research: 1989–1991. In: *Drug Abuse and Drug Abuse Research: The Fourth Triennial Report to Congress From the Secretary, Department of Health and Human Services.* Rockville, MD: National Institute on Drug Abuse, 1992 (unpublished).

Annis, H.M., and Davis, C.S. Self-efficacy and the prevention of alcoholic relapse: Initial findings from a treatment trial. In: Baker, T., and Cannon, D., eds. *Assessment and Treatment of Addictive Disorders.* New York: Praeger, 1988. pp. 88–112.

Annis, H.M., and Davis, C.S. Relapse prevention. *Alcohol Health and Research World* 15:204–212, 1991.

Annis, H.M., and Graham, J.M. *Situational Confidence Questionnaire (SCQ-39): User's Guide.* Toronto, ON: Addiction Research Foundation, 1988.

Annis, H.M., and Graham, J.M. *Situational Confidence Questionnaire.* Toronto, ON: Addiction Research Foundation, 1990.

Annis, H.M., and Graham, J.M. Profile types on the Inventory of Drinking Situations: Implications for relapse prevention counseling. *Psychology of Addictive Behaviors* 9:176–182, 1995.

Appelbaum, A. A critical re-examination of the concept of "motivation for change" in psychoanalytic treatment. *International Journal of Psychoanalysis* 53:51–59, 1972.

Aubrey, L.L. "Motivational interviewing with adolescents presenting for outpatient substance abuse treatment." Ph.D. diss., University of New Mexico. *Dissertation Abstracts International*, 59-03B, 1357, 1998.

Azrin, N.H., and Besalel, V.A. *Job Club Counselor's Manual. A Behavioral Approach to Vocational Counseling.* Baltimore, MD: University Park Press, 1980.

Azrin, N.H., and Besalel, V.A. *Finding a Job.* Berkeley, CA: Ten Speed Press, 1982.

Azrin, N.H.; Sisson, R.W.; Meyers, R.J.; and Godley, M.D. Alcoholism treatment by disulfiram and community reinforcement therapy. *Journal of Behavior Therapy and Experimental Psychiatry* 13(2):105–112, 1982.

Babor, T.F., and Grant, M., eds. *Project on Identification and Management of Alcohol-Related Problems. Report on Phase II: A Randomized Clinical Trial of Brief Interventions in Primary Health Care.* Geneva, Switzerland: World Health Organization, 1992.

Baer, J.S.; Marlatt, G.A.; Kivlahan, D.R.; Fromme, K.; Larimer, M.E.; and Williams, E. Experimental test of three methods of alcohol risk reduction with young adults. *Journal of Consulting and Clinical Psychology* 60(6):974–979, 1992.

Bandura, A. Human agency in social cognitive theory. *American Psychologist* 44:1175–1184, 1989.

Bandura, A. *Self-Efficacy: The Exercise of Control.* New York: W.H. Freeman, 1997.

Baumeister, R.F. The crystallization of discontent in the process of major life change. In: Heatherton, T.F., and Weinberger, J.L., eds. *Can Personality Change?* Washington, DC: American Psychological Association, 1994. pp. 281–294.

Beck, A.T.; Wright, F.D.; Newman, C.F.; and Liese, B.S. *Cognitive Therapy of Substance Abuse.* New York: Guilford Press, 1993.

Beckman, L.J. An attributional analysis of Alcoholics Anonymous. *Journal of Studies on Alcohol* 41:714–726, 1980.

Bernstein E.; Bernstein, J.; and Levenson, S. Project ASSERT: An ED-based intervention to increase access to primary care, preventive services, and the substance abuse treatment system. *Annals of Emergency Medicine* 30(2):181–197, 1997a.

Bernstein, E.; Bernstein, J.; Schulz, C.; and Shepard, D.S. *Substance Abuse in New Hampshire: Intervention.* Waltham, MA: Institute for Health Policy, Brandeis University, 1997b.

Bien, T.H. "Motivational intervention with alcohol outpatients." Ph.D. diss., University of New Mexico, 1992.

Bien, T.H.; Miller, W.R.; and Boroughs, J.M. Motivational interviewing with alcohol outpatients. *Behavioral and Cognitive Psychotherapy* 21:347–356, 1993a.

Bien, T.H.; Miller, W.R.; and Tonigan, J.S. Brief interventions for alcohol problems: A review. *Addiction* 88:315–336, 1993b.

Blomqvist, J. Paths to recovery from substance misuse: Change of lifestyle and the role of treatment. *Substance Use and Misuse* 31(13):1807–1852, 1996.

Borysenko, J., and Borysenko, M. *The Power of the Mind to Heal: Renewing Body, Mind, and Spirit.* Carson, CA: Hay House, 1995.

Brecht, M.L., and Anglin, M.D. Conditional factors of maturing out: Legal supervision and treatment. *International Journal of the Addictions* 25:395–407, 1990.

Brehm, S.S., and Brehm, J.W. *Psychological Reactance: A Theory of Freedom and Control.* New York: Academic Press, 1981.

Breslin, F.C.; Sobell, L.C.; Sobell, M.B.; and Buchan, G. "A comparison of a brief and long format for the Situational Confidence Questionnaire." Poster presented at the 31st Annual Meeting of the Association for Advancement of Behavior Therapy. Miami Beach, FL. November 1997.

Brown, J.M., and Miller, W.R. Impact of motivational interviewing on participation in residential alcoholism treatment. *Psychology of Addictive Behaviors* 7:211–218, 1993.

Brown, S.A. Drug effect expectancies and addictive behavior change. *Experimental and Clinical Psychopharmacology* 1:55–67, 1993.

Brown, S.A.; Christiansen, B.A.; and Goldman, M.S. The Alcohol Expectancy Questionnaire: An instrument for the assessment of adolescent and adult alcohol expectancies. *Journal of Studies on Alcohol* 48:483–491, 1987.

Brown, V.B.; Huba, G.J.; and Melchior, L.A. Level of burden: Women with more than one co-occurring disorder. *Journal of Psychoactive Drugs* 27(4):339–346, 1995.

Brown, V.B.; Melchior, L.A.; and Huba, G.J. Level of burden among women diagnosed with severe mental illness and substance abuse. *Journal of Psychoactive Drugs* 31(1):31–40, 1999.

Brown, V.B.; Melchior, L.A.; Panter, A.T.; Slaughter, R.; and Huba, G.J. Women's steps of change and entry into drug abuse treatment: A multidimensional stages of change model. *Journal of Substance Abuse Treatment*, in press.

Brownell, K.D.; Marlatt, G.A.; Lichtenstein, E.; and Wilson, G.T. Understanding and preventing relapse. *American Psychologist* 41:765–782, 1986.

Budman, S., and Gurman, A. *Theory and Practice of Brief Therapy.* New York: Guilford Press, 1988.

Budney, A.J., and Higgins, S.T. *Therapy Manuals for Drug Addiction. A Community Reinforcement Plus Vouchers Approach: Treating Cocaine Addiction.* DHHS Pub. No. 98-4309, Washington, DC: U.S. Government Printing Office, 1998.

Carey, K.B. Substance use reduction in the context of outpatient psychiatric treatment: A collaborative, motivational, harm reduction approach. *Community Mental Health Journal* 32:291–306, 1996.

Carpenter, R.A.; Lyons, C.A.; and Miller, W.R. Peer-managed self-control program for prevention of alcohol abuse in American Indian high school students: A pilot evaluation study. *International Journal of the Addictions* 20:299–310, 1985.

Carroll, M.E. The economic context of drug and non-drug reinforcers affects acquisition and maintenance of drug-reinforced behavior and withdrawal effects. *Drug and Alcohol Dependence* 33:201–210, 1993.

Center for Substance Abuse Treatment. *Screening and Assessment for Alcohol and Other Drug Abuse Among Adults in the Criminal Justice System.* Treatment Improvement Protocol (TIP) Series, Number 7. DHHS Pub. No. (SMA) 94-2076. Washington, DC: U.S. Government Printing Office, 1994a.

Center for Substance Abuse Treatment. *Assessment and Treatment of Patients with Coexisting Mental Illness and Alcohol and Other Drug Abuse.* Treatment Improvement Protocol (TIP) Series, Number 9. DHHS Pub. No. (SMA) 94-2078. Washington, DC: U.S. Government Printing Office, 1994b.

Center for Substance Abuse Treatment. *Assessment of Cocaine-Abusing Methadone-Maintained Patients.* Treatment Improvement Protocol (TIP) Series, Number 10. DHHS Pub. No. (SMA) 94-3003, Washington, DC: U.S. Government Printing Office, 1994c.

Center for Substance Abuse Treatment. *Simple Screening Instruments for Outreach for Alcohol and Other Drug Abuse and Infectious Diseases.* Treatment Improvement Protocol (TIP) Series, Number 11. DHHS Pub. No. (SMA) 94-2094. Washington, DC: U.S. Government Printing Office, 1994d.

Center for Substance Abuse Treatment. *Combining Substance Abuse Treatment With Intermediate Sanctions for Adults in the Criminal Justice System.* Treatment Improvement Protocol (TIP) Series, Number 12. DHHS Pub. No. (SMA) 94-3004. Washington, DC: U.S. Government Printing Office, 1994e.

Center for Substance Abuse Treatment. *The Role and Current Status of Patient Placement Criteria in the Treatment of Substance Use Disorders.* Treatment Improvement Protocol (TIP) Series, Number 13. DHHS Pub. No. (SMA) 95-3021. Washington, DC: U.S. Government Printing Office, 1995a.

Center for Substance Abuse Treatment. *Planning for Alcohol and Other Drug Abuse Treatment for Adults in the Criminal Justice System.* Treatment Improvement Protocol (TIP) Series, Number 17. DHHS Pub. No. (SMA) 95-3039. Washington, DC: U.S. Government Printing Office, 1995b.

Center for Substance Abuse Treatment. *Matching Treatment to Patient Needs in Opioid Substitution Therapy.* Treatment Improvement Protocol (TIP) Series, Number 20. DHHS Pub. No. (SMA) 95-3049. Washington, DC: U.S. Government Printing Office, 1995c.

Center for Substance Abuse Treatment. *A Guide to Substance Abuse Services for Primary Care Clinicians.* Treatment Improvement Protocol (TIP) Series, Number 24. DHHS Pub. No. (SMA) 97-3139. Washington, DC: U.S. Government Printing Office, 1997.

Center for Substance Abuse Treatment. *Substance Use Disorder Treatment for People With Physical and Cognitive Disabilities.* Treatment Improvement Protocol (TIP) Series, Number 29. DHHS Pub. No. (SMA) 98-3249. Washington, DC: U.S. Government Printing Office, 1998a.

Center for Substance Abuse Treatment. *Continuity of Offender Treatment for Substance Use Disorders From Institution to Community.* Treatment Improvement Protocol (TIP) Series, Number 30. DHHS Pub. No. (SMA) 98-3245. Washington, DC: U.S. Government Printing Office, 1998b.

Center for Substance Abuse Treatment. *Brief Interventions and Brief Therapies for Substance Abuse.* Treatment Improvement Protocol (TIP) Series. DHHS Pub. No. (SMA) 99-3353. Washington, DC: U.S. Government Printing Office, in press (a).

Center for Substance Abuse Treatment. *Substance Abuse Treatment for Persons With Child Abuse and Neglect Issues.* Treatment Improvement Protocol (TIP) Series. Washington, DC: U.S. Government Printing Office, in press (b).

Chafetz, M.E.; Blane, H.T.; Abram, H.S.; Clark, E.; Golner, J.; Hastie, E.L.; and McCourt, W.F. Establishing treatment relations with alcoholics: A supplementary report. *Journal of Nervous and Mental Disease* 138:390–393, 1964.

Chafetz, M.E.; Blane, H.T.; Abram, H.S.; Golner, J.; Lacy, E.; McCourt, W.F.; Clark, E.; and Meyers, W. Establishing treatment relations with alcoholics. *Journal of Nervous and Mental Disease* 134:395–409, 1962.

Chamberlain, P.; Patterson, G.; Reid, J.; Kavanaugh, K.; and Forgatch, M. Observation of client resistance. *Behavior Therapy* 15:144–155, 1984.

Chapman, P.L.H., and Huygens, I. An evaluation of three treatment programmes for alcoholism: An experimental study with 6- and 18-month follow-up. *British Journal of Addiction* 83:67–81, 1988.

Chen, K., and Kandel, D.B. The natural history of drug use from adolescence to mid-thirties in a general population sample. *American Journal of Public Health* 85(1):41–47, 1995.

Chick, J.; Lloyd, G.; and Crombie, E. Counselling problem drinkers in medical wards: A controlled study. *British Medical Journal* 290:965–967, 1985.

Chick, J.; Ritson, B.; Connaughton, J.; Stewart, A; and Chick, J. Advice versus extended treatment for alcoholism: A controlled study. *British Journal of Addiction* 83:159–170, 1988.

Christiansen, B.A.; Goldman, M.S.; and Inn, A. Development of alcohol-related expectancies in adolescents: Separating pharmacological from social learning influences. *Journal of Consulting and Clinical Psychology* 50:336–344. 1982.

Colby, S.M.; Monti, P.M.; Barnett, N.P.; Rohsenow, D.J.; Weissman, K.; Spirito, A.; Woolard, R.H.; and Lewander, W.J. Brief motivational interviewing in a hospital setting for adolescent smoking: A preliminary study. *Journal of Consulting and Clinical Psychology* 66:574–578, 1998.

Collins, R.L.; Lapp, W.M.; Emmons, K.M.; and Isaac, L.M. Endorsement and strength of alcohol expectancies. *Journal of Studies on Alcohol* 51(4):336–342, 1990.

Colten, M.E., and Janis, I.L. Effects of moderate self-disclosure and the balance sheet procedure. In: Janis, I.L., ed. *Counseling on Personal Decisions: Theory and Research on Short-Term Help Relationships.* New Haven, CT: Yale University Press, 1982. pp. 159–171.

Connors, G.J., and Maisto, S.A. Alcohol expectancy construct: Overview and clinical applications. *Cognitive Therapy and Research* 12:487–504, 1988.

Connors, G.J.; O'Farrell, T.J.; Cutter, H.S.G.; and Thompson, D.L. Dose-related effects of alcohol among male alcoholics, problem drinkers, and nonproblem drinkers. *Journal of Studies on Alcohol* 48:461–466, 1987.

Costello, R.M. Alcoholism treatment and evaluation: In search of methods. II. Collation of two-year follow-up studies. *International Journal of the Addictions* 10:857–867, 1975.

Cota, A.A.; Longman, R.S.; Evans, C.R.; Dion, K.L.; and Kilik, L. Using and misusing factor analysis to explore group cohesion. *Journal of Clinical Psychology* 51:308–316, 1995.

Cox, W.M.; Klinger, E.; and Blount, J.P. Alcohol use and goal hierarchies: Systematic motivational counseling for alcoholics. In: Miller, W.R., and Rollnick, S., eds. *Motivational Interviewing: Preparing People To Change Addictive Behaviors.* New York: Guilford Press, 1993. pp. 260–271.

Cummings, C.; Gordon, J.R.; and Marlatt, G.A. Relapse: Prevention and prediction. In: Miller, W.R., ed. *The Addictive Behaviors: Treatment of Alcoholism, Drug Abuse, Smoking, and Obesity.* Oxford: Pergamon Press, 1980. pp. 291–321.

Cunningham, J.A.; Sobell, L.C.; Gavin, D.R.; Sobell, M.B.; and Breslin, F.C. Assessing motivation for change: Preliminary development and evaluation of a scale measuring the costs and benefits of alcohol or drug use. *Psychology of Addictive Behaviors* 11(2):107–114, 1997.

Cunningham, J.A.; Sobell, M.B.; Sobell, L.C.; Gavin, D.R.; and Annis, H.M. Heavy drinking and negative affective situations in a general population and a treatment sample: Alternative explanations. *Psychology of Addictive Behaviors* 9:123–127, 1995.

Daley, D.C.; Salloum, I.M.; Zuckoff, A.; Kiricsi, L.; and Thase, M.E. Increasing treatment adherence among outpatients with depression and cocaine dependence: Results of a pilot study. *American Journal of Psychiatry* 155:1611–1613, 1998.

Daniels, V.; Somers, M.; and Orford, J. How can risk drinking amongst medical patients be modified? The effects of computer screening and advice and a self-help manual. *Behavioral Psychotherapy* 20:47–60, 1992.

Davidson, R. Can psychology make sense of change? In: Edwards, G., and Lader, M., eds. *Addiction: Processes of Change.* Society for the Study of Addiction Monograph No. 3. New York: Oxford University Press, 1994. pp. 51–78.

Deci, E.L. *Intrinsic Motivation.* New York: Plenum Press, 1975.

Deci, E.L. *The Psychology of Self-Determination.* Lexington, MA: Lexington Books, 1980.

De Leon, G.; Melnick, G.; Kressel, D.; and Jainchill, N. Circumstances, motivation, readiness, and suitability (the CMRS Scales): Predicting retention in therapeutic community treatment. *American Journal of Drug and Alcohol Abuse* 20(4):495–515, 1994.

DiClemente, C.C. Motivational interviewing and the stages of change. In: Miller, W.R., and Rollnick, S., eds. *Motivational Interviewing: Preparing People To Change Addictive Behavior.* New York: Guilford Press, 1991. pp. 191–202.

DiClemente, C.C.; Carbonari, J.P.; Montgomery, R.P.G.; and Hughes, S.O. The Alcohol Abstinence Self-Efficacy Scale. *Journal of Studies on Alcohol* 55(2):141–148, 1994.

DiClemente, C.C., and Prochaska, J.O. Processes and stages of self-change: Coping and competence in smoking behavior change. In: Shiffman, S., and Wills, T.A., eds. *Coping and Substance Abuse.* New York: Academic Press, 1985. pp. 319–343.

DiClemente, C.C., and Prochaska, J.O. Toward a comprehensive transtheoretical model of change: Stages of change and addictive behaviors. In: Miller, W.R., and Heather, N., eds. *Treating Addictive Behaviors,* 2nd ed. New York: Plenum Press, 1998.

DiClemente, C.C., and Scott, C.W. Stages of change: Interactions with treatment compliance and involvement. In: Onken, L.S.; Blaine, J.D.; and Boren, J.J., eds. *Beyond the Therapeutic Alliance: Keeping the Drug-Dependent Individual in Treatment.* NIDA Research Monograph Series, Number 165. DHHS Pub. No. (ADM) 97-4142. Rockville, MD: National Institute on Drug Abuse, 1997. pp. 131–156.

Dies, R.R., ed. *The Therapist's Role in Group Treatments.* New York: Guilford Press, 1994.

D'Onofrio, G.; Bernstein, E.; Bernstein, J.; Woolard, R.H.; Brewer, P.A.; Craig, S.A.; and Zink, B.J. Patients with alcohol problems in the emergency department, Part 2: Intervention and referral. *Academic Emergency Medicine* 5:1210–1217, 1998.

Drummond, D.C. Alcohol interventions: Do the best things come in small packages? *Addiction* 92(4):375–379, 1997.

Drummond, D.C.; Thom, B.; Brown, C.; Edwards, G.; and Mullan, M.J. Specialist versus general practitioner treatment of problem drinkers. *Lancet* 336:915–918, 1990.

Eastwood, G.L., and Avunduk, C. *Manual of Gastroenterology: Diagnosis and Therapy*, 2nd ed. New York: Little, Brown and Company, 1994.

Edwards, G.; Orford, J.; Egert, S.; Guthrie, S.; Hawken, A.; Hensman, C.; Mitcheson, M.; Oppenheimer, E.; and Taylor, C. Alcoholism: A controlled trial of "treatment" and "advice." *Journal of Studies on Alcohol* 38:1004–1031, 1977.

Ellis, A., and Velten, E. *When AA Doesn't Work for You: Rational Steps to Quitting Alcohol.* Fort Lee, NJ: Barricade Books, 1992.

Elvy, G.A.; Wells, J.E.; and Baird, K.A. Attempted referral as intervention for problem drinking in the general hospital. *British Journal of Addiction* 83:83–89, 1988.

Fleming, M.F.; Barry, K.L.; Manwell, L.B.; Johnson, K.; and London, R. Brief physician advice for problem alcohol drinkers: A randomized controlled trial in community-based primary care practices. *JAMA* 277(13):1039–1045, 1997.

Fosnocht, K.M. Cost-effectiveness of the AHCPR guidelines for smoking. *JAMA* 279(11):837, 1998.

Galanter, M.; Keller, D.S.; and Dermatis, H. Network Therapy for addiction: Assessment of the clinical outcome of training. *American Journal of Drug and Alcohol Abuse* 23:355–367, 1997.

Gavin, D.R.; Sobell, L.C.; and Sobell, M.B. Evaluation of the Readiness to Change Questionnaire with problem drinkers in treatment. *Journal of Substance Abuse* 10:53–58, 1998.

Goddard, L., ed. *An African Centered Model of Prevention for African-American Youth at High Risk.* Washington, DC: U.S. Government Printing Office, 1992.

Gordon, T. *Parent Effectiveness Training: The No-Lose Program for Raising Responsible Children.* New York: Wyden, 1970.

Grills, C., and Rowe, D. African traditional medicine: Implications for African centered approaches to healing. In: Jones, R., ed. *African American Mental Health.* Hampton, VA: Cobb and Henry, 1998.

Handmaker, N.S.; Miller, W.R.; and Manicke, M. Findings of a pilot study of motivational interviewing with pregnant drinkers. *Journal of Studies on Alcohol* 60(2):285–287, 1999.

Harris, K.B., and Miller, W.R. Behavioral self-control training for problem drinkers: Components of efficacy. *Psychology of Addictive Behaviors* 4:82–90, 1990.

Heather, N. Interpreting the evidence on brief interventions for excessive drinkers: The need for caution. *Alcohol and Alcoholism* 30(3):287–296, 1995.

Heather, N.; Kissoon-Singh, J.; and Fenton, G.W. Assisted natural recovery from alcohol problems: Effects of a self-help manual with and without supplementary telephone contact. *British Journal of Addiction* 85:1177–1185, 1990.

Heather, N.; Luce, A.; Peck, D.; and Dunbar, B. "Development of the Readiness to Change Questionnaire (Treatment Version)." Report to the Northern and Yorkshire R&D Directorate, 1996a.

Heather N.; Robertson, I.; MacPherson, B.; Allsop, S.; and Fulton, A. Effectiveness of a controlled drinking self-help manual: One year follow-up results. *British Journal of Clinical Psychology* 26:279–287, 1987.

Heather, N.; Rollnick, S.; and Bell, A. Predictive validity of the Readiness to Change Questionnaire. *Addiction* 88:1667–1677, 1993.

Heather, N.; Rollnick, S.; Bell, A.; and Richmond, R. Effects of brief counseling among male heavy drinkers identified on general hospital wards. *Drug and Alcohol Review* 15:29–38, 1996b.

Heather, N.; Whitton, B.; and Robertson, I. Evaluation of a self-help manual for media-recruited problem drinkers: Six month follow-up results. *British Journal of Clinical Psychology* 25:19–34, 1986.

Helzer, J.E., and Pryzbeck, T.R. Co-occurrence of alcoholism with other psychiatric disorders in the general population and its impact on treatment. *Journal of Studies on Alcohol* 49:219–224, 1988.

Higgins, S.T.; Bickel, W.K.; and Hughes, J.R. Influence of an alternative reinforcer on human cocaine self-administration. *Life Sciences* 55:179–187, 1994a.

Higgins, S.T., and Budney, A.J. Treatment of cocaine dependence through the principles of behavior analysis and behavioral pharmacology. In: Onken, L.S.; Blaine, J.D.; and Boren, J.J., eds. *Behavioral Treatments for Drug Abuse and Dependence.* Rockville, MD: National Institute on Drug Abuse, 1993. pp. 97–121.

Higgins, S.T.; Budney, A.J.; Bickel, W.K.; Badger, G.J.; Foerg, F.E.; and Ogden, D. Outpatient behavioral treatment for cocaine dependence: One-year outcome. *Experimental and Clinical Psychopharmacology* 3:205–212, 1995.

Higgins, S.T.; Budney, A.J.; Bickel, W.K.; Foerg, F.; Donham, R.; and Badger, M.S. Incentives improve outcome in outpatient behavioral treatment of cocaine dependence. *Archives of General Psychiatry* 51:568–576, 1994b.

Higgins, S.T.; Budney, A.J.; Bickel, W.K.; Hughes, J.R.; Foerg, F.; and Badger, G. Achieving cocaine abstinence with a behavioral approach. *American Journal of Psychiatry* 150:763–769, 1993.

Higgins, S.T., and Silverman, K. *Motivating Behavior Change Among Illicit Drug Abusers: Research on Contingency Management Interventions.* Washington, DC: American Psychological Association, 1999.

Holder, H.; Longabaugh, R.; Miller, W.R.; and Rubonis, A.V. The cost effectiveness of treatment for alcoholism: A first approximation. *Journal of Studies on Alcohol* 52(6):517–540, 1991.

Hunt, G.M., and Azrin, N.H. A community-reinforcement approach to alcoholism. *Behavioral Research and Therapy* 11(1):91–104, 1973.

Hurt, R.D.; Offord, K.P.; Croghan, I.T.; Gomez-Dahl, L.; Kottke, T.E.; Morse, R.M.; and Melton, J. Mortality following inpatient addictions treatment: Role of tobacco use in a community-based cohort. *JAMA* 25:1097–1103, 1996.

Inciardi, J.A; Tims, F.M.; and Fletcher, B. *Innovative Approaches to the Treatment of Drug Abuse: Program Models and Strategies.* Westport, CT: Greenwood, 1993.

Ingersoll, K.S., and Wagner, C.C. *Motivational Enhancement Groups for the Virginia Substance Abuse Treatment Outcomes Evaluation (SATOE) Model: Theoretical Background and Clinical Guidelines.* Richmond, VA: Office of Mental Health Services, Department of Mental Health, Mental Retardation and Substance Abuse Services, 1997.

Institute of Medicine. *Broadening the Base of Treatment for Alcohol Problems.* Report of a Study by a Committee of the Institute of Medicine, Division of Mental Health and Behavioral Medicine. Washington, DC: National Academy Press, 1990a.

Institute of Medicine. *Treating Drug Problems.* Washington, DC: National Academy Press, 1990b.

Intagliata, J. A telephone follow-up procedure for increasing the effectiveness of a treatment program for alcoholics. *Journal of Studies on Alcohol* 37:1330–1335, 1976.

Ivey, A.E.; Gluckstern, N.B.; and Ivey, M.B. *Basic Influencing Skills.* 3rd ed. North Amherst, MA: Microtraining Associates, 1997.

Jaffee, J.H. The swinging pendulum: The treatment of drug users in America. In: Dupont, R.L.; Goldstein, A.; O'Donnell, J.; and Brown, B., eds. *Handbook on Drug Abuse.* Rockville, MD: National Institute on Drug Abuse, 1979. pp. 3–16.

Janis, I.L., and Mann, L. *Decision Making: A Psychological Analysis of Conflict, Choice, and Commitment.* London: Cassel and Collier Macmillan, 1977.

Johnson, V.E. *I'll Quit Tomorrow.* New York: Harper & Row, 1973.

Jones, R.A. *Self-Fulfilling Prophecies: Social, Psychological, and Physiological Effects of Expectancies.* Hillsdale, NJ: L. Erlbaum, 1977.

Kahan, M.; Wilson, L.; and Becker, L. Effectiveness of physician-based interventions with problem drinkers: A review. *Canadian Medical Association Journal* 152(6):851–859, 1995.

Kanfer, F.H. Self-regulation: Research, issues, and speculations. In: Neuringer, C., and Michael, J.L., eds. *Behavior Modification in Clinical Psychology.* New York: Appleton-Century-Crofts, 1970. pp. 178–220.

Kanfer, F.H., and Schefft, B.K. *Guiding the Process of Therapeutic Change.* Champaign, IL: Research Press, 1988.

Keller, D.S.; Galanter, M.; and Weinberg, S. Validation of a scale for network therapy: A technique for systematic use of peer and family support in addiction treatment. *American Journal of Drug and Alcohol Abuse* 23:115–127, 1997.

Kent, R. Motivational interviewing and the maintenance of change. In: Miller, W.R., and Rollnick, S., eds. *Motivational Interviewing: Preparing People To Change Addictive Behavior.* New York: Guilford Press, 1991. pp. 191–202.

Khantzian, E.J. An ego/self theory of substance dependence: A contemporary psychoanalytic perspective. In: Lettieri, D.J.; Sayers, M.; and Pearson, H.W., eds. *Theories on Drug Abuse: Selected Contemporary Perspectives.* NIDA Research Monograph Series, Number 30. DHHS Publication No. (ADM) 80-967. Washington, DC: U.S. Government Printing Office, 1980. pp. 29–33.

Khantzian, E.J.; Halliday, K.S.; and McAuliffe, W.E. *Addiction and the Vulnerable Self: Modified Dynamic Group Therapy for Substance Abusers.* New York: Guilford Press, 1990.

Kilpatrick, D.G.; Roitzsch, J.C.; Best, C.L.; McAlhany, D.A.; Sturgis, E.T.; and Miller, W.C. Treatment goal preference and problem perception of chronic alcoholics: Behavioral and personality correlates. *Addictive Behaviors* 3:107–116, 1978.

Klingemann, H.K. The motivation for change from problem alcohol and heroin use. *British Journal of Addiction* 86:727–744, 1991.

Kolden, G.G.; Howard, K.I.; Bankoff, E.A.; Maling, M.S.; and Martinovich, Z. Factors associated with treatment continuation: Implications for the treatment of drug dependence. In: Onken, L.S.; Blaine, J.D.; and Boren, J.J., eds. *Beyond the Therapeutic Alliance: Keeping the Drug-Dependent Individual in Treatment.* NIDA Research Monograph Series, Number 165. DHHS Pub. No. (ADM) 97-4142. Rockville, MD: National Institute on Drug Abuse, 1997. pp. 110–130.

Kopel, S., and Arkowitz, H. The role of attribution and self-perception in behavior change: Implications for behavior therapy. *Genetic Psychology Monographs* 92:175–212, 1975.

Koumans, A.J.R., and Muller, J.J. Use of letters to increase motivation in alcoholics. *Psychology Reports* 16:1152, 1965.

Kris, A.O. The conflict of ambivalence. *Psychoanalytical Study of the Child* 39:213–234, 1984.

Kristenson, H.; Öhlin, H.; Hultén-Nosslin, M.B.; Trell, E.; and Hood, B. Identification and intervention of heavy drinking in middle-aged men: Results and follow-up of 24–60 months of long-term study with randomized controls. *Alcoholism: Clinical and Experimental Research* 7:203–209, 1983.

Kuchipudi, V.; Hobein, K.; Flickinger, A.; and Iber, F.L. Failure of a 2-hour motivational intervention to alter recurrent drinking behavior in alcoholics with gastrointestinal disease. *Journal of Studies on Alcohol* 51:356–360, 1990.

Landry, M.J. *Overview of Addiction Treatment Effectiveness.* DHHS Pub. No. (SMA) 96-3081. Rockville, MD: Substance Abuse and Mental Health Services Administration, Office of Applied Studies, 1996.

Landry, M.J.; Smith, D.E.; and Steinberg, J.R. Anxiety, depression, and substance use disorders: Diagnosis, treatment, and prescribing practices. *Journal of Psychoactive Drugs* 23(4):397–416, 1991.

Leake, G.J., and King, S.A. Effect of counselor expectations on alcoholic recovery. *Alcohol Health and Research World* 11(3):16–22, 1977.

Leigh, B.C. Confirmatory factor analysis of alcohol expectancy scales. *Journal of Studies on Alcohol* 50:268–277, 1989a.

Leigh, B.C. In search of the seven dwarves: Issues of measurement and meaning in alcohol expectancy research. *Psychological Bulletin* 105:361–373, 1989b.

Leukefeld, C.G., and Tims, F.M. Compulsory treatment: A review of findings. In: Leukefeld, C.G., and Tims, F.M., eds. *Compulsory Treatment of Drug Abuse: Research and Clinical Practice.* NIDA Research Monograph Series, Number 86. DHHS Pub. No. (ADM) 88-1578. Rockville, MD: National Institute on Drug Abuse, 1988. pp. 236–251.

Leventhal, H. Fear appeals and persuasion: The differentiation of a motivational construct. *American Journal of Public Health* 61:1208–1224, 1971.

Liepman, M.R.; Nirenberg, T.D.; and Begin, A.M. Evaluation of a program designed to help family and significant others to motivate resistant alcoholics into recovery. *American Journal of Drug and Alcohol Abuse* 15(2):209–221, 1989.

Løberg, T., and Miller, W.R. Personality, cognitive, and neuropsychological correlates of harmful alcohol consumption: A cross-national comparison of clinical samples. *Annals of the New York Academy of Sciences* 472:75–97, 1986.

Loneck, B.; Garrett, J.A.; and Banks, S.M. A comparison of the Johnson intervention with four other methods of referral to outpatient treatment. *American Journal of Drug and Alcohol Abuse* 22(2):233–246, 1996a.

Loneck, B.; Garrett, J.A.; and Banks, S.M. The Johnson intervention and relapse during outpatient treatment. *American Journal of Drug and Alcohol Abuse* 22(3):363–375, 1996b.

Longabaugh, R.; Beattie, M.; Noel, N.; Stout, R.; and Malloy, P. The effect of social investment on treatment outcome. *Journal of Studies on Alcohol* 54(4):465–478, 1993.

Longshore, D., and Grills, C. Drug problem recognition among African American drug-using arrestees. *Addictive Behaviors* 23(2):275–279, 1998.

Longshore, D.; Grills, C.; Anglin, D.; and Annon, K. Treatment motivation among African-American drug using arrestees. *Journal of Black Psychology* 24(2):126–144, 1998.

Luborsky, L.; McLellan, A.T.; Woody, G.E.; O'Brien, C.P.; and Auerbach, A. Therapist success and its determinants. *Archives of General Psychiatry* 42:602–611, 1985.

Luke, D. "Teens' images of smoking and smokers." Paper presented at the annual meeting of the Society for Research on Nicotine and Tobacco, New Orleans, LA, 1998.

MacKenzie, K.R., ed. *The Clinical Application of a Group Climate Measure*. New York: International Universities Press, 1983.

Marlatt, G.A.; Baer, J.S.; Kivlahan, D.R.; Dimeff, L.A., Larimer, M.E., Quigley, L.A.; Somers, J.M.; and Williams, E. Screening and brief intervention for high-risk college student drinkers: Results from a 2-year follow-up assessment. *Journal of Consulting and Clinical Psychology* 66:604–615, 1998.

Marlatt, G.A., and George, W.H. Relapse prevention: Introduction and overview of the model. *British Journal of Addiction* 79:261–273, 1984.

Marlatt, G.A., and Gordon, J.R., eds. *Relapse Prevention: Maintenance Strategies in the Treatment of Addictive Behaviors*. New York: Guilford Press, 1985.

Marlatt, G.A., and Kristeller, J. Mindfulness and meditation. In: Miller, W.R., ed. *Integrating Spirituality Into Treatment: Resources for Practitioners*. Washington, DC: American Psychological Association, 1999.

Mattick, R.P., and Jarvis, T. Brief or minimal intervention for 'alcoholics'? The evidence suggests otherwise. *Drug and Alcohol Review* 13:137–144, 1994.

McAuliffe, W.E., and Gordon, R.A. Reinforcement and the combination of effects: Summary of a theory of opiate addiction. In: Lettieri, D.J.; Sayers, M.; and Wallenstein-Pearson, H., eds. *Theories on Drug Abuse: Selected Contemporary Perspectives*. NIDA Research Monograph Series, Number 30. DHHS Pub. No. (ADM) 80-967. Washington, DC: U.S. Government Printing Office, 1980. pp. 137–141.

McCaul, M.E., and Svikis, D.S. Improving client compliance in outpatient treatment: Counselor-targeted interventions. In: Pickens, R.W.; Leukefeld, C.G.; and Schuster, C.R. *Improving Drug Abuse Treatment.* NIDA Research Monograph Series, Number 106. Rockville, MD: National Institute on Drug Abuse, 1991. pp. 204–217.

McConnaughy, E.A.; Prochaska, J.O.; and Velicer, W.F. Stages of change in psychotherapy: Measurement and sample profiles. *Psychotherapy: Theory, Research and Practice* 20:368–375, 1983.

McLellan, A.T.; Alterman, A.I.; Metzger, D.S.; Grisson, G.R.; Woody, G.E.; Luborsky, L.; and O'Brien, C.P. Similarity of outcome predictors across opiate, cocaine, and alcohol treatments: Role of treatment services. *Journal of Consulting and Clinical Psychology* 62(6):1141–1158, 1994.

Melchior, L.A.; Huba, G.J.; Brown, V.B.; and Slaughter, R. Evaluation of the effects of outreach to women with multiple vulnerabilities on entry into substance abuse treatment. *Evaluation and Program Planning,* in press.

Meyers, R.J., and Smith, J.E. *Clinical Guide to Alcohol Treatment: The Community Reinforcement Approach.* New York: Guilford Press, 1995.

Meyers, R.J., and Smith, J.E. Getting off the fence: Procedures to engage treatment-resistant drinkers. *Journal of Substance Abuse Treatment* 14(5):467–472, 1997.

Miller, L. Neuropsychological assessment of substance abusers: Review and recommendations. *Journal of Substance Abuse Treatment* 2(1):5–17, 1985a.

Miller, W.R. Alcoholism scales and objective assessment methods: A review. *Psychological Bulletin* 98:84–107, 1976.

Miller, W.R. Motivational interviewing with problem drinkers. *Behavioural Psychotherapy* 11:147–172, 1983.

Miller, W.R. Motivation for treatment: A review with special emphasis on alcoholism. *Psychological Bulletin* 98(1):84–107, 1985b.

Miller, W.R. Increasing motivation for change. In: Hester, R.K., and Miller, W.R., eds. *Handbook of Alcoholism Treatment Approaches: Effective Alternatives,* 2nd ed. Boston: Allyn & Bacon, 1995. pp. 89–104.

Miller, W.R. What is a relapse? Fifty ways to leave the wagon. *Addiction* 91(Suppl.):S15–S27, 1996.

Miller, W.R.; Andrews, N.R.; Wilbourne, P.; and Bennett, M.E. A wealth of alternatives: Effective treatments for alcohol problems. In: Miller, W.R., and Heather, N., eds. *Treating Addictive Behaviors: Processes of Change,* 2nd ed. New York: Plenum Press, 1998. pp. 203–216.

Miller, W.R., and Baca, L.M. Two-year follow-up of bibliotherapy and therapist-directed controlled drinking training for problem drinkers. *Behavior Therapy* 14:441–448, 1983.

Miller, W.R.; Benefield, R.G.; and Tonigan, J.S. Enhancing motivation for change in problem drinking: A controlled comparison of two therapist styles. *Journal of Consulting and Clinical Psychology* 61(3):455–461, 1993.

Miller, W.R.; Brown, J.M.; Simpson, T.L.; Handmaker, N.S.; Bien, T.H.; Luckie, L.F.; Montgomery, H.A.; Hester, R.K.; and Tonigan, J.S. What works? A methodological analysis of the alcohol treatment outcome literature. In: Hester, R.K., and Miller, W.R., eds. *Handbook of Alcoholism Treatment Approaches: Effective Alternatives,* 2nd ed. Boston: Allyn & Bacon, 1995a. pp. 12–44.

Miller, W.R., and C'de Baca, J. Quantum change: Toward a psychology of transformation. In: Heatherton, T., and Weinberger, J., eds. *Can Personality Change?* Washington, DC: American Psychological Association, 1994. pp. 253–280

Miller, W.R.; Gribskov, C.J.; and Mortell, R.L Effectiveness of a self-control manual for problem drinkers with and without therapist contact. *International Journal of the Addictions* 16:1247–1254, 1981.

Miller, W.R., and Heather, N., eds. *Treating Addictive Behaviors,* 2nd ed. New York: Plenum Press, 1998.

Miller, W.R., and Kurtz, E. Models of alcoholism used in treatment: Contrasting AA and other perspectives with which it is often confused. *Journal of Studies on Alcohol* 55:159–166, 1994.

Miller, W.R.; Leckman, A.L; Delaney, H.D.; and Tinkcom, M. Long-term follow-up of behavioral self-control training. *Journal of Studies on Alcohol* 53(3):249–261, 1992.

Miller, W.R., and Meyers, R.J. Engaging unmotivated individuals in treatment for alcohol problems: A comparison of three intervention strategies. *Journal of Consulting and Clinical Psychology,* in press.

Miller, W.R., and Page, A.C. Warm turkey: Other routes to abstinence. *Journal of Substance Abuse Treatment* 8:227–232, 1991.

Miller, W.R., and Pechacek, T.F. New roads: Assessing and treating psychological dependence. *Journal of Substance Abuse Treatment* 4:73–77, 1987.

Miller, W.R., and Rollnick, S. *Motivational Interviewing: Preparing People To Change Addictive Behavior.* New York: Guilford Press, 1991.

Miller, W.R., and Sanchez, V.C. Motivating young adults for treatment and lifestyle change. In: Howard, G., and Nathan, P.E., eds. *Alcohol Use and Misuse by Young Adults.* Notre Dame, IN: University of Notre Dame Press, 1994.

Miller, W.R., and Saucedo, C.F. Assessment of neuropsychological impairment and brain damage in problem drinkers. In: Golden, C.J.; Moses, J.A., Jr.; Coffman, J.A.; Miller, W.R.; and Strider, F.D., eds. *Clinical Neuropsychology: Interface With Neurologic and Psychiatric Disorders.* New York: Grune & Stratton, 1983. pp. 141–195.

Miller, W.R., and Sovereign, R.G. The check-up: A model for early intervention in addictive behaviors. In: Løberg, T.; Miller, W.R.; Nathan, P.E.; and Marlatt, G.A., eds. *Addictive Behaviors: Prevention and Early Intervention.* Amsterdam: Swets & Zeitlinger, 1989. pp. 219–231.

Miller, W.R.; Sovereign, R.G.; and Krege, B. Motivational interviewing with problem drinkers: II. The Drinker's Check-up as a preventive intervention. *Behavioural Psychotherapy* 16:251–268, 1988.

Miller, W.R., and Taylor, C.A. Relative effectiveness of bibliotherapy, individual and group self-control training in the treatment of problem drinkers. *Addictive Behaviors* 5:13–24, 1980.

Miller, W.R.; Taylor, C.A.; and West, J.C. Focused versus broad-spectrum behavior therapy for problem drinkers. *Journal of Consulting and Clinical Psychology* 48:590–601, 1980.

Miller, W.R., and Tonigan, J.S. Assessing drinkers' motivation for change: The Stages of Change Readiness and Treatment Eagerness Scale (SOCRATES). *Psychology of Addictive Behaviors* 10(2):81–89, 1996.

Miller, W.R.; Westerberg, V.S.; and Waldron, H.B. Evaluating alcohol problems. In: Hester, R.K., and Miller, W.R., eds. *Handbook of Alcoholism Treatment Approaches: Effective Alternatives*, 2nd ed. Boston: Allyn & Bacon, 1995b. pp. 61–88.

Miller, W.R.; Zweben, A.; DiClemente, C.C.; and Rychtarik, R.G. *Motivational Enhancement Therapy Manual: A Clinical Research Guide for Therapists Treating Individuals With Alcohol Abuse and Dependence*. Project MATCH Monograph Series, Vol. 2. NIH Pub. No. 94-3723. Rockville, MD: National Institute on Alcohol Abuse and Alcoholism, 1995c.

Moos, R.H.; Brennan, P.L.; Fondacaro, M.R.; and Moos, B.S. Approach and avoidance coping responses among older problem and nonproblem drinkers. *Psychology and Aging* 5(1):31–40, 1990.

Najavits, L.M., and Weiss, R.D. Variations in therapist effectiveness in the treatment of patients with substance use disorders: An empirical review. *Addiction* 89(6):679–688, 1994.

Nir, Y., and Cutler, R. The unmotivated patient syndrome: Survey of therapeutic interventions. *American Journal of Psychiatry* 135:442–447, 1978.

Nirenberg, T.D.; Sobell, L.C.; and Sobell, M.B. Effective and inexpensive procedures for decreasing client attrition in an outpatient alcohol treatment program. *American Journal of Drug and Alcohol Abuse* 7:73–82, 1980.

Noonan, W.C., and Moyers, T.B. Motivational interviewing. *Journal of Substance Misuse* 2:8–16, 1997.

Obert, J.L.; Rawson, R.A.; and Miotto, K. Substance abuse treatment for "hazardous users": An early intervention. *Journal of Psychoactive Drugs* 29(3):291–298, 1997.

Ockene, J.K.; Wheeler, E.V.; Adams, A.; Hurley, T.G.; and Hebert, J. Provider training for patient-centered alcohol counseling in a primary care setting. *Archives of Internal Medicine* 157(20):2334–2341, 1997.

O'Farrell, T.J., ed. *Treating Alcohol Problems: Marital and Family Interventions*. New York: Guilford Press, 1993.

Orford, J. *Excessive Appetites: A Psychological View of Addictions*. New York: John Wiley and Sons, 1985.

Orford, J. Empowering family and friends: A new approach to the secondary prevention of addiction. *Drug and Alcohol Review* 13:417–429, 1994.

Orleans, C.T.; Schoenbach, V.J.; Wagner, E.H.; Quade, D.; Salmon, M.A.; Pearson, D.C.; Fiedler, J.; Porter, C.Q.; and Kaplan, B.H. Self-help quit smoking interventions: Effects of self-help materials, social support instructions, and telephone counseling. *Journal of Consulting and Clinical Psychology* 59:439–448, 1991.

Panepinto, W.C., and Higgins, M.J. Keeping alcoholics in treatment: Effective follow-through procedures. *Quarterly Journal of Studies on Alcohol* 30:414–419, 1969.

Parker, M.W.; Winstead, D.K.; and Willi, F.J. Patient autonomy in alcohol rehabilitation: I. Literature review. *International Journal of the Addictions* 14:1015–1022, 1979.

Pattison, E.M.; Sobell, M.B.; and Sobell, L.C. *Emerging Concepts of Alcohol Dependence*. New York: Springer, 1977.

Persson, J., and Magnusson, P.H. Early intervention in patients with excessive consumption of alcohol: A controlled study. *Alcohol: An International Biomedical Journal* 6:403–408, 1989.

Perz, C.A.; DiClemente, C.C.; and Carbonari, J.P. Doing the right thing at the right time? The interaction of stages and processes of change in successful smoking cessation. *Health Psychology* 15:462–468, 1996.

Peterson, L.; Gable, S.; and Saldana, L. Treatment of maternal addiction to prevent child abuse and neglect. *Addictive Behaviors* 21: 789–801, 1996.

Pickens, R.W., and Fletcher, B.W. Overview of treatment issues. In: Pickens, R.W.; Leukefeld, C.G.; and Schuster, C.R., eds. *Improving Drug Abuse Treatment.* NIDA Research Monograph Series, Number 106. DHHS Pub. No. (ADM) 91-1754. Rockville, MD: National Institute on Drug Abuse, 1991. pp. 1–19.

Polich, J.M.; Armor, D.J.; and Braiker, H.B. *The Course of Alcoholism: Four Years After Treatment.* New York: John Wiley and Sons, 1981.

Prochaska, J.O. *Systems of Psychotherapy: A Transtheoretical Analysis.* Homewood, IL: Dorsey Press, 1979.

Prochaska, J.O., and DiClemente, C.C. Stages and processes of self-change of smoking: Toward an integrated model of change. *Journal of Consulting and Clinical Psychology* 51:390–395, 1983.

Prochaska, J.O., and DiClemente, C.C. *The Transtheoretical Approach: Crossing Traditional Boundaries of Therapy.* Homewood, IL: Dow Jones-Irwin, 1984.

Prochaska, J.O., and DiClemente, C.C. Stages of change in the modification of problem behaviors. In: Hersen, M.; Eisler, R.M.; and Miller, P.M., eds. *Progress in Behavior Modification.* Sycamore, IL: Sycamore Publishing Company, 1992. pp. 184–214.

Prochaska, J.O; DiClemente, C.C.; and Norcross, J.C. Changing: Process approaches to initiation and maintenance of changes. In: Klar, Y.; Fisher, J.D.; Chinsky, J.M.; and Nadler, A., eds. *Self-Change: Social, Psychological, and Clinical Perspectives.* New York: Springer-Verlag, 1992a. pp. 87–114.

Prochaska, J.O.; DiClemente, C.C.; and Norcross, J.C. In search of how people change: Applications to addictive behaviors. *American Psychologist* 47:1102–1114, 1992b.

Prochaska, J.O., and Goldstein, M.G. Process of smoking cessation: Implications for clinicians. *Clinical Chest Medicine* 12:727–735, 1991.

Prochaska, J.O.; Velicer, W.F.; Rossi, J.S.; Goldstein, M.G.; Marcus, B.H.; Rakowski, W.; Fiore, C.; Harlow, L.L.; Redding, C.A., Rosenbloom, D.; and Rossi, S.R. Stages of change and decisional balance for 12 problem behaviors. *Health Psychology* 13(1):39–46, 1994.

Project MATCH Research Group. Matching alcoholism treatments to client heterogeneity: Project MATCH posttreatment drinking outcomes. *Journal of Studies on Alcohol* 58:7–29, 1997a.

Project MATCH Research Group. Matching alcoholism treatments to client heterogeneity: Project MATCH three-year drinking outcomes. *Alcoholism: Clinical and Experimental Research* 22:1300–1311, 1998a.

Project MATCH Research Group. Project MATCH secondary a priori hypotheses. *Addiction* 92:1671–1698, 1997b.

Project MATCH Research Group. Therapist effects in three treatments for alcohol problems. *Psychotherapy Research* 8(4):455–474, 1998b.

Rawson, R.A.; Obert, J.L.; McCann, M.J.; Smith, D.P.; and Scheffey, E.H. *The Neurobehavioral Treatment Manual.* Beverly Hills, CA: Matrix, 1989.

Rawson, R.A.; Shoptaw, S.J.; Obert, J.L.; McCann, M.J.; Hasson, A.L.; Marinelli-Casey, P.J.; Brethen, P.R.; and Ling, W. An intensive outpatient approach for cocaine abuse treatment: The Matrix model. *Journal of Substance Abuse Treatment* 12(2):117–127, 1995.

Regier, D.A.; Farmer, M.E.; Rae, D.S.; Locke, B.Z.; Keith, S.J.; Judd, L.L.; and Goodwin, F.K. Comorbidity of mental disorders with alcohol and other drug abuse. *JAMA* 264:2511–2518, 1990.

Richmond, R.L.; Kehoe, L.A.; and Webster, I.W. Multivariate models for predicting abstention following interventions to stop smoking by general practitioners. *Addiction* 88:1127–1135, 1993.

Robertson, I.; Heather, N.; Dzialdowski, A.; Crawford, J.; and Winton, M. Comparison of minimal versus intensive controlled drinking treatment interventions for problem drinkers. *British Journal of Clinical Psychology* 25:185–194, 1986.

Robins, L.N.; Davis, D.H.; and Goodwin, D.W. Drug use by U.S. Army enlisted men in Vietnam: A follow-up on their return home. *American Journal of Epidemiology* 99:235–249, 1974.

Rogers, C.R. A theory of therapy, personality, and interpersonal relationships as developed in the client-centered framework. In: Koch, S., ed. *Psychology: A Study of a Science.* Vol. 3, *Formulations of the Person and the Social Context.* New York: McGraw-Hill, 1959. pp. 184–256.

Rogers, R.W.; Deckner, C.W.; and Mewborn, C.R. An expectancy-value theory approach to the long-term modification of smoking behavior. *Journal of Clinical Psychology* 34:562–566, 1978.

Rokeach, M. *The Nature of Human Values.* New York: Free Press, 1973.

Rokeach, M. *Rokeach Value Survey.* Palo Alto, CA: Consulting Psychologists Press, 1983.

Rollnick, S.; Heather, N.; and Bell, A. Negotiating behavior change in medical settings: The development of brief motivational interviewing. *Journal of Mental Health* 1:25–37, 1992a.

Rollnick, S.; Heather, N.; Gold, R.; and Hall, W. Development of a short "readiness to change" questionnaire for use in brief, opportunistic interventions among excessive drinkers. *British Journal of Addiction* 87:743–754, 1992b.

Rollnick, S., and Miller, W.R. What is motivational interviewing? *Behavioral and Cognitive Psychotherapy* 23:325–334, 1995.

Romelsjo, A.; Andersson, L.; Barrner, H.; Borg, S.; Granstrand, C.; Hultman, O.; Hassler, A.; Kallqvist, A.; Magnusson, P.; Morgell, R.; Hyman, K.; Olofsson, A.; Olsson, E.; Rhedin, A.; and Wikblad, O. Randomized study of secondary prevention of early stage problem drinkers in primary health care. *British Journal of Addiction* 84:1319–1327, 1989.

Rowe, D., and Grills, C. African-centered drug treatment: An alternative conceptual paradigm for drug counseling with African-American clients. *Journal of Psychoactive Drugs* 25:21–33, 1993.

Ryan, R.M.; Plant, R.W.; and O'Malley, S. Initial motivations for alcohol treatment: Relations with patient characteristics, treatment involvement, and dropout. *Addictive Behaviors* 20(3):279–297, 1995.

Samet, J.H., and O'Connor, P.G. Alcohol abusers in primary care: Readiness to change behavior. *American Journal of Medicine* 105:302–306, 1998.

Samet, J.H.; Rollnick, S.; and Barnes, H. Beyond CAGE: A brief clinical approach after detection of substance abuse. *Archives of Internal Medicine* 156:2287–2293, 1996.

Sannibale, C. The differential effect of a set of brief interventions on the functioning of a group of "early-stage" problem drinkers. *Australian Drug and Alcohol Review* 7:147–155, 1988.

Satterfield, J.M. Integrating group dynamics and cognitive-behavioral groups: A hybrid model. *Clinical Psychology: Science and Practice* 1:185–196, 1994.

Saunders, B.; Wilkinson, C.; and Allsop, S. Motivational intervention with heroin users attending a methadone clinic. In: Miller, W.R., and Rollnick, S., eds. *Motivational Interviewing: Preparing People To Change Addictive Behavior.* New York: Guilford Press, 1991. pp. 279–292.

Saunders, B.; Wilkinson, C.; and Phillips, M. The impact of a brief motivational intervention with opiate users attending a methadone programme. *Addiction* 90(3):415–424, 1995.

Scales, R. "Motivational interviewing and skills-based counseling in cardiac rehabilitation: The Cardiovascular Health Initiative and Lifestyle Intervention (CHILE) Study." Ph.D. diss., University of New Mexico. *Dissertation Abstracts International*, 59-03A, 0741, 1998.

Schafer, J., and Brown, S.A. Marijuana and cocaine effect expectancies and drug use patterns. *Journal of Consulting and Clinical Psychology* 59:558–565, 1991.

Senft, R.A.; Polen, M.R.; Freeborn, D.K.; and Hollis, J.F. Brief intervention in a primary care setting for hazardous drinkers. *American Journal of Preventive Medicine* 13:464–470, 1997.

Silverman, K.; Chutuape, M.D.; Bigelow, G.E.; and Stitzer, M.L. Reinforcement of cocaine abstinence in treatment-resistant patients: Effects of reinforcer magnitude. In: Harris, L.S., ed. *Problems of Drug Dependence, 1996.* NIDA Research Monograph Series, Number 174. DHHS Pub. No. (ADM) 97-4236, Rockville, MD: National Institute on Drug Abuse, 1997. p. 74.

Silverman, K.; Higgins, S.T.; Brooner, R.K.; Montoya, I.D.; Cone, E.J.; Schuster, C.R.; and Preston, K.L. Sustained cocaine abstinence in methadone maintenance patients through voucher-based reinforcement therapy. *Archives of General Psychiatry* 53:409–415, 1996.

Simpson, D.D., and Joe, G.W. Motivation as a predictor of early dropout from drug abuse treatment. *Psychotherapy* 30(2):357–368, 1993.

Simpson, D.D.; Joe, G.W.; and Brown, B.S. Treatment retention and follow-up outcomes in the Drug Abuse Treatment Outcome Study (DATOS). *Psychology of Addictive Behaviors* 11:294–307, 1997.

Sisson, R.W., and Azrin, N.H. Family member involvement to initiate and promote treatment of problem drinkers. *Journal of Behavior Therapy and Experimental Psychiatry* 17(1):15–21, 1986.

Sklar, S.M.; Annis, H.M.; and Turner, N.E. Development and validation of the Drug-Taking Confidence Questionnaire: A measure of coping self-efficacy. *Addictive Behaviors: An International Journal* 22:655–670, 1997.

Skutle, A., and Berg, G. Training in controlled drinking for early-stage problem drinkers. *British Journal of Addiction* 82:493–501, 1987.

Smith, D.E.; Heckemeyer, C.M.; Kratt, P.P.; and Mason, D.A. Motivational interviewing to improve adherence to a behavioral weight-control program for older obese women with NIDDM: A pilot study. *Diabetes Care* 20:53–54, 1997.

Sobell, L.C. Bridging the gap between science and practitioners: The challenge before us. *Behavior Therapy* 27:297–320, 1996.

Sobell, L.C.; Breslin, F.C.; and Sobell, M.B. Substance-related disorders (alcohol). In: Turner, S., and Hersen, M., eds. *Adult Psychopathology and Diagnostic Issues*, 3rd ed. New York: John Wiley and Sons, 1997. pp. 128–159.

Sobell, L.C.; Cunningham, J.A.; and Sobell, M.B. Recovery from alcohol problems with and without treatment: Prevalence in two population surveys. *American Journal of Public Health* 86:966–972, 1996a.

Sobell, L.C.; Cunningham, J.A.; Sobell, M.B.; Agrawal, S.; Gavin, D.R.; Leo, G.I.; and Singh, K.N. Fostering self-change among problem drinkers: A proactive community intervention. *Addictive Behaviors* 21(6):817–833, 1996b.

Sobell, L.C., and Sobell, M.B, eds. Alcohol consumption measures. In: Allen, J.P., and Columbus, M., eds. *Assessing Alcohol Problems: A Guide for Clinicians and Researchers*. Treatment Handbook Series 4. Bethesda, MD: National Institute on Alcohol Abuse and Alcoholism, 1995a. pp. 55–74.

Sobell, L.C., and Sobell, M.B. *Timeline Follow Back (TLFB)*. Toronto, ON: Addiction Research Foundation, 1996.

Sobell, L.C.; Sobell, M.B.; Brown, J.; and Cleland, P.A. "A randomized trial comparing group versus individual guided self-change treatment for alcohol and drug abusers." Poster presented at the 29th Annual Meeting of the Association for Advancement of Behavior Therapy, Washington, DC, 1995.

Sobell, L.C.; Sobell, M.B.; and Leo, G.I. "Spousal social support: A motivational intervention for alcohol abusers." Poster presented at the annual meeting of the Association for the Advancement of Behavior Therapy, Atlanta, GA, 1993a.

Sobell, L.C.; Sobell, M.B.; Toneatto, T.; and Leo, G.I. What triggers the resolution of alcohol problems without treatment? *Alcoholism: Clinical and Experimental Research* 17:217–224. 1993b.

Sobell, L.C.; Toneatto, T.; and Sobell, M.B. Behavioral assessment and treatment planning for alcohol, tobacco, and other drug problems: Current status with an emphasis on clinical applications. *Behavior Therapy* 25:533–580, 1994.

Sobell, M.B.; Buchan, G.; and Sobell, L.C. "Relationship of goal choices by substance abusers in guided self-change treatment to subject characteristics and treatment outcome." Poster presented at the annual meeting of the Association for Advancement of Behavior Therapy, New York, 1996c.

Sobell, M.B., and Sobell, L.C. *Problem Drinkers: Guided Self-Change Treatment*. New York: Guilford Press, 1993.

Sobell, M.B., and Sobell, L.C. "Group versus individual guided self-change treatment for problem drinkers." Paper presented at the World Congress on Behavioral and Cognitive Therapies, Copenhagen, Denmark, 1995b.

Sobell, M.B., and Sobell, L.C. Guiding self-change. In: Miller, W.R., and Heather, N., eds. *Treating Addictive Behaviors*, 2nd ed. New York: Plenum, 1998. pp. 189–202.

Sobell, M.B., and Sobell, L.C. Stepped care for alcohol problems: An efficient method for planning and delivering clinical services. In: Tucker, J.A.; Donovan, D.M.; and Marlatt, G.A., eds. *Changing Addictive Behavior: Bridging Clinical and Public Health Strategies.* New York: Guilford Press, 1999. pp. 331–343.

Southwick, L.; Steele, C.; Marlatt, A.; and Lindell, M. Alcohol-related expectancies: Defined by phase of intoxication and drinking experience. *Journal of Consulting and Clinical Psychology* 49:713–721, 1981.

Stanton, M.D. The role of family and significant others in the engagement and retention of drug-dependent individuals. In: Onken, L.S.; Blaine, J.D.; and Boren, J.J., eds. *Beyond the Therapeutic Alliance: Keeping the Drug-Dependent Individual in Treatment.* NIDA Research Monograph Series, Number 165. DHHS Pub. No. (ADM) 97-4142. Rockville, MD: National Institute on Drug Abuse, 1997. pp. 157–180.

Stephens, R.S.; Roffman, R.A.; Cleaveland, B.L.; Curtin, L.; and Wertz, J. "Extended versus minimal intervention with marijuana-dependent adults." Paper presented at the annual meeting of the Association for Advancement of Behavior Therapy, San Diego, CA, 1994.

Strang, J.; Bacchus, L.; Howes, S.; and Watson, P. Turned away from treatment: Maintenance-seeking opiate addicts at two-year follow-up. *Addiction Research* 6:71–81, 1997.

Sutton, S. Can stages of change provide guidelines in the treatment of addictions? In: Edwards, G., and Dare, C., eds. *Psychotherapy, Psychological Treatments and the Addictions.* New York: Cambridge University Press, 1996.

Swanson, A.J.; Pantalon, M.V.; and Cohen, K.R. Motivational interviewing and treatment adherence among psychiatric and dually-diagnosed patients. *Journal of Nervous and Mental Disease*, in press.

Taleff, M.J. *A Handbook To Assess and Treat Resistance in Chemical Dependency.* Dubuque, IA: Kendall/Hunt, 1997.

Thomas, E.J., and Ager, R.D. Unilateral family therapy with spouses of uncooperative alcohol abusers. In: O'Farrell, T.J., ed. *Treating Alcohol Problems: Marital and Family Interventions.* New York: Guilford Press, 1993. pp. 3–33.

Thombs, D.L. *Introduction to Addictive Behaviors.* New York: Guilford Press, 1994.

Tonigan, J.S.; Toscova, R.T.; and Connors, G.J. Spirituality and the 12-Step programs: A guide for clinicians. In: Miller, W.R., ed. *Integrating Spirituality Into Treatment: Resources for Practitioners.* Washington, DC: American Psychological Association, 1999.

Trigwell, P.; Grant, P.J.; and House, A. Motivation and glycemic control in diabetes mellitus. *Journal of Psychosomatic Research* 43:307–315, 1997.

Truax, C.B., and Carkhuff, R.R. *Toward Effective Counseling and Psychotherapy.* Chicago: Aldine, 1967.

Tuchfield, B. Spontaneous remission in alcoholics: Empirical observations and theoretical implications. *Journal of Studies on Alcohol* 42:626–641, 1981.

Tucker, J.A. Predictors of help-seeking and the temporal relationship of help to recovery among treated and untreated recovered problem drinkers. *Addiction* 90(6):805–809, 1995.

Tucker, J.A.; Vuchinich, R.E.; and Gladsjo, J.A. Environmental events surrounding natural recovery from alcohol-related problems. *Journal of Studies on Alcohol* 55:401–411, 1994.

Tucker, J.A.; Vuchinich, R.E.; and Pukish, M.M. Molar environmental contexts surrounding recovery from alcohol problems by treated and untreated problem drinkers. In: Marlatt, G.A., and Vanden Bos, G.R., eds. *Addictive Behaviors: Readings on Etiology, Prevention, and Treatment.* Washington, DC: American Psychological Association, 1997. pp. 581–601.

Vaillant, G.E. *The Natural History of Alcoholism Revisited.* Cambridge, MA: Harvard University Press, 1995.

Van Bilsen, H.P. Motivational interviewing: perspectives from the Netherlands with particular emphasis on heroin-dependent clients. In: Miller, W.R., and Rollnick, S. *Motivational Interviewing: Preparing People To Change Addictive Behavior.* New York: Guilford Press, 1991. pp. 214–235.

Van Bremen, J.R., and Chasnoff, I.J. Policy issues for integrating parenting interventions and addiction treatment for women. *Topics in Early Childhood Special Education* 14:254–274, 1994.

Varney, S.M.; Rohsenow, D.J.; Dey, A.N.; Myers, M.G.; Zwick, W.R.; and Monti, P.M. Factors associated with help seeking and perceived dependence among cocaine users. *American Journal of Drug and Alcohol Abuse* 21(1): 81–91, 1995.

Victorio-Estrada, A., and Mucha, R.F. The Inventory of Drinking Situations (IDS) in current drinkers with different degrees of alcohol problems. *Addictive Behaviors* 22:557–565, 1997.

Wagner, C.C.; Ingersoll, K.S.; Horvatich, P.; May, J.; Fornili, K.; and Gharib, S. *A Technology Transfer Case Study: Part II. Motivational Enhancement Therapy as First Stage Treatment.* Scottsdale, AZ: College on Problems of Drug Dependence, 1998.

Wahlberg, J. Personal growth and self-esteem through cultural spiritualism: A Native-American experience. In: Rivas, R.F., and Hull, G.H., eds. *Case Studies in Generalist Practice.* Belmont, CA: Wadsworth, 1996. pp. 65–71.

Wallace, J. The new disease model of alcoholism. *Western Journal of Medicine* 152(5):502–505, 1990.

Wallace, P.; Cutler, S.; and Haines, A. Randomized controlled trial of general practitioner intervention in patients with excessive alcohol consumption. *British Medical Journal* 297:663–668, 1988.

Walters, S.T.; Bennett, M.E.; and Miller, J.E. Reducing alcohol use in college students: A controlled trial of two brief interventions. *Journal of Drug Education,* in press.

Watson, A.L., and Sher, K.J. Resolution of alcohol problems without treatment: Methodological issues and future directions of natural recovery research. *Clinical Psychology: Science and Practice* 5:1–18, 1998.

Wetter, D.W.; Fiore, M.C.; Gritz, E.R.; Lando, H.A.; Stitzer, M.L.; Hasselblad, V.; and Baker, T.B. The Agency for Health Care Policy and Research: Smoking cessation clinical practice guideline—Findings and implications for psychologists. *American Psychologist* 53:657–669, 1998.

Wilbanks, W.L. Drug addiction should be treated as a lack of self-discipline. In: Leone, B., ed. *Chemical Dependency: Opposing Viewpoints.* San Diego, CA: Greenhaven, 1989.

Wilk, A.I.; Jensen, N.M.; and Havighurst, T.C. Meta-analysis of randomized control trials addressing brief interventions in heavy alcohol drinkers. *Journal of General Internal Medicine* 12(5):274–283, 1997.

Williams, R., and Williams, V. *Anger Kills: Seventeen Strategies for Controlling the Hostility That Can Harm Your Health*. New York: HarperCollins, 1994.

Yahne, C.E., and Miller, W.R. Evoking hope. In: Miller, W.R., ed. *Integrating Spirituality Into Treatment: Resources for Practitioners*. Washington, DC: American Psychological Association, 1999.

Zacny, J.P.; Divane, W.T.; and de Wit, H. Assessment of magnitude and availability of a non-drug reinforcer on preference for a drug reinforcer. *Human Psychopharmacology* 7:281–286, 1992.

Ziedonis, D., and Fisher, W. Motivation-based assessment and treatment of substance abuse in patients with schizophrenia. *Directions in Psychiatry* 16(11):1–8, 1996.

Zweben, A., and Barrett, D. Brief couples treatment for alcohol problems. In: O'Farrell, T.J., ed. *Treating Alcohol Problems: Marital and Family Interventions*. New York: Guilford Press, 1993. pp. 353–380.

Zweben, A.; Bonner, M.; Chaim, G.; and Santon, P. Facilitative strategies for retaining the alcohol-dependent client in outpatient treatment. *Alcoholism Treatment Quarterly* 5:3–24, 1988.

Zweben, A., and Fleming, M.F. Brief interventions for alcohol and drug problems. In: Tucker, J.A.; Donovan, D.M.; and Marlatt, G.A., eds. *Changing Addictive Behavior*. New York: Guilford Press, in press.

Zweben, A., and Li, S. Efficacy of role induction in preventing early dropout from outpatient treatment of drug dependency. *American Journal of Drug and Alcohol Abuse* 8:171–183, 1981.

Zweben, A.; Pearlman, S.; and Li, S. A comparison of brief advice and conjoint therapy in the treatment of alcohol abuse: The results of the Marital Systems Study. *British Journal of Addiction* 83(8):899–916, 1988.

Zweben, J.E. Counseling issues in methadone maintenance treatment. *Journal of Psychoactive Drugs* 23(2):177–190, 1991.

Appendix B
Screening and Assessment Instruments

This appendix includes

- Alcohol and Drug Consequences Questionnaire (ADCQ)
- Alcohol (and Illegal Drugs) Decisional Balance Scale
- Alcohol Effects Questionnaire
- Alcohol Expectancy Questionnaire—III (Adult)
- Alcohol Use Disorders Identification Test (AUDIT)
- Brief Situational Confidence Questionnaire (BSCQ)
- Personal Feedback Report
  - Understanding Your Personal Feedback Report
- Readiness To Change Questionnaire (Treatment Version) (RCQ-TV)
- Situational Confidence Questionnaire (SCQ-39)
- Stages of Change Readiness and Treatment Eagerness Scale (SOCRATES 8A, 8D)
- University of Rhode Island Change Assessment Scale (URICA)
- What I Want From Treatment

Ordering information for these instruments, along with other resources, appears in Appendix C.

Alcohol and Drug Consequences Questionnaire (ADCQ)

There can be good and bad consequences to any change. These consequences may not be the same for everyone. In thinking about your decision to change your alcohol or drug use, we would like to know what consequences are important to you. This is **not** a test: There are no right or wrong answers. We simply want to know what you think.

My primary problem drug is (write in name of primary drug, e.g., alcohol, cocaine)

_____

All questions below refer to my primary drug use.
*When I consider **stopping or cutting down** my primary drug use, the following reasons are **important to me**.*
    "IF I STOP OR CUT DOWN . . . . "

Circle the number which applies to you.

	Not Important	Slightly Important	Moderately Important	Very Important	Extremely Important	Not Applicable
1. I will feel better physically.	1	2	3	4	5	0
2. I will have difficulty relaxing.	1	2	3	4	5	0
3. I will change a lifestyle I enjoy.	1	2	3	4	5	0
4. I will have fewer problems with my family.	1	2	3	4	5	0
5. I will feel frustrated and anxious.	1	2	3	4	5	0
6. I will have more money to do other things with.	1	2	3	4	5	0
7. I will be more active and alert.	1	2	3	4	5	0
8. I will get depressed.	1	2	3	4	5	0
9. I will have fewer problems with friends.	1	2	3	4	5	0

	Not Important	Slightly Important	Moderately Important	Very Important	Extremely Important	Not Applicable
	1	2	3	4	5	0
10. I will feel better about myself.	1	2	3	4	5	0
11. I will regain some self-respect.	1	2	3	4	5	0
12. I will accomplish more of the things I want to get done.	1	2	3	4	5	0
13. I will have a better relationship with my family.	1	2	3	4	5	0
14. I will have difficulty coping with my problems.	1	2	3	4	5	0
15. I will feel withdrawal or craving.	1	2	3	4	5	0
16. I will have too much time on my hands.	1	2	3	4	5	0
17. I will have difficulty not drinking or using drugs.	1	2	3	4	5	0
18. My health will improve.	1	2	3	4	5	0
19. I will live longer.	1	2	3	4	5	0
20. I will be more in control of life.	1	2	3	4	5	0
21. I will feel bored.	1	2	3	4	5	0
22. I will be irritable.	1	2	3	4	5	0
23. I will be more financially stable.	1	2	3	4	5	0
24. I will miss the taste.	1	2	3	4	5	0

	Not Important	Slightly Important	Moderately Important	Very Important	Extremely Important	Not Applicable
25. I will have a better relationship with my friends.	1	2	3	4	5	0
26. I will feel stressed out.	1	2	3	4	5	0
27. I will save more money.	1	2	3	4	5	0
28. I will miss the feeling of being high.	1	2	3	4	5	0

Alcohol (and Illegal Drugs) Decisional Balance Scale

Client ID#_____

Date: _____/ _____/ _____

Assessment Point: _____

THE FOLLOWING STATEMENTS MAY PLAY A PART IN MAKING A DECISION ABOUT USING ALCOHOL (AND DRUGS). WE WOULD LIKE TO KNOW HOW IMPORTANT EACH STATEMENT IS TO YOU <u>AT THE PRESENT TIME</u> IN RELATION TO MAKING A DECISION ABOUT YOUR USING ALCOHOL (AND DRUGS). PLEASE RATE THE LEVEL OF IMPORTANCE TO EACH STATEMENT ON THE FOLLOWING 5 POINTS:

> 1 = Not important at all
> 2 = Slightly important
> 3 = Moderately important
> 4 = Very important
> 5 = Extremely important

PLEASE READ EACH STATEMENT AND CIRCLE THE NUMBER ON THE <u>RIGHT</u> TO INDICATE HOW YOU RATE ITS LEVEL OF IMPORTANCE AS IT RELATES TO YOUR MAKING A DECISION ABOUT WHETHER TO DRINK (OR USE DRUGS) AT THE PRESENT TIME.

How important is this to me?	Importance in making a decision about drinking:				
	Not At All	Slightly	Moderately	Very	Extremely
1. My drinking (drug use) causes problems with others.	1	2	3	4	5
2. I like myself better when I am drinking (using drugs).	1	2	3	4	5
3. Because I continue to drink (use drugs) some people think I lack the character to quit.	1	2	3	4	5
4. Drinking (drug use) helps me deal with problems.	1	2	3	4	5
5. Having to lie to others about my drinking (drug use) bothers me.	1	2	3	4	5
6. Some people try to avoid me when I drink (use drugs).	1	2	3	4	5

How important is this to me?	Not At All	Slightly	Moderately	Very	Extremely
7. Drinking (drug use) helps me to have fun and socialize.	1	2	3	4	5
8. Drinking (drug use) interferes with my functioning at home or/and at work.	1	2	3	4	5
9. Drinking (drug use) makes me more of a fun person.	1	2	3	4	5
10. Some people close to me are disappointed in me because of my drinking (drug use).	1	2	3	4	5
11. Drinking (drug use) helps me to loosen up and express myself.	1	2	3	4	5
12. I seem to get myself into trouble when drinking (using drugs).	1	2	3	4	5
13. I could accidentally hurt someone because of my drinking (drug use).	1	2	3	4	5
14. Not drinking (using drugs) at a social gathering would make me feel too different.	1	2	3	4	5
15. I am losing the trust and respect of my coworkers and/or spouse because of my drinking (drug use).	1	2	3	4	5
16. My drinking (drug use) helps give me energy and keeps me going.	1	2	3	4	5
17. I am more sure of myself when I am drinking (using drugs).	1	2	3	4	5
18. I am setting a bad example for others with my drinking (drug use).	1	2	3	4	5

The header "Importance in making a decision about drinking:" spans the columns Not At All, Slightly, Moderately, Very, and Extremely.

How important is this to me?		Importance in making a decision about drinking:			
	Not At All	Slightly	Moderately	Very	Extremely
19. Without alcohol (illegal drugs), my life would be dull and boring.	1	2	3	4	5
20. People seem to like me better when I am drinking (using drugs).	1	2	3	4	5

Scoring:

Pros of drinking (drug use) are items: 2, 4, 7, 9, 11, 14, 16, 17, 19, 20.

Cons of drinking (drug use) are items: 1, 3, 5, 6, 8, 10, 12, 13, 15, 18.

To get the average number of pros endorsed, add up the total number of points from the items and divide by 10. Example: Pros of drinking (drug use) = $\dfrac{\text{Sum of items } (2+4+7+9+11+14+16+17+19+20)}{10}$

To get the average number of cons endorsed, add up the total number of points from the items and divide by 10. Example: Cons of drinking (drug use) = $\dfrac{\text{Sum of items } (1+3+5+6+8+10+12+13+15+18)}{10}$

Alcohol Effects Questionnaire

This questionnaire consists of a series of statements that describe possible effects following alcohol use. We would like to find out about your present beliefs about alcohol.

Please read each of the statements and respond according to your experiences with a **heavy (5 drinks or more per occasion)** amount of alcohol. If you believe alcohol sometimes or always has the stated effect on you, check <u>AGREE</u>. If you believe alcohol never has the stated effect on you, check <u>DISAGREE.</u>

Then, in the column to the far right, fill in the number that **best corresponds to the strength of your belief**, according to the following scale:

1	2	3	4	5	6	7	8	9	10
Mildly Believe									Strongly Believe

For example, if you strongly believe that alcohol makes you more intelligent, you would check AGREE and enter a "10" in the far column.

Please answer every question without skipping any.

For a **HEAVY (5 or more drinks per occasion)** amount of alcohol

	Agree	Disagree	Strength of Belief
1. Drinking makes me feel flushed.	____	____	____
2. Alcohol decreases muscular tension in my body.	____	____	____
3. Drinking makes me feel less shy.	____	____	____
4. Alcohol enables me to fall asleep much more easily.	____	____	____
5. I feel powerful when I drink, as if I can really influence others to do what I want.	____	____	____
6. I'm more clumsy after I drink.	____	____	____
7. I'm more romantic when I drink.	____	____	____
8. Drinking makes the future seem brighter to me.	____	____	____
9. If I have had alcohol it is easier for me to tell someone off.	____	____	____
10. I can't act as quickly when I've been drinking.	____	____	____
11. Alcohol can act as an anesthetic for me; that is, it can deaden the pain.	____	____	____

	Agree	Disagree	Strength of Belief
12. I often feel sexier after I've been drinking.	____	____	____
13. Drinking makes me feel good.	____	____	____
14. Alcohol makes me careless about my actions.	____	____	____
15. Alcohol has a pleasant, cleansing, tingly taste to me.	____	____	____
16. Drinking increases my aggressiveness.	____	____	____
17. Alcohol seems like magic to me.	____	____	____
18. Alcohol makes it hard for me to concentrate.	____	____	____
19. After drinking, I'm a better lover.	____	____	____
20. When I'm drinking, it is easier to open up and express my feelings.	____	____	____
21. Drinking adds a certain warmth to social occasions for me.	____	____	____
22. If I'm feeling restricted in any way, drinking makes me feel better.	____	____	____
23. I can't think as quickly after I drink.	____	____	____
24. Having drinks is a nice way for me to celebrate special occasions.	____	____	____
25. Alcohol makes me worry less.	____	____	____
26. Drinking makes me inefficient.	____	____	____
27. Drinking is pleasurable because it's enjoyable for me to join in with other people who are enjoying themselves.	____	____	____
28. After drinking, I am more sexually responsive.	____	____	____
29. I feel more coordinated after I drink.	____	____	____
30. I'm more likely to say embarrassing things after drinking.	____	____	____
31. I enjoy having sex more if I've had alcohol.	____	____	____
32. I'm more likely to get into an argument if I've had alcohol.	____	____	____

	Agree	Disagree	Strength of Belief
33. Alcohol makes me less concerned about doing things well.	____	____	____
34. Alcohol helps me sleep better.	____	____	____
35. Drinking gives me more confidence in myself.	____	____	____
36. Alcohol makes me more irresponsible.	____	____	____
37. After drinking it is easier for me to pick a fight.	____	____	____
38. Alcohol makes it easier for me to talk to people.	____	____	____
39. If I have alcohol it is easier for me to express my feelings.	____	____	____
40. Alcohol makes me more interesting.	____	____	____

Alcohol Expectancy Questionnaire—III (Adult)

The following pages contain statements about the effects of alcohol. Read each statement carefully and respond according to your own personal thoughts, feelings, and beliefs about alcohol now. We are interested in what you think about alcohol, regardless of what other people might think.

If you think that the statement is true, or mostly true, or true some of the time, then mark (X) "Agree" on the answer sheet. If you think the statement is false, or mostly false, then mark (X) "Disagree" on the answer sheet. When the statements refer to drinking alcohol you may think in terms of drinking any alcoholic beverage, such as beer, wine, whiskey, liquor, rum, scotch, vodka, gin, or various alcoholic mixed drinks. Whether or not you have had actual drinking experiences yourself, **you are to answer in terms of your beliefs about alcohol**. It is important that you respond to **every question**.

PLEASE BE HONEST. REMEMBER, YOUR ANSWERS ARE CONFIDENTIAL.

RESPOND TO THESE ITEMS ACCORDING TO WHAT YOU PERSONALLY BELIEVE TO BE TRUE ABOUT ALCOHOL

(Mark "X" according to your beliefs)

	Agree	Disagree
1. Alcohol can transform my personality.	____	____
2. Drinking helps me feel whatever way I want to feel.	____	____
3. Some alcohol has a pleasant, cleansing, tingly taste.	____	____
4. Alcohol makes me feel happy.	____	____
5. Drinking adds a certain warmth to social occasions.	____	____
6. Sweet mixed drinks taste good.	____	____
7. When I am drinking, it is easier to open up and express my feelings.	____	____
8. Time passes quickly when I am drinking.	____	____
9. When they drink, women become more sexually relaxed.	____	____
10. Drinking makes me feel flushed.	____	____
11. I feel powerful when I drink, as if I can really influence others to do as I want.	____	____
12. Drinking increases male aggressiveness.	____	____

ANSWER ACCORDING TO WHAT YOU PERSONALLY BELIEVE NOW

	Agree	Disagree
13. Alcohol lets my fantasies flow more easily.	———	———
14. Drinking gives me more confidence in myself.	———	———
15. Drinking makes me feel good.	———	———
16. I feel more creative after I have been drinking.	———	———
17. Having a few drinks is a nice way to celebrate special occasions.	———	———
18. I can discuss or argue a point more forcefully after I have had a few drinks.	———	———
19. When I am drinking, I feel free to be myself and to do whatever I want.	———	
20. Drinking makes it easier to concentrate on the good feelings I have at the time.	———	———
21. Alcohol allows me to be more assertive.	———	———
22. When I feel "high" from drinking, everything seems to feel better.	———	———
23. A drink or two makes the humorous side of me come out.	———	———
24. If I am nervous about having sex, alcohol makes me feel better.	———	———
25. Drinking relieves boredom.	———	———
26. I find that conversing with members of the opposite sex is easier for me after I have had a few drinks.	———	———
27. After a few drinks, I feel less sexually inhibited.	———	———
28. Drinking is pleasurable because it is enjoyable to join in with people who are enjoying themselves.	———	———
29. I like the taste of some alcoholic beverages.	———	———
30. If I am feeling restricted in any way, a few drinks make me feel better.	———	———
31. Men are friendlier when they drink.	———	———

ANSWER ACCORDING TO WHAT YOU PERSONALLY BELIEVE NOW

	Agree	Disagree

32. It is easier for me to meet new people if I've been drinking.

33. After a few drinks it is easier to pick a fight.

34. Alcohol can eliminate feelings of inferiority.

35. Alcohol makes women more sensuous.

36. If I have a couple of drinks, it is easier to express my feelings.

37. I feel less bothered by physical ills after a few drinks.

38. Alcohol makes me need less attention from others than I usually do.

39. Alcohol makes me more outspoken or opinionated.

40. After a few drinks, I feel more self-reliant than usual.

41. After a few drinks, I don't worry as much about what other people think of me.

42. When drinking, I do not consider myself totally accountable or responsible for my behavior.

43. Alcohol enables me to have a better time at parties.

44. Anything that requires a relaxed style can be facilitated by alcohol.

45. Drinking makes the future seem brighter.

46. I am not as tense if I am drinking.

47. I often feel sexier after I have had a couple of drinks.

48. Having a few drinks helps me relax in a social situation.

49. I drink when I am feeling mad.

50. Drinking alone or with one other person makes me feel calm and serene.

ANSWER ACCORDING TO WHAT YOU PERSONALLY BELIEVE NOW

	Agree	Disagree
51. After a few drinks, I feel brave and more capable of fighting.	_____	_____
52. Drinking can make me more satisfied with myself.	_____	_____
53. There is more camaraderie in a group of people who have been drinking.	_____	_____
54. My feelings of isolation and alienation decrease when I drink.	_____	_____
55. A few drinks make me feel less in touch with what is going on around me.	_____	_____
56. Alcohol makes me more tolerant of people I do not enjoy.	_____	_____
57. Alcohol helps me sleep better.	_____	_____
58. Drinking increases female aggressiveness.	_____	_____
59. I am a better lover after a few drinks.	_____	_____
60. Women talk more after they have had a few drinks.	_____	_____
61. Alcohol decreases muscular tension.	_____	_____
62. Alcohol makes me worry less.	_____	_____
63. A few drinks make it easier to talk to people.	_____	_____
64. After a few drinks, I am usually in a better mood.	_____	_____
65. Alcohol seems like magic.	_____	_____
66. Women can have orgasms more easily if they have been drinking.	_____	_____
67. At times, drinking is like permission to forget problems.	_____	_____
68. Drinking helps me get out of a depressed mood.	_____	_____

ANSWER ACCORDING TO WHAT YOU PERSONALLY BELIEVE NOW

	Agree	Disagree
69. After I have had a couple of drinks, I feel I am more of a caring, sharing person.	_____	_____
70. Alcohol decreases my feelings of guilt about not working.	_____	_____
71. I feel more coordinated after I drink.	_____	_____
72. Alcohol makes me more interesting.	_____	_____
73. A few drinks make me feel less shy.	_____	_____
74. If I am tense or anxious, having a few drinks makes me feel better.	_____	_____
75. Alcohol enables me to fall asleep more easily.	_____	_____
76. If I am feeling afraid, alcohol decreases my fears.	_____	_____
77. A couple of drinks make me more aroused or physiologically excited.	_____	_____
78. Alcohol can act as an anesthetic; that is, it can deaden pain.	_____	_____
79. I enjoy having sex more if I have had some alcohol.	_____	_____
80. I am more romantic when I drink.	_____	_____
81. I feel more masculine/feminine after a few drinks.	_____	_____
82. When I am feeling antisocial, drinking makes me more gregarious.	_____	_____
83. Alcohol makes me feel better physically.	_____	_____
84. Sometimes when I drink alone or with one other person it is easy to feel cozy and romantic.	_____	_____
85. I feel like a more happy-go-lucky person when I drink.	_____	_____
86. Drinking makes get-togethers more fun.	_____	_____

ANSWER ACCORDING TO WHAT YOU PERSONALLY BELIEVE NOW

	Agree	Disagree
87. Alcohol makes it easier to forget bad feelings.	_____	_____
88. After a few drinks, I am more sexually responsive.	_____	_____
89. If I am cold, having a few drinks will give me a sense of warmth.	_____	_____
90. It is easier to act on my feelings after I have had a few drinks.	_____	_____
91. I become lustful when I drink.	_____	_____
92. A couple of drinks make me feel more outgoing.	_____	_____
93. A drink or two can make me feel more wide awake.	_____	_____
94. Alcohol decreases my hostilities.	_____	_____
95. Alcohol makes me feel closer to people.	_____	_____
96. I tend to be less self-critical when I have something alcoholic to drink.	_____	_____
97. I find that conversing with members of the opposite sex is easier for me after I have had a few drinks.	_____	_____
98. Drinking makes me feel flushed.	_____	_____
99. It is easier to remember funny stories or jokes when I have been drinking.	_____	_____
100. After a few drinks, I am less submissive to those in positions of authority.	_____	_____
101. Alcohol makes me more talkative.	_____	_____
102. I am more romantic when I drink.	_____	_____
103. Men can have orgasms more easily if they have had a drink.	_____	_____
104. A drink or two is really refreshing after strenuous physical activity.	_____	_____
105. Alcohol enables me to have a better time at parties.	_____	_____
106. I can be more persuasive if I have had a few drinks.	_____	_____

ANSWER ACCORDING TO WHAT YOU PERSONALLY BELIEVE NOW

	Agree	Disagree
107. Drinking makes people feel more at ease in social situations.	_____	_____
108. Alcohol helps me sleep better.	_____	_____
109. After a drink, things like muscle aches and pains do not hurt as much.	_____	_____
110. Women are friendlier after they have had a few drinks.	_____	_____
111. Alcohol makes me worry less.	_____	_____
112. Alcohol makes it easier to act impulsively or make decisions quickly.	_____	_____
113. Alcohol makes me feel less shy.	_____	_____
114. Alcohol makes me more tolerant of people I do not enjoy.	_____	_____
115. Alcohol makes me need less attention from others than I usually do.	_____	_____
116. A drink or two can slow me down, so I do not feel so rushed or pressured for time.	_____	_____
117. I feel more sexual after a few drinks.	_____	_____
118. Alcohol makes me feel better physically.	_____	_____
119. Having a drink in my hand can make me feel secure in a difficult social situation.	_____	_____
120. Things seem funnier when I have been drinking, or at least I laugh more.	_____	_____

Alcohol Use Disorders Identification Test (AUDIT)

Please answer each question by checking one of the circles in the second column.

Q1	O Never O Monthly or less O 2-4 times per month O 2-3 times per week O 4+ times per week	How often do you have a drink containing alcohol?
Q2	O 1 or 2 O 3 or 4 O 5 or 6 O 7 to 9 O 10 or more	How many drinks containing alcohol do you have on a typical day when you are drinking?
Q3	O Never O Less than monthly O Monthly O Weekly O Daily or almost daily	How often do you have six or more drinks on one occasion?
Q4	O Never O Less than monthly O Monthly O Weekly O Daily or almost daily	How often during the last year have you found that you were not able to stop drinking once you had started?
Q5	O Never O Less than monthly O Monthly O Weekly O Daily or almost daily	How often in the last year have you failed to do what was normally expected of you because you were drinking?
Q6	O Never O Less than monthly O Monthly O Weekly O Daily or almost daily	How often during the last year have you needed a first drink in the morning to get yourself going after a heavy drinking session?
Q7	O Never O Less than monthly O Monthly O Weekly O Daily or almost daily	How often during the last year have you had a feeling of guilt or remorse about drinking?

Q8	O Never O Less than monthly O Monthly O Weekly O Daily or almost daily	How often during the last year have you been unable to remember what happened the night before because you had been drinking?
Q9	O No O Yes, but not in the last year O Yes, during the last year	Have you or someone else been injured as a result of your drinking?
Q10	O No O Yes, but not in the last year O Yes, during the last year	Has a relative, friend, doctor, or other health worker been concerned about your drinking or suggested that you cut down?

Your score on the AUDIT is _____.

A score of **eight points or less** is considered nonalcoholic, while **nine points and above** indicates alcoholism.

Your score of _____ does not indicate a problem with alcoholism.

Brief Situational Confidence Questionnaire (BSCQ)

Name: _____   Date: _____

Listed below are eight types of situations in which some people experience an alcohol or drug problem. Imagine yourself as you are right now in each of the following types of situations. Indicate on the scale provided how confident you are right now that you will be able to resist drinking heavily or resist the urge to use your primary drug in each situation by placing an "X" along the line, from 0% "Not at all confident" to 100% "Totally confident" as in the example below.

I feel...

|————————X———————————————|

0%   100%

Not at all confident   Totally confident

Right now I would be able to resist the urge to drink heavily or use my primary drug in situations involving...

1. **UNPLEASANT EMOTIONS** (e.g., If I were depressed about things in general; if everything were going badly for me).

I feel...

|—————————————————————| _____

0%   100%

Not at all confident   Totally confident

2. **PHYSICAL DISCOMFORT** (e.g., If I were to have trouble sleeping; if I felt jumpy and physically tense).

I feel...

|—————————————————————| _____

0%   100%

Not at all confident   Totally confident

3. **PLEASANT EMOTIONS** (e.g., If something good happened and I felt like celebrating; if everything were going well).

I feel...

|—————————————————————| _____

0%   100%

Not at all confident   Totally confident

Right now I would be able to resist the urge to drink heavily or use my primary drug in situations involving…

4. **TESTING CONTROL OVER MY USE OF ALCOHOL OR DRUGS** (e.g., If I were to start to believe that alcohol or drugs were no longer a problem for me; if I felt confident that I could handle drugs or several drinks).

I feel…

0%	100%
Not at all confident	Totally confident

_____

5. **URGES AND TEMPTATIONS** (e.g., If I suddenly had an urge to drink or use drugs; if I were in a situation where I had often used drugs or drank heavily).

I feel…

0%	100%
Not at all confident	Totally confident

_____

6. **CONFLICT WITH OTHERS** (e.g., If I had an argument with a friend; if I were not getting along well with others at work).

I feel…

0%	100%
Not at all confident	Totally confident

_____

7. **SOCIAL PRESSURE TO USE** (e.g., If someone were to pressure me to "be a good sport" and drink or use drugs with him; if I were invited to someone's home and he offered me a drink or drugs).

I feel…

0%	100%
Not at all confident	Totally confident

_____

8. **PLEASANT TIMES WITH OTHERS** (e.g., If I wanted to celebrate with a friend; if I were enjoying myself at a party and wanted to feel even better).

I feel…

0%	100%
Not at all confident	Totally confident

_____

Personal Feedback Report

Location: _____

Name: _____ ID: _____

1. YOUR DRINKING _____

Number of standard "drinks" per week: _____ drinks

Your drinking relative to American adults (same sex): _____ percentile

2. LEVEL OF INTOXICATION _____

Estimated Blood Alcohol Concentration (BAC) peaks:

in a typical week: _____ mg %

on a heavier day of drinking: _____ mg %

3. RISK FACTORS _____

Tolerance Level:

_____ Low (0–60)   _____ Medium (61–120)   _____ High (121–180)   _____ Very High (181 +)

Other Drug Risk:

_____ Low   _____ Medium   _____ High

Family Risk: _____

Low: 0–1   Medium: 2–3   High: 4–6   Very High: 7 +

MacAndrew Score: _____

Normal Range: 0–23   Medium Risk: 24–29   High Risk: 30 +

Age at Onset: _____ years

Under 25 Higher Risk   25–39 Medium Risk   40 + Lower Risk

4. NEGATIVE CONSEQUENCES _____

Severity of Problems

	Low	Medium	High	Very High
AUDIT	0–7	8–15	16–25	26–40

Your Score: _____

DRINC: Ever happened	Low	Medium	High	Very High
	55–60	61–75	76–90	91 +

Your Score: _____

(Additional information on attached sheet.)

5. BLOOD TESTS _____

SGOT (AST): _____ Normal range: 5–35

GGTP (GGT): _____ Normal range: 0–30 Low Normal   31–50 High Normal
                                       51 + Elevated/Abnormal

SGPT (ALT): _____ Normal range: 7–56

Uric Acid: _____ Normal range: 2.6–5.6

Bilirubin: _____ Normal range: 0.2–1.2

6. NEUROPSYCHOLOGICAL TESTS _____

	Well Above Average	Above Average	Average	Below Average	Well Below Average
SV	1	2	3	4	5
TMTA	1	2	3	4	5
TMTB	1	2	3	4	5
SYDM	1	2	3	4	5
SHVA	1	2	3	4	5

Therapist: _____

Understanding Your Personal Feedback Report

The Personal Feedback Report summarizes results from your pretreatment evaluation. Your therapist has explained these to you. This information is to help you understand the written report you have received and to remember what your therapist told you.

Your report consists of two sheets. The first sheet provides information from your pretreatment interviews. Attached to this is a second sheet summarizing your answers to a questionnaire, the Alcohol Use Inventory. The following information is presented section by section to help you understand what your results mean.

1. *Your drinking*

The first line in this section shows the number of drinks that you reported having in a typical drinking week. Because different alcohol beverages vary in their strength, we have converted your regular drinking pattern into standard "one drink" units. In this system, one drink is equal to

10 ounces of beer	(5 percent alcohol) or
4 ounces of table wine	(12 percent alcohol) or
2.5 ounces of fortified wine	
(sherry, port, etc.)	(20 percent alcohol) or
1.25 ounces of 80 proof liquor	(40 percent alcohol) or
1 ounce of 100 proof liquor	(50 percent alcohol)

All of these drinks contain the same amount of the same kind of alcohol: one-half ounce of pure ethyl alcohol.

ONE STANDARD DRINK IS:

Beer	10 oz
Wine	4 oz
80 proof liquor	1¼ oz
100 proof liquor	1 oz

This first piece of information, then, tells you how many of these standard drinks you have been consuming per week of drinking, according to what you reported in your interview. (If you have not been drinking for a period of time recently, this refers to your pattern of drinking before you stopped.)

To give you an idea of how this compares with the drinking of American adults in general, the second number in section 1 is a *percentile* figure. This tells you what percentage of U.S. men (if you are a man) or women (if you are a woman) drink *less* than you reported drinking in a typical week of drinking. If this number were 60, for example, it would mean that your drinking is higher than 60 percent of Americans of your sex (or that 40 percent drink as much as you reported, or more).

How much is too much? It depends on many factors. Current research indicates that people who average *three* or more standard drinks per day have much higher risk of health and social problems. For some people, however, even 1–2 drinks per day would be too many. Pregnant women, for example, are best advised to abstain from alcohol altogether, because even small amounts of regular drinking have been found to increase risk for the unborn child. Certain health problems (such as liver disease) make even moderate drinking unsafe. Some people find that they are unable to drink moderately, and having even one or two drinks leads to intoxication.

Your total number of drinks per week tells only part of the story. It is *not* healthy, for example, to have 12 drinks per week by saving them all up for Saturdays. Neither is it safe to have even a few drinks and then drive. This raises the important question of level of intoxication.

2. *Level of intoxication*

A second way of looking at your past drinking is to ask what level of intoxication you have been reaching. It is possible to estimate the amount of alcohol that would be circulating in your bloodstream, based on the pattern of drinking you reported. Blood alcohol concentration (BAC) is an important indication of the extent to which alcohol would be affecting your body and behavior. It is used by police and the courts, for example, to determine whether a driver is too impaired to operate a motor vehicle.

To understand better what BAC means, consider the list of common effects of different levels of intoxication.

Common Effects of Different Levels of Intoxication	
20–60 mg %	This is the "normal" social drinking range. NOTE: Driving, even at these levels, is unsafe.
80 mg %	Memory, judgment, and perception are impaired. Legally intoxicated in some States.
100 mg %	Reaction time and coordination of movement are affected. Legally intoxicated in all States.
150 mg %	Vomiting may occur in normal drinkers; balance is often impaired.
200 mg %	Memory "blackout" may occur, causing loss of recall for events occurring while intoxicated.
300 mg %	Unconsciousness in a normal person, although some remain conscious at levels in excess of 600 mg % if tolerance is very high.
400–500 mg %	Fatal dose for a normal person, although some survive higher levels if tolerance is very high.

The two figures shown in section 2 are computer-calculated estimates of your highest (peak) BAC level during a typical week of drinking and during one of your heaviest days of drinking.

It is important to realize that there is no known "safe" level of intoxication when driving or engaging in other potentially hazardous activities (such as swimming, boating, hunting, and operating tools or machinery). Blood alcohol levels as low as 40–60 mg % can decrease crucial abilities. Adding to the danger, drinkers typically do not *realize* that they are impaired. The only safe BAC when driving is *zero*. If you must drive after drinking, plan to allow enough time for all of the alcohol to be eliminated from your body before driving. The tables below can be helpful in determining how long it takes to eliminate alcohol completely:

Approximate hours from first drink to zero alcohol concentration levels for MEN								
Number of Drinks	**Your weight in pounds**							
	120	**140**	**160**	**180**	**200**	**220**	**240**	**260**
1	2	2	2	1.5	1	1	1	1
2	4	3.5	3	3	2.5	2	2	2
3	6	5	4.5	4	3.5	3.5	3	3
4	8	7	6	5.5	5	4.5	4	3.5
5	10	8.5	7.5	6.5	6	5.5	5	4.5

One drink = 10 oz of beer or 4 oz of wine or 1 oz of liquor (100 proof)

Approximate hours from first drink to zero alcohol concentration levels for WOMEN								
Number of Drinks	**Your weight in pounds**							
	120	**140**	**160**	**180**	**200**	**220**	**240**	**260**
1	3	2.5	2	2	2	1.5	1.5	1
2	6	5	4	4	3.5	3	3	2.5
3	9	7.5	6.5	5.5	5	4.5	4	4
4	12	9.5	8.5	7.5	6.5	6	5.5	5
5	15	12	10.5	9.5	8	7.5	7	6

One drink = 10 oz of beer or 4 oz of wine or 1 oz of liquor (100 proof)

3. Risk factors

It is clear that some people have a much higher risk of alcohol and other drug problems. This section provides you with some information about your own level of risk, based on your personal characteristics. "High risk" does not mean that one will definitely have serious problems with alcohol or other drugs. Neither does "low risk" mean that one will be free of such problems. High-risk people, however, have greater chances of developing serious problems.

Tolerance

Your peak BAC levels, given in section 2, are one reasonably good reflection of your level of *tolerance* for alcohol. If you are reaching BAC levels beyond the normal social drinking range (especially if you are not feeling some of the normal effects of lower BACs), it means that you have a higher tolerance for alcohol. This is partly hereditary and partly the result of changes in the body that occur with heavier drinking. Some people are proud of this tolerance—the ability "to hold your liquor"—and think it means they are not being harmed by alcohol. Actually, the opposite is true. Tolerance for alcohol may be a serious *risk factor* for alcohol problems. The person with a high tolerance for alcohol reaches high BAC levels, which can damage the brain and other organs of the body but has *no built-in warning* that it is happening. Tolerance is not a protection against being harmed by drinking; to the contrary, it makes damage more likely because of the false confidence that it encourages. It is a bit like a person who has no sense of pain.

Pain is an important warning signal. People who feel no pain can seriously injure themselves without realizing it. It is the same with people who have a high tolerance for alcohol.

Many people believe that tolerance ("holding your liquor") means that a person gets rid of alcohol at a faster rate than others. Although people do differ in how quickly their bodies can clear alcohol, tolerance has more to do with actually *being* at a high blood alcohol level and not feeling it.

Other drug use

A person who uses other drugs besides alcohol runs several additional risks. Decreased use of one drug may simply result in the increased use of another. The effects of different drugs can multiply when they are taken together, with dangerous results. A tolerance to one drug can increase tolerance to another, and it is common for multiple drug users to become addicted to several drugs. The use of other drugs, then, increases your risk for serious problems. Based on the lifetime drug use that you reported during your interview, your risk in this regard was judged to be low, medium, or high.

Family risk

People who have a family history of alcohol or other drug problems among their blood relatives clearly are at higher risk themselves. The exact reason for this higher risk is unknown, but it appears that the risk is inherited to an important extent. People may inherit a higher tolerance for alcohol or a body that is particularly sensitive to alcohol in certain ways. In any event, a family history of alcohol problems increases personal risk.

Personality pattern

Although there is no single personality style associated with alcohol and drug problems, certain patterns are linked to higher risk. One questionnaire you completed—the MacAndrew Scale—measures this particular kind of risk. People who score higher on this scale as teenagers, for example, have been found to have higher risk for developing serious problems with alcohol in adulthood.

Age at onset

Recent research indicates that the younger a person is when drinking problems start, the greater the person's risk for developing serious consequences and dependence. Although serious problems can occur at any time of life, a younger beginning does represent a significant risk factor.

4. Negative consequences

From your pretreatment interview, two scores were calculated to reflect the current overall severity of your negative consequences from drinking.

AUDIT

The AUDIT is a scale devised by the World Health Organization to evaluate a person's problematic involvement with alcohol. Higher scores reflect recent problems related to drinking.

DRINC

Another way to look at risks and effects of drinking is to add up alcohol's negative effects throughout one's lifetime. Your score on this scale reflects the extent to which your drinking has had negative effects over the course of your life thus far. The higher your score, the more harm has resulted from your drinking.

5. *Blood tests*

Your pretreatment evaluation also included a blood sample. These particular blood tests were chosen because they have been shown in previous research to be negatively affected by heavy drinking. You should realize that normal results on these tests do not guarantee that you are in good health (for example, that your liver is functioning completely normally). An abnormal score on one or more of these tests, however, probably reflects unhealthy changes in your body resulting from excessive use of alcohol and/or other drugs.

Research indicates that modestly abnormal scores on the blood tests reported here will often show improvement and a return to normal range when harmful drinking and other drug use patterns are changed. The longer one continues drinking, however, the more difficult it is to reverse the physical damage.

These tests are directly related to how the liver is working. Your liver is extremely important to your health. It is involved in producing energy, and it filters and neutralizes impurities and poisons in your bloodstream. Alcohol damages the liver, and after a long period of heavy drinking, parts of the liver begin to die. This is the process of cirrhosis, but physical changes in the liver can be caused by drinking long before cirrhosis appears. As the liver becomes damaged, it begins to leak enzymes into the blood and is less efficient in doing its work. This can be reflected in abnormally elevated values on the tests reported in this section.

Elevated values on any of these tests should be taken seriously. They do not happen by chance and are very likely related to physical changes in the body caused by excessive drinking. Consult a physician who is knowledgeable about the effects of alcohol on the body.

6. *Neuropsychological tests*

Some of the earliest damaging effects of drinking may be seen in certain types of abilities that are affected by alcohol. Certain patterns of brain impairment have been shown to be especially related to heavy drinking. The brain is very vulnerable to alcohol, and over a long span of time, a substantial amount of damage can occur in a heavy drinker. (Brain impairment from the use of certain other drugs has also been shown.)

Such damage occurs gradually. In later stages, it can be seen in x-rays of the brain, which show actual shrinkage and other changes in shape and density. Long before this occurs, however, harmful changes in brain functioning can be measured by psychological tests, several of which you completed. Research indicates that such negative effects can often be reversed, sometimes completely, if the individual stops or reduces drinking.

The four tests included in section 6 have been found to be related to heavy drinking. For comparison purposes, we include one test (SV) that is not usually affected by drinking to give you an idea of where your scores might normally be expected to fall. People who are heavy drinkers tend to score more poorly (higher) on the four alcohol-sensitive tests (TMTA, TMTB, SYDM, and SHVA) than on SV.

A high score on any one scale is not necessarily reason for concern. There are many reasons why a single score might be elevated. A *pattern* of elevated scores, however, resembles the kinds of problems that emerge among excessive drinkers. Studies of individuals currently in treatment for alcohol problems consistently show impairment on these measures.

Alcohol's effects on the brain have sometimes been described as "premature aging." The abnormal changes in the brain of a heavy drinker do resemble normal changes that occur with advanced age. For this reason, your scores reflected above take into account your present age. Scores of 4 or 5 represent below-average performance relative to others in your age group.

Summary

Your Personal Feedback Report summarizes a large amount of information that you provided during your pretreatment interviews. Sometimes this information can seem surprising or even discouraging. The best use of feedback like this is to consider it as you decide what, if anything, you will do about your drinking. Many of the kinds of problems covered in your Personal Feedback Report do improve when heavy drinking is stopped. What you do with this information is up to you. Your report is designed to give you a clear picture of where you are at present so that you can make good decisions about where you want to go from here.

Readiness To Change Questionnaire (Treatment Version) (RCQ-TV)

The following questionnaire is designed to identify how you personally feel about your drinking <u>right now</u>. Please think about your <u>current</u> situation and drinking habits, even if you have given up drinking completely. Read each question below carefully, and then decide whether you agree or disagree with the statements. Please tick the answer of your choice to each question. If you have any problems, please ask the questionnaire administrator.

<u>**Your answers are completely private and confidential**</u>

<u>Key:</u> **SD** = Strongly Disagree   **D** = Disagree   **U** = Unsure
A = Agree   **SA** = Strongly Agree

		SD	D	U	A	SA	For office use only
1.	There is no need for me to change my drinking habits.	☐	☐	☐	☐	☐	PC
2.	I enjoy my drinking, but sometimes I drink too much.	☐	☐	☐	☐	☐	C
3.	I have reached the stage where I should seriously think about giving up or drinking less alcohol.	☐	☐	☐	☐	☐	PA
4.	I am trying to stop drinking or drink less than I used to.	☐	☐	☐	☐	☐	A
5.	I was drinking too much at one time, but now I've managed to cut down (or stop) my drinking.	☐	☐	☐	☐	☐	M
6.	It's a waste of time thinking about my drinking because I do not have a problem.	☐	☐	☐	☐	☐	PC
7.	Sometimes I think I should quit or cut down on my drinking.	☐	☐	☐	☐	☐	C

		SD	D	U	A	SA	For office use only
8.	I have decided to do something about my drinking.	☐	☐	☐	☐	☐	PA
9.	I know that my drinking has caused problems, and I'm now trying to correct this.	☐	☐	☐	☐	☐	A
10.	I have changed my drinking habits (either cut down or quit), and I'm trying to keep it that way.	☐	☐	☐	☐	☐	M
11.	There is nothing seriously wrong with my drinking.	☐	☐	☐	☐	☐	PC
12.	My drinking is a problem sometimes.	☐	☐	☐	☐	☐	C
13.	I'm preparing to change my drinking habits (either cut down or give up completely).	☐	☐	☐	☐	☐	PA
14.	Anyone can talk about wanting to do something about their drinking, but I am actually doing something about it.	☐	☐	☐	☐	☐	A
15.	It is important for me to hold onto the changes I've made, now that I've cut down (or quit) drinking.	☐	☐	☐	☐	☐	M
16.	I am a fairly normal drinker.	☐	☐	☐	☐	☐	PC
17.	I am weighing up the advantages and disadvantages of my present drinking habits.	☐	☐	☐	☐	☐	C
18.	I have made a plan to stop or cut down drinking, and I intend to put this plan into practice.	☐	☐	☐	☐	☐	PA

		SD	D	U	A	SA	For office use only
19.	I am actually changing my drinking habits right now (either cutting down or quitting).	☐	☐	☐	☐	☐	A
20.	I have already done something about my drinking (either cut down or stopped completely), and I'm trying to avoid slipping back.	☐	☐	☐	☐	☐	M
21.	Giving up or drinking less alcohol would be pointless for me.	☐	☐	☐	☐	☐	PC
22.	I'm uncertain whether or not I drink too much.	☐	☐	☐	☐	☐	C
23.	I have a drinking problem, and I really want to do something about it.	☐	☐	☐	☐	☐	PA
24.	I have started to carry out a plan to cut down or quit drinking.	☐	☐	☐	☐	☐	A
25.	I am working hard to prevent having a relapse of my drinking problem.	☐	☐	☐	☐	☐	M
26.	There is nothing I really need to change about my drinking.	☐	☐	☐	☐	☐	PC
27.	Sometimes I wonder if my drinking is out of control.	☐	☐	☐	☐	☐	C
28.	If I don't change my drinking soon, my problems will just get worse.	☐	☐	☐	☐	☐	PA
29.	I am actively working on my drinking problem.	☐	☐	☐	☐	☐	A
30.	I've succeeded in stopping or cutting down drinking.	☐	☐	☐	☐	☐	M

Situational Confidence Questionnaire (SCQ-39)

Listed below are a number of situations or events in which some people experience a drinking problem.

Imagine yourself as you are right now in each of these situations. Indicate on the scale provided how confident you are that you would be able to resist the urge to drink heavily in that situation.

Circle **100** if you are 100 percent confident right now that you could resist the urge to drink heavily; **80** if you are 80 percent confident; **60** if you are 60 percent confident. If you are more unconfident than confident, circle **40** to indicate that you are only 40 percent confident that you could resist the urge to drink heavily; **20** for 20 percent confident; **0** if you have no confidence at all about that situation.

I would be able to resist the urge to drink heavily

	not at all confident					very confident
1. If I felt that I had let myself down	0	20	40	60	80	100
2. If there were fights at home	0	20	40	60	80	100
3. If I had trouble sleeping	0	20	40	60	80	100
4. If I had an argument with a friend	0	20	40	60	80	100
5. If other people didn't seem to like me	0	20	40	60	80	100
6. If I felt confident and relaxed	0	20	40	60	80	100
7. If I were out with friends and they stopped by the bar for a drink	0	20	40	60	80	100
8. If I were enjoying myself at a party and wanted to feel even better	0	20	40	60	80	100
9. If I remembered how good it tasted	0	20	40	60	80	100
10. If I convinced myself that I was a new person and could take a few drinks	0	20	40	60	80	100
11. If I were afraid that things weren't going to work out	0	20	40	60	80	100

I would be able to resist the urge to drink heavily

	not at all confident					very confident
12. If other people interfered with my plans	0	20	40	60	80	100
13. If I felt drowsy and wanted to stay alert	0	20	40	60	80	100
14. If there were problems with people at work	0	20	40	60	80	100
15. If I felt uneasy in the presence of someone	0	20	40	60	80	100
16. If everything were going well	0	20	40	60	80	100
17. If I were at a party and other people were drinking	0	20	40	60	80	100
18. If I wanted to celebrate with a friend	0	20	40	60	80	100
19. If I passed by a liquor store	0	20	40	60	80	100
20. If I wondered about my self-control over alcohol and felt like having a drink to try it out	0	20	40	60	80	100
21. If I were angry at the way things had turned out	0	20	40	60	80	100
22. If other people treated me unfairly	0	20	40	60	80	100
23. If I felt nauseous	0	20	40	60	80	100
24. If pressure built up at work because of the demands of my supervisor	0	20	40	60	80	100
25. If someone criticized me	0	20	40	60	80	100
26. If I felt satisfied with something I had done	0	20	40	60	80	100

I would be able to resist the urge to drink heavily

	not at all confident					very confident
27. If I were relaxed with a good friend and wanted to have a good time	0	20	40	60	80	100
28. If I were in a restaurant, and the people with me ordered drinks	0	20	40	60	80	100
29. If I unexpectedly found a bottle of my favorite booze	0	20	40	60	80	100
30. If I started to think that just one drink could cause no harm	0	20	40	60	80	100
31. If I felt confused about what I should do	0	20	40	60	80	100
32. If I felt under a lot of pressure from family members at home	0	20	40	60	80	100
33. If my stomach felt like it was tied in knots	0	20	40	60	80	100
34. If I were not getting along well with others at work	0	20	40	60	80	100
35. If other people around me made me tense	0	20	40	60	80	100
36. If I were out with friends "on the town" and wanted to increase my enjoyment	0	20	40	60	80	100
37. If I met a friend and he/she suggested that we have a drink together	0	20	40	60	80	100
38. If I suddenly had an urge to drink	0	20	40	60	80	100
39. If I wanted to prove to myself that I could take a few drinks without becoming drunk	0	20	40	60	80	100

Stages of Change Readiness and Treatment Eagerness Scale (SOCRATES 8A)

INSTRUCTIONS: Please read the following statements carefully. Each one describes a way that you might (or might not) feel *about your drinking*. For each statement, circle one number from 1 to 5, to indicate how much you agree or disagree with it *right now*. Please circle one and only one number for every statement.

	NO! Strongly Disagree	No Disagree	? Undecided or Unsure	Yes Agree	YES! Strongly Agree
1. I really want to make changes in my drinking.	1	2	3	4	5
2. Sometimes I wonder if I am an alcoholic.	1	2	3	4	5
3. If I don't change my drinking soon, my problems are going to get worse.	1	2	3	4	5
4. I have already started making some changes in my drinking.	1	2	3	4	5
5. I was drinking too much at one time, but I've managed to change my drinking.	1	2	3	4	5
6. Sometimes I wonder if my drinking is hurting other people.	1	2	3	4	5
7. I am a problem drinker.	1	2	3	4	5
8. I'm not just thinking about changing my drinking, I'm already doing something about it.	1	2	3	4	5
9. I have already changed my drinking, and I am looking for ways to keep from slipping back to my old pattern.	1	2	3	4	5
10. I have serious problems with drinking.	1	2	3	4	5
11. Sometimes I wonder if I am in control of my drinking.	1	2	3	4	5
12. My drinking is causing a lot of harm.	1	2	3	4	5
13. I am actively doing things now to cut down or stop drinking.	1	2	3	4	5

	NO! Strongly Disagree	No Disagree	? Undecided or Unsure	Yes Agree	YES! Strongly Agree
14. I want help to keep from going back to the drinking problems that I had before.	1	2	3	4	5
15. I know that I have a drinking problem.	1	2	3	4	5
16. There are times when I wonder if I drink too much.	1	2	3	4	5
17. I am an alcoholic.	1	2	3	4	5
18. I am working hard to change my drinking.	1	2	3	4	5
19. I have made some changes in my drinking, and I want some help to keep from going back to the way I used to drink.	1	2	3	4	5

For scoring and interpretation information of SOCRATES, see pp. 221–223.

Stages of Change Readiness and Treatment Eagerness Scale (SOCRATES 8D)

INSTRUCTIONS: Please read the following statements carefully. Each one describes a way that you might (or might not) feel *about your drug use.* For each statement, circle one number from 1 to 5, to indicate how much you agree or disagree with it *right now*. Please circle one and only one number for every statement.

	NO! Strongly Disagree	No Disagree	? Undecided or Unsure	Yes Agree	YES! Strongly Agree
1. I really want to make changes in my use of drugs.	1	2	3	4	5
2. Sometimes I wonder if I am an addict.	1	2	3	4	5
3. If I don't change my drug use soon, my problems are going to get worse.	1	2	3	4	5
4. I have already started making some changes in my use of drugs.	1	2	3	4	5
5. I was using drugs too much at one time, but I've managed to change that.	1	2	3	4	5
6. Sometimes I wonder if my drug use is hurting other people.	1	2	3	4	5
7. I have a drug problem.	1	2	3	4	5
8. I'm not just thinking about changing my drug use, I'm already doing something about it.	1	2	3	4	5
9. I have already changed my drug use, and I am looking for ways to keep from slipping back to my old pattern.	1	2	3	4	5
10. I have serious problems with drugs.	1	2	3	4	5
11. Sometimes I wonder if I am in control of my drug use.	1	2	3	4	5
12. My drug use is causing a lot of harm.	1	2	3	4	5

	NO! Strongly Disagree	No Disagree	? Undecided or Unsure	Yes Agree	YES! Strongly Agree
13. I am actively doing things now to cut down or stop my use of drugs.	1	2	3	4	5
14. I want help to keep from going back to the drug problems that I had before.	1	2	3	4	5
15. I know that I have a drug problem.	1	2	3	4	5
16. There are times when I wonder if I use drugs too much.	1	2	3	4	5
17. I am a drug addict.	1	2	3	4	5
18. I am working hard to change my drug use.	1	2	3	4	5
19. I have made some changes in my drug use, and I want some help to keep from going back to the way I used before.	1	2	3	4	5

SOCRATES Scoring Form (19-Item Version 8)

Transfer the client's answers from questionnaire (see note below):

Recognition	Ambivalence	Taking Steps
1 _____	2 _____	4 _____
3 _____		5 _____
	6 _____	
7 _____		8 _____
		9 _____
10 _____	11 _____	
12 _____		13 _____
		14 _____
15 _____	16 _____	
17 _____		18 _____
		19 _____

Totals: Re: _____	Am: _____	Ts: _____
Possible Range: 7–35	4–20	8–40

223

SOCRATES Profile Sheet (19-Item Version 8A)

INSTRUCTIONS: From the SOCRATES Scoring Form (19-Item Version) transfer the total scale scores into the empty boxes at the bottom of the Profile Sheet. Then for each scale, CIRCLE the same value above it to determine the decile range.

DECILE SCORES	Recognition	Ambivalence	Taking Steps
90 (Very High)		19–20	39–40
80		18	37–38
70 (High)	35	17	36
60	34	16	34–35
50 (Medium)	32–33	15	33
40	31	14	31–32
30 (Low)	29–30	12–13	30
20	27–28	9–11	26–29
10 (Very Low)	7–26	4–8	8–25
RAW SCORES (from Scoring Sheet)	Re=	Am=	Ts=

These interpretive ranges are based on a sample of 1,726 adult men and women presenting for treatment of alcohol problems through Project MATCH. Note that individual scores are therefore being ranked as low, medium, or high *relative to people already presenting for alcohol treatment.*

Guidelines for Interpretation of SOCRATES-8 Scores

Using the SOCRATES Profile Sheet, circle the client's raw score within each of the three scale columns. This provides information as to whether the client's scores are low, average, or high *relative to people already seeking treatment for alcohol problems.* The following are provided as general guidelines for interpretation of scores, but it is wise in an individual case also to examine individual item responses for additional information.

RECOGNITION

HIGH scorers directly acknowledge that they are having problems related to their drinking, tending to express a desire for change and to perceive that harm will continue if they do not change.

LOW scorers deny that alcohol is causing them serious problems, reject diagnostic labels such as "problem drinker" and "alcoholic," and do not express a desire for change.

AMBIVALENCE

HIGH scorers say that they sometimes *wonder* if they are in control of their drinking, are drinking too much, are hurting other people, and/or are alcoholic. Thus a high score reflects ambivalence or uncertainty. A high score here reflects some openness to reflection, as might be particularly expected in the contemplation stage of change.

LOW scorers say that they *do not wonder* whether they drink too much, are in control, are hurting others, or are alcoholic. Note that a person may score low on ambivalence *either* because he "knows" his drinking is causing problems (high Recognition), *or* because he "knows" that he does not have drinking problems (low Recognition). Thus a low Ambivalence score should be interpreted in relation to the Recognition score.

TAKING STEPS

HIGH scorers report that they are already doing things to make a positive change in their drinking and may have experienced some success in this regard. Change is under way, and they may want help to persist or to prevent backsliding. A high score on this scale has been found to be predictive of successful change.

LOW scorers report that they are not currently doing things to change their drinking and have not made such changes recently.

University of Rhode Island Change Assessment Scale (URICA)

Each statement below describes how a person might feel when starting therapy or approaching problems in his life. Please indicate the extent to which you tend to agree or disagree with each statement. In each case, make your choice in terms of how you feel right now, not what you have felt in the past or would like to feel. For all the statements that refer to your "problem," answer in terms of problems related to your drinking (illegal drug use). The words "here" and "this place" refer to your treatment center.

There are five possible responses to each of the items in the questionnaire:

1 = Strongly Disagree
2 = Disagree
3 = Undecided
4 = Agree
5 = Strongly Agree

Circle the number that best describes how much you agree or disagree with each statement.

	STRONGLY DISAGREE	DISAGREE	UNDECIDED	AGREE	STRONGLY AGREE
1. As far as I'm concerned, I don't have any problems that need changing.	1	2	3	4	5
2. I think I might be ready for some self-improvement.	1	2	3	4	5
3. I am doing something about the problems that had been bothering me.	1	2	3	4	5
4. It might be worthwhile to work on my problem.	1	2	3	4	5
5. I'm not the problem one. It doesn't make much sense for me to consider changing.	1	2	3	4	5
6. It worries me that I might slip back on a problem I have already changed, so I am looking for help.	1	2	3	4	5
7. I am finally doing some work on my problem.	1	2	3	4	5

		STRONGLY DISAGREE	DISAGREE	UNDECIDED	AGREE	STRONGLY AGREE
8.	I've been thinking that I might want to change something about myself.	1	2	3	4	5
9.	I have been successful in working on my problem, but I'm not sure I can keep up the effort on my own.	1	2	3	4	5
10.	At times my problem is difficult, but I'm working on it.	1	2	3	4	5
11.	Trying to change is pretty much a waste of time for me because the problem doesn't have to do with me.	1	2	3	4	5
12.	I'm hoping that I will be able to understand myself better.	1	2	3	4	5
13.	I guess I have faults, but there's nothing that I really need to change.	1	2	3	4	5
14.	I am really working hard to change.	1	2	3	4	5
15.	I have a problem, and I really think I should work on it.	1	2	3	4	5
16.	I'm not following through with what I had already changed as well as I had hoped, and I want to prevent a relapse of the problem.	1	2	3	4	5
17.	Even though I'm not always successful in changing, I am at least working on my problem.	1	2	3	4	5

	STRONGLY DISAGREE	DISAGREE	UNDECIDED	AGREE	STRONGLY AGREE
18. I thought once I had resolved the problem I would be free of it, but sometimes I still find myself struggling with it.	1	2	3	4	5
19. I wish I had more ideas on how to solve my problem.	1	2	3	4	5
20. I have started working on my problem, but I would like help.	1	2	3	4	5
21. Maybe someone or something will be able to help me.	1	2	3	4	5
22. I may need a boost right now to help me maintain the changes I've already made.	1	2	3	4	5
23. I may be part of the problem, but I don't really think I am.	1	2	3	4	5
24. I hope that someone will have some good advice for me.	1	2	3	4	5
25. Anyone can talk about changing; I'm actually doing something about it.	1	2	3	4	5
26. All this talk about psychology is boring. Why can't people just forget about their problems?	1	2	3	4	5
27. I'm struggling to prevent myself from having a relapse of my problem.	1	2	3	4	5
28. It is frustrating, but I feel I might be having a recurrence of a problem I thought I had resolved.	1	2	3	4	5

		STRONGLY DISAGREE	DISAGREE	UNDECIDED	AGREE	STRONGLY AGREE
29.	I have worries, but so does the next guy. Why spend time thinking about them?	1	2	3	4	5
30.	I am actively working on my problem.	1	2	3	4	5
31.	I would rather cope with my faults than try to change them.	1	2	3	4	5

What I Want From Treatment

William R. Miller and Janice M. Brown

Instructions

People have different ideas about what they want, need, and expect from treatment.

This questionnaire is designed to help you explain what you would *like* to have happen in your treatment. Many possibilities are listed. For each one, please indicate how much you would like for this to be part of your treatment.

You can do this by circling one number (0, 1, 2, or 3) for each item. This is what the numbers mean:

0 NO   means that you definitely do **NOT** want or need this from treatment.
1 ?   means that you are **UNSURE**. **MAYBE** you want this from treatment.
2 YES   means that you **DO** want or need this from treatment.
3 YES! means that you **DEFINITELY** want or need this from treatment.

FOR EXAMPLE:

Consider item #1, which says, "I want to receive detoxification." If you definitely do NOT want or need to receive detoxification, you would circle **0.** If you are UNSURE whether you want or need detoxification, you would circle **1.** If you DO want detoxification, you would circle **2.** If you DEFINITELY know that detoxification is an important goal for your treatment, you would circle **3.**

If you have any questions about how to use this questionnaire, ask for assistance before you begin.

DO YOU WANT THIS FROM TREATMENT? ↘	NO 0	Maybe 1	Yes 2	YES! 3
1. I want to receive detoxification, to ease my withdrawal from alcohol or other drugs.	0	1	2	3
2. I want to find out for sure whether I have a problem with alcohol or other drugs.	0	1	2	3
3. I want help to stop drinking alcohol completely.	0	1	2	3
4. I want help to decrease my drinking.	0	1	2	3
5. I want help to stop using drugs (other than alcohol).	0	1	2	3

DO YOU WANT THIS FROM TREATMENT? ↘	NO 0	Maybe 1	Yes 2	YES! 3
6. I want to stop using tobacco.	0	1	2	3
7. I want to decrease my use of tobacco.	0	1	2	3
8. I want help with an eating problem.	0	1	2	3
9. I want help with a gambling problem.	0	1	2	3
10. I want to take Antabuse (a medication to help me stop drinking).	0	1	2	3
11. I want to take Trexan (a medication to help me stop using alcohol or heroin).	0	1	2	3
12. I want to take methadone.	0	1	2	3
13. I want to learn more about alcohol/drug problems.	0	1	2	3
14. I want to learn some skills to keep from returning to alcohol or other drugs.	0	1	2	3
15. I would like to learn more about 12-Step programs like Alcoholics Anonymous (AA) or Narcotics Anonymous (NA).	0	1	2	3
16. I would like to talk about some personal problems.	0	1	2	3
17. I need to fulfill a requirement of the courts.	0	1	2	3
18. I would like help with problems in my marriage or close relationship.	0	1	2	3
19. I want help with some health problems.	0	1	2	3
20. I want help to decrease my stress and tension.	0	1	2	3
21. I would like to improve my health by learning more about nutrition and exercise.	0	1	2	3
22. I want help with depression or moodiness.	0	1	2	3

DO YOU WANT THIS FROM TREATMENT? ↘	NO 0	Maybe 1	Yes 2	YES! 3
23. I want to work on my spiritual growth.	0	1	2	3
24. I want to learn how to solve problems in my life.	0	1	2	3
25. I want help with angry feelings and how I express them.	0	1	2	3
26. I want to have healthier relationships.	0	1	2	3
27. I would like to discuss sexual problems.	0	1	2	3
28. I want to learn how to express my feelings in a more healthy way.	0	1	2	3
29. I want to learn how to relax better.	0	1	2	3
30. I want help in overcoming boredom.	0	1	2	3
31. I want help with feelings of loneliness.	0	1	2	3
32. I want to discuss having been physically abused.	0	1	2	3
33. I want help to prevent violence at home.	0	1	2	3
34. I want to discuss having been sexually abused.	0	1	2	3
35. I want to work on having better self-esteem.	0	1	2	3
36. I want help with sleep problems.	0	1	2	3
37. I want help with legal problems.	0	1	2	3
38. I want advice about financial problems.	0	1	2	3
39. I would like help in finding a place to live.	0	1	2	3
40. I could use help in finding a job.	0	1	2	3

DO YOU WANT THIS FROM TREATMENT? ↘	NO 0	Maybe 1	Yes 2	YES! 3
41. Someone close to me has died or left, and I would like to talk about it.	0	1	2	3
42. I have thoughts about suicide, and I would like to discuss this.	0	1	2	3
43. I want help with personal fears and anxieties.	0	1	2	3
44. I want help to be a better parent.	0	1	2	3
45. I feel very confused and would like help with this.	0	1	2	3
46. I would like information about or testing for HIV/AIDS.	0	1	2	3
47. I want someone to listen to me.	0	1	2	3
48. I want to learn to have fun without drugs or alcohol.	0	1	2	3
49. I want someone to tell me what to do.	0	1	2	3
50. I want help in setting goals and priorities in my life.	0	1	2	3
51. I would like to learn how to manage my time better.	0	1	2	3
52. I want help to receive SSI/disability payments.	0	1	2	3
53. I want to find enjoyable ways to spend my free time.	0	1	2	3
54. I want help in getting my child(ren) back.	0	1	2	3
55. I would like to talk about my past.	0	1	2	3
56. I need help in getting motivated to change.	0	1	2	3
57. I would like to see a female counselor.	0	1	2	3
58. I would like to see a male counselor.	0	1	2	3
59. I would like to see the counselor I had before.	0	1	2	3

DO YOU WANT THIS FROM TREATMENT? ↘	NO 0	Maybe 1	Yes 2	YES! 3
60. I would like to see a doctor or nurse about medical problems.	0	1	2	3
61. I want to receive medication.	0	1	2	3
62. I would like my spouse or partner to be in treatment with me.	0	1	2	3
63. I would like to have private, individual counseling.	0	1	2	3
64. I would like to be in a group with people who are dealing with problems similar to my own.	0	1	2	3
65. I need someone to care for my children while I am in treatment.	0	1	2	3
66. I want my treatment to be short.	0	1	2	3
67. I believe I will need to be in treatment for a long time.	0	1	2	3

Is there anything else you would like from treatment? If so, please write on the back of this sheet.

Appendix C
Ordering Information for Assessment Instruments

Alcohol and Drug Consequences Questionnaire (ADCQ)

This instrument is not copyrighted and may be obtained by writing its developer:

John A. Cunningham, Ph.D.
Clinical Research Dissemination Unit
Addiction Research Foundation
33 Russell Street
Toronto, ON
Canada M5S 2S1
Phone: (416) 595-6701
Fax: (416) 595-6617
E-mail: jcunning@arf.org

Alcohol Effects Questionnaire (AEQ)

This instrument is in the public domain and may be downloaded from the Web site at
http://silk.nih.gov/silk/niaaa1/publication/insaeq.htm

Alcohol Expectancy Questionnaire

This instrument is in the public domain and may be downloaded from the Web site at
http://silk.nih.gov/silk/niaaa1/publication/instable.htm

Alcohol Use Disorders Identification Test (AUDIT)

This instrument is in the public domain and may be downloaded from the Web site at
http://silk.nih.gov/silk/niaaa1/publication/instable.htm

Brief Situational Confidence Questionnaire (BSCQ)

This instrument is copyrighted and may be obtained by writing its author:

Linda Sobell, Ph.D.
NOVA Southeastern University
Center for Psychological Studies
3301 College Avenue
Fort Lauderdale, FL 33314
Phone: (954) 262-5811
Fax: (954) 262-3895
E-mail: sobelll@cps.nova.edu

Personal Feedback Report

This instrument is not copyrighted and may be obtained by writing its developer:

Project MATCH Series
National Institute on Alcohol Abuse and Alcoholism
P.O. Box 10686
Rockville, MD 10849-0686

Readiness To Change Questionnaire (Treatment Version) (RCQ-TV)

This instrument is copyrighted and may be obtained by contacting:

Professor Nick Heather
Consultant Clinical Psychologist
Newcastle City Health NHS Trust
Northern Regional Drug and Alcohol Service
Newcastle upon Tyne
United Kingdom
Fax: 44 191 219-5601

Situational Confidence Questionnaire (SCQ-39)

This instrument is copyrighted and may be obtained by writing the copyright holder:

Marketing Services
Addiction Research Foundation
33 Russell Street
Toronto, ON
Canada M5S 2S1
Phone: (416) 595-6557
Fax: (416) 593-4694

Stages of Change Readiness and Treatment Eagerness Scale (SOCRATES)

This instrument is in the public domain and may be obtained by contacting its author:

> William R. Miller, Ph.D.
> Director
> Center on Alcoholism, Substance Abuse, and Addictions
> 2350 Alamo SE
> University of New Mexico
> Albuquerque, NM 87106
> Phone: (505) 768-0100
> Fax: (505) 768-0113
> E-mail: wrmiller@unm.edu

University of Rhode Island Change Assessment Scale (URICA)

This instrument is in the public domain and may be obtained by contacting its author:

> Carlo C. DiClemente, Ph.D.
> Professor and Chair
> University of Maryland Baltimore County
> Department of Psychology
> 1000 Hilltop Circle
> Baltimore, MD 21250
> Phone: (410) 455-2415
> Fax: (410) 455-1055
> E-mail: diclemen@umbc.edu

Other Resources

Allen, J.P., and Columbus, M. *Assessing Alcohol Problems: A Guide for Clinicians and Researchers.* Rockville, MD: National Institute on Alcohol Abuse and Alcoholism, 1995.

This volume contains psychometrically sound assessment instruments. A brief discussion is provided for each instrument, along with a copy of the instrument and scoring instructions. Examples of assessment instruments that may be used to enhance motivation include the Situational Confidence Questionnaire; AUDIT; self-monitoring form; the alcohol timeline; and daily drinking feedback. Free copies may be obtained by calling the National Clearinghouse for Alcohol and Drug Information at (800) 729-6686.

Sobell, L.C., and Sobell, M.B. *Timeline Follow-Back (TLFB).* Toronto: Addiction Research Foundation, 1996.

Software is available to provide visual, easily understood feedback on individual consumption of alcohol, marijuana, cigarettes, or other substance use compared with norms. This interactive version allows the treatment provider or client to complete calendars onscreen and to generate printouts. A user's guide contains a paper and pencil version of the calendar method. In addition, a video demonstrates techniques for conducting interviews using timeline follow-back data. To order, please contact the following:

Addiction Research Foundation
Marketing Services
33 Russell Street
Toronto, ON
Canada M5S 2S1
(800) 661-1111

Appendix D
Resource Panel

Peter J. Cohen, M.D., J.D.
    Adjunct Professor of Law
    Georgetown University Law Center
    Washington, D.C.

Frances Cotter, M.A., M.P.H.
    Senior Public Health Advisor
    Office of Managed Care
    Center for Substance Abuse and Treatment
    Rockville, Maryland

Dorynne Czechowicz, M.D.
    Associate Director
    Division of Clinical and Services Research
    Treatment Research Branch
    National Institute on Drug Abuse
    Bethesda, Maryland

Gil Hill
    Director
    Office of Substance Abuse
    American Psychological Association
    Washington, D.C.

Linda Kaplan
    Executive Director
    National Association of Alcoholism and
        Drug Abuse Counselors
    Arlington, Virginia

Pedro Morales, J.D.
    Director
    Equal Employment Civil Rights
    Substance Abuse and Mental Health Services
        Administration
    Rockville, Maryland

Harold I. Perl, Ph.D.
    Public Health Analyst
    Division of Clinical and Prevention Research
    National Institute on Alcohol Abuse and
        Alcoholism
    Bethesda, Maryland

Barbara J. Silver, Ph.D.
    Center for Mental Health Services
    Substance Abuse and Mental Health Services
        Administration
    Department of Health and Human Services
    Rockville, Maryland

Lucretia Vigil
    Policy Advisor
    National Coalition of Hispanic Health and
        Human Services Organization (COSSMO)
    Washington, D.C.

Appendix E
Field Reviewers

Noel Brankenhoff, L.M.F.T., L.C.D.P.
Child and Family Services
Middletown, Rhode Island

Rodolfo Briseno, L.C.D.C.
Coordinator for Cultural/Special
Populations and Youth Treatment
Program Services, Program Initiatives
Texas Commission on Alcohol and Drug
Abuse
Austin, Texas

Richard L. Brown, M.D., M.P.H.
Associate Professor
Department of Family Medicine
University of Wisconsin School of Medicine
Madison, Wisconsin

Michael Burke
Senior Substance Abuse Specialist
Student Health
Rutgers University
New Brunswick, New Jersey

Kate Carey, Ph.D.
Associate Professor
Department of Psychology
Syracuse University
Syracuse, New York

Anthony J. Cellucci, Ph.D.
Director of Idaho State University Clinic
Associate Professor of Psychology
Idaho State University
Pocatello, Idaho

Gerard Connors, Ph.D.
Research Institute on Alcoholism
1021 Main Street
Buffalo, New York

John Cunningham, Ph.D.
Scientist
Addiction Research Foundation Division
Centre for Addiction and Mental Health
Toronto, Ontario

Janie Dargan, M.S.W.
Senior Policy Analyst
Office of National Drug Control Policy/EOP
Washington, D.C.

George De Leon, Ph.D.
Center for Theraputic Community Research
New York, New York

Nereida Diaz-Rodriguez, L.L.M., J.D.
Project Director
Director to the Master in Health Science in
Substance Abuse
Centro de Entudion on Adiccion (Altos Salud
Mental)
Edif. Hosp. Regional de Bayamon
Santa Juanita, Bayamon, Puerto Rico

Thomas Diklich, B.A.
Portsmouth CSR
Portsmouth, Virginia

Chris Dunn, Ph.D., M.A.C., C.D.C.
Psychologist
University of Washington
Psychiatry and Behavioral Science
Seattle, Washington

Madeline Dupree, L.P.C.
Harrisonburg-Rockingham CSB
Harrisonburg, Virginia

Gary L. Fisher, Ph.D.
Nevada Addiction Technology Transfer
Center
College of Education
University of Nevada at Reno
Reno, Nevada

Cynthia Flackus, M.S.W., L.I.C.S.W.
Therapist
Camp Share Renewal Center
Walker, Minnesota

Stephen T. Higgins, Ph.D.
Professor
Departments of Psychiatry and Psychology
University of Vermont
Burlington, Vermont

Col. Kenneth J. Hoffman, M.D., M.P.H., M.C.F.S.
Preventive Medicine Consultant
HHC 18th Medical Command
Seoul, Korea

James Robert Holden, M.A.
Program Director
Partners in Drug Abuse Rehabilitation
Counseling
Washington, D.C.

Ron Jackson, M.S.W.
Executive Director
Evergreen Treatment Services
Seattle, Washington

Linda Kaplan
Executive Director
National Association of Alcoholism and
Drug Abuse Counselors
Arlington, Virginia

Matthew Kelly, Ph.D.
Clinical Director
Robert Wood Johnson Foundation
Northwest Mexico Fighting Back, Inc.
Gallup, New Mexico

Karen Kelly-Woodall, M.S., M.A.C., N.C.A.C.II
Criminal Justice Coordinator
Cork Institute
Morehouse School of Medicine
Atlanta, Georgia

Richard Laban, Ph.D.
Laban's Training
Harrisburg, Pennsylvania

Lauren Lawendowski, Ph.D.
Acting Project Director
Center on Alcoholism, Substance Abuse, and
Addiction
University of New Mexico
Albuquerque, New Mexico

Bruce R. Lorenz, N.C.A.C. II
Director
Thresholds, Inc.
Dover, Delaware

Russell P. MacPherson, Ph.D., C.A.P., C.A.P.P.,
C.C.P., D.A.C., D.V.C.
President
RPM Addiction Prevention Training
Deland, Florida

George Medzerian, Ph.D.
Pensacola, Florida

Lisa A. Melchior, Ph.D.
Vice President
The Measurement Group
Culver City, California

Paul Nagy, M.S., C.S.A.C.
Director
Duke Alcoholism and Addictions Program
Duke University Medical Center
Durham, North Carolina

Tracy A. O'Leary, Ph.D.
Clinical Supervisor
Assistant Project Coordinator
Center for Alcohol and Addiction Studies
Brown University
Providence, Rhode Island

Gwen M. Olitsky, M.S.
CEO
The Self-Help Institute for Training and
Therapy
Lansdale, Pennsylvania

Michele A. Packard, Ph.D.
Executive Director
SAGE Institute
Training and Consulting
Boulder, California

Michael Pantalon, Ph.D.
Yale School of Medicine
New Haven, Connecticut

Joe Pereira, L.I.C.S.W., C.A.S.
Recovery Strategies
Medford, Massachusetts

Harold Perl, Ph.D.
Public Health Analyst
Division of Clinical and Prevention Research
National Institute on Alcoholism and
Alcohol Abuse
Bethesda, Maryland

Raul G. Rodriguez, M.D.
Medical Director
La Hacienda Treatment Center
Hunt, Texas

Richard T. Suchinsky, M.D.
Associate Director for Addictive Disorders
and Psychiatric Rehabilitation
Mental Health and Behavioral Sciences
Services
Department of Veterans Affairs
Washington, D.C.

Suzan Swanton, M.S.W.
Clinical Director
R.E.A.C.H. Mobile Home Services
Baltimore, Maryland

Michael J. Taleff, Ph.D., C.A.C., M.A.C.,
N.C.A.C.II
Assistant Professor and Coordinator
Graduate Programs in Chemical Dependency
Counselor Education
Department of Counselor Education
Counseling Psychology and Rehabilitation
Services
Pennsylvania State University
University Park, Pennsylvania

Nola C. Veazie, Ph.D., L.P.C., C.A.D.A.C.
Superintendent
Medical Services Department
United States Air Force
Family Therapist/Drug and Alcohol
Counselor
Veazie Family Therapy
Santa Maria, California

Mary Velasquez, Ph.D.
Psychology Department
University of Houston
Houston, Texas

Christopher Wagner, Ph.D.
Division of Substance Abuse Medicine
Virginia Commonwealth University
Richmond, Virginia